M343
Applications of probability

BOOK 4
Random processes in continuous time

About M343

M343 *Applications of probability* is about the application of probability to modelling real-life situations. It follows the level 2 module M248 *Analysing data* and develops ideas about probability and random processes that are introduced there. Software for exploring properties of random processes is supplied as part of M343; its use is covered in the *Computer Book*.

The Open University, Walton Hall, Milton Keynes MK7 6AA.

First published 2012.

Edited, designed and typeset by The Open University, using the Open University TEX System.

Printed in the United Kingdom by Hobbs the Printers Limited, Brunel Road, Totton, Hampshire SO40 3WX.

ISBN 978 1 8487 3626 9

1.1

Contents

Study guide   **6**

Introduction   **8**

Part I   Birth and death processes   **9**
Introduction to Part I   9

1   Arrivals, births and deaths   **9**
   1.1   The Poisson process   10
   1.2   The simple birth process   11
   1.3   The pure death process   14
   1.4   Markov processes   16

2   The distribution of $X(t)$ **19**
   2.1   Differential–difference equations   19
   2.2   Functions of two variables   22
   2.3   Probability generating function approach   24
   2.4   Lagrange's equation   26

3   Solving Lagrange's equation   **27**
   3.1   The general solution   27
   3.2   Particular solutions   33
   3.3   Lagrange's method   35

4   Two growing populations   **38**
   4.1   The simple birth process   38
   4.2   The immigration–birth process   40

5   Birth and death processes   **44**
   5.1   Markov processes   44
   5.2   Birth and death processes   44
   5.3   The immigration–birth–death process   47

6   The simple birth–death process   **48**
   6.1   The size of the population   49
   6.2   Extinction   51
   6.3   The embedded random walk   53

7   The immigration–death process   **56**
   7.1   The size of the population   57
   7.2   What happens in the long run?   58

8   Deterministic models   **60**

Part II   Queues   **66**
    Introduction to Part II   66

9   Models and notation   **66**

10 The simple queue   **68**
    10.1 Queue size   69
    10.2 The equilibrium queue size   69
    10.3 Queueing time   72
    10.4 Idle periods and busy periods   74

11 Markov queues   **77**
    11.1 The $M/M/n$ queue   77
    11.2 Other Markov queues   82

12 General service times   **83**
    12.1 The $M/G/1$ queue   84
    12.2 More than one server   86

Part III   Epidemics   **87**
    Introduction to Part III   87

13 Modelling the spread of an infectious disease   **88**

14 The simple epidemic   **90**
    14.1 The model   91
    14.2 The deterministic model   92
    14.3 The stochastic model: waiting times   93
    14.4 The stochastic model: distribution of $Y(t)$ 95

15 The general epidemic   **99**
    15.1 The stochastic model   99
    15.2 The deterministic model   100
    15.3 A variation on the model   105

16 The stochastic general epidemic model   **106**

17 The threshold phenomenon   **111**
    17.1 Exploring the stochastic model   111
    17.2 The threshold phenomenon for the stochastic general
          epidemic model   112

18 Other models for epidemics   **114**

Part IV   More population models   **115**
    Introduction to Part IV   115

19 Modelling lifetimes   **116**

20 Life tables   **121**

21 Stationary populations   **125**

22 Stable populations   **131**
    22.1 The growth of a stable population   131
    22.2 Stable populations and stationary populations 133

23 Population pyramids   **136**

24 Exercises on Book 4   **140**
    24.1 Routine exercises   140
    24.2 Further exercises   143

Summary of Book 4   **146**
    Learning outcomes   147

Solutions to Activities   **149**

Solutions to Exercises   **172**

Index   **190**

Study guide

You should schedule 22 study sessions for this book. This includes time for working through one chapter of the computer book, answering the TMA and CMA questions, and consolidating your work on this book. You should schedule nine study sessions for Part I, four for Part II, five for Part III and four for Part IV.

The analysis of the models described in Parts II and III depends on some of the ideas introduced in Part I, so you are recommended to work through Part I first. However, Parts II, III and IV do not depend on each other, so although we recommend that you study them in the order in which they appear, it would be possible to study them in a different order.

The sections vary in length. In Part I, Section 3 is longer than average, but Sections 7 and 8 are both quite short. In Part II, Sections 9, 11 and 12 are all shorter than average. In Part III, Sections 13 and 18 are very short. In Part IV, Sections 20, 22 and 23 are all quite short.

As you study this book, you will be asked to work through one chapter of the computer book. We recommend that you work through it at the point indicated in the text (in Section 17).

One possible study pattern is as follows.

Part I

Study session 1: Section 1.

Study session 2: Section 2.

Study session 3: Section 3.

Study session 4: Section 4.

Study session 5: Section 5.

Study session 6: Section 6.

Study session 7: Sections 7 and 8.

Study sessions 8 and 9: TMA and CMA questions on Part I, and consolidation of your work on Part I.

Part II

Study session 10: Sections 9 and 10.

Study session 11: Section 11.

Study session 12: Section 12.

Study session 13: TMA and CMA questions on Part II, and consolidation of your work on Part II.

Part III

Study session 14: Sections 13 and 14.

Study session 15: Section 15.

Study session 16: Section 16.

Study session 17: Sections 17 and 18. You will need access to your computer for this session.

Study session 18: TMA and CMA questions on Part III, and consolidation of your work on Part III.

Part IV

Study session 19: Sections 19 and 20.

Study session 20: Section 21.

Study session 21: Sections 22 and 23.

Study session 22: TMA and CMA questions on Part IV, and consolidation of your work on Part IV.

Introduction

Discrete-valued random processes $\{X(t); t \geq 0\}$ developing in continuous time are studied in this book. Specifically, situations where the random variable $X(t)$ takes non-negative integer values are considered. For example, $X(t)$ may be the number of events that have happened by time t, or the number of individuals alive at time t in an evolving community, or the length of a queue at time t, or the number of individuals in a community who, by time t, have caught a disease.

Some stochastic processes are non-decreasing. For instance, $X(t)$ might be the number of arrivals at a particular location by time t, where individuals arrive according to a Poisson process. Another example of a non-decreasing process is the *simple birth process*: individuals born into a community themselves independently generate further offspring according to a Poisson process. The more individuals there are alive at any time, the more frequent the incidence of births is likely to be.

Many stochastic processes are subject to decrease as well as increase. For instance, the individuals in a population may generate offspring as in a simple birth process, but instead of living forever, they die (at some random age). Hence the population size goes down as well as up. Similarly, if departures occur as well as arrivals, then the number of individuals present at a location can fall as well as rise. Examples of this type include the number of aircraft on the ground at an airport, and the number of customers present in a supermarket.

In Part I, models involving one or more of arrivals, births and deaths are studied. These models belong to a class of models known as birth and death processes. Several models for queues are discussed in Part II. These models involve arrivals and departures, but not births and deaths.

The control of infectious diseases is a major concern of medical science, and mathematical models have a part to play in helping us to understand how epidemics of such diseases spread, and how they can be controlled. In Part III, some basic epidemic models are described.

The models discussed in Part IV attempt to describe the way in which populations grow. Such models are used in demography (the study of human populations) and in population ecology (the study of how more general biological populations interact with their environment and with other populations). For the models involving deaths discussed in Part I, the lifetimes of individuals are assumed to be exponentially distributed. The implications of other lifetime distributions for the growth and age-structure of a population are investigated in Part IV.

Part I   Birth and death processes

Introduction to Part I

Several models for the development of a population are described in Part I. The Poisson process, which you studied in *Book 2*, is fundamental to all these models. In Section 1, the Poisson process is reviewed briefly, and two models are introduced – the *simple birth process* and the *pure death process*. These three random processes are used to model the arrivals of individuals to join a population, technically known as **immigration**, and the births and deaths of individuals in a population. The distribution of the waiting times between events in these models is investigated, and some properties of the models, including the Markov property, are discussed briefly.

In *Book 2*, the distribution of the number of events that occur by time t in a Poisson process was found by obtaining a set of differential–difference equations for the probabilities and solving them recursively. The method introduced in Section 2 of this book involves the solution of a particular form of differential equation known as *Lagrange's equation*. A technique for solving Lagrange's equation is described in Section 3. This technique is applied in Section 4, where two models for growing populations are studied – the simple birth process and the immigration–birth process. The Markov property for random processes in continuous time and Markov processes are discussed briefly in Section 5. Some properties of processes that belong to the class of processes known as birth and death processes are also described, and the immigration–birth–death process is introduced. This model allows for arrivals, births and deaths. Some of the ideas and techniques discussed in Sections 1 to 5 are applied in Sections 6 and 7. The simple birth–death process is analysed in Section 6, and the immigration–death process is discussed in Section 7.

The deterministic version of a model ignores random fluctuations in a random process and investigates only the 'average' behaviour of the process. Deterministic analogues for some of the models introduced in Sections 1 to 7 are discussed briefly in Section 8.

1   Arrivals, births and deaths

Three models for the development of a population in continuous time are described in this section. The Poisson process is reviewed briefly in Subsection 1.1, and the simple birth process and the pure death process are introduced in Subsections 1.2 and 1.3. All three processes are Markov processes; that is, they possess the Markov property. Markov processes, and the Markov property as it applies to random processes in continuous time, are discussed briefly in Subsection 1.4.

1.1 The Poisson process

The Poisson process is the basic building block for all the models described in Part I of this book, and for many of those discussed in Parts II and III. It can be used as a model in many situations – for example, in counting radioactive emissions from an isotope, or recording arrivals at a bank or at a doctor's surgery. When discussing applications, it is sometimes referred to as an **arrival process**, or more commonly using the technical term **immigration process**.

The Poisson process is a model for the occurrence of events in continuous time in which events occur singly, the rate of occurrence of events remains constant, and the incidence of future events is independent of the past. These assumptions are expressed mathematically in the following box.

Postulates for the Poisson process

A Poisson process with rate λ is specified by three postulates.

I   The probability that (exactly) one event occurs in any small time interval $[t, t + \delta t]$ is equal to $\lambda \, \delta t + o(\delta t)$.

II   The probability that two or more events occur in any small time interval $[t, t + \delta t]$ is equal to $o(\delta t)$.

III The occurrence of events after any time t is independent of the occurrence of events before time t.

The number of events that occur by time t is denoted $X(t)$, and the integer-valued process $\{X(t); t \geq 0\}$ is a non-decreasing process developing in continuous time. The times at which events occur and the total number of events that occur by time t in a realisation of a Poisson process are represented in Figure 1.1.

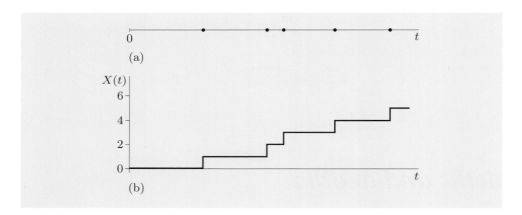

Figure 1.1   Realisation of a Poisson process: (a) times at which events occur; (b) number of events that occur by time t

The time from the start of observation to the first event is denoted T_1, and the times between subsequent events are denoted $T_2, T_3, \ldots$. The time at which the nth event occurs is denoted W_n. So $W_1 = T_1$, and for $n = 2, 3, \ldots$, $W_n = T_1 + \cdots + T_n$.

Two key results for a Poisson process are stated in the following box.

These results were derived in Book 2.

The Poisson process: two results

Suppose that events occur at random at rate λ in such a way that their occurrence may be modelled as a Poisson process. Then:

◇ $N(t)$, the number of events that occur during an interval of length t, has a Poisson distribution with parameter λt: $N(t) \sim \text{Poisson}(\lambda t)$;

◇ T, the waiting time between successive events, has an exponential distribution with parameter λ: $T \sim M(\lambda)$.

The first result implies that $X(t)$, the number of events that occur by time t, has a Poisson distribution with parameter λt. The second result means that for $i = 2, 3, \ldots, T_i \sim M(\lambda)$, and since an exponential distribution has the memoryless property, $T_1 \sim M(\lambda)$. Since W_n is the sum of n independent exponential variates, each with parameter λ, it follows that W_n has a gamma distribution with parameters n and λ; that is, $W_n \sim \Gamma(n, \lambda)$.

This result is in the Handbook.

1.2   The simple birth process

The simple birth process is used to model the growth of a population whose size increases with time as offspring are born to existing individuals in the population. For simplicity, suppose that at time $t = 0$ there is a single individual, and that this individual gives birth to further individuals according to a Poisson process with rate β. As soon as a new individual is born, it also starts giving birth independently at the same rate β. There are no deaths; the population simply increases as time passes. This model is called the **simple birth process** with (**individual**) **birth rate** β. It is a reasonable model for the increase in a colony of bacteria or cells where reproduction occurs by splitting of cells and is independent of the age of the individual, and where resources are abundant so that deaths need not be considered.

There are several sequences of random variables associated with a simple birth process. For example, $\{X(t); t \geq 0\}$, where $X(t)$ is the size of the population at time t; $\{T_n; n = 1, 2, \ldots\}$, where T_1 is the time to the first birth, and for $n \geq 2$, T_n is the time between the $(n-1)$th birth and the nth birth; and $\{W_n; n = 1, 2, \ldots\}$, where W_n is the time up to the nth birth, that is, until the population reaches size $n + 1$.

The distribution of T_n can be found using the following result from *Book 1* for a minimum of exponential variates: if $X_1, \ldots, X_n$ are independent exponential variates with parameters $\lambda_1, \ldots, \lambda_n$ and $X = \min\{X_1, \ldots, X_n\}$, then $X \sim M(\lambda_1 + \cdots + \lambda_n)$.

This result is in the Handbook.

Suppose that a population starts with one individual. Then after $n - 1$ births there are n individuals alive. Each of these individuals is giving birth independently according to a Poisson process with rate β. Therefore, considering the process as a whole, the time until the next birth (the nth) is the minimum of n exponential variates, each with distribution $M(\beta)$. Hence

$$T_n \sim M(n\beta).$$

That is, the time between the $(n-1)$th birth and the nth birth has an exponential distribution with parameter $n\beta$, and hence mean $1/(n\beta)$. As the size of the population increases, the rate of births increases and the population grows more rapidly. Thus the distribution of T_1, the waiting time to the first birth, is $M(\beta)$, the distribution of T_2, the waiting time from the first birth to the second birth, is $M(2\beta)$, the distribution of T_3, the waiting time from the second birth to the third birth, is $M(3\beta)$, and so on.

A realisation of a simple birth process can be obtained by simulating the times between successive births. Figure 1.2 shows the graph of a realisation of $X(t)$, the size of the population in a simple birth process at time t, up to $X(t) = 20$.

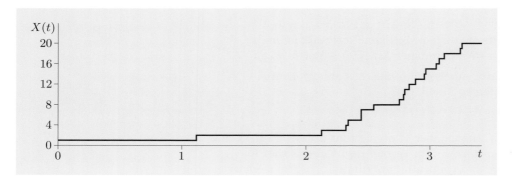

Figure 1.2   Realisation of a simple birth process

Although the waiting times between successive births are all exponentially distributed, the parameters of the distributions are different. Therefore the distribution of $W_n = T_1 + T_2 + \cdots + T_n$, the waiting time to the nth birth, is not a standard distribution. However, since $T_1, T_2, \ldots, T_n$ are independent, expressions for the mean and variance of W_n can be obtained, as follows.

If $X \sim M(\lambda)$, then $E(X) = 1/\lambda$ and $V(X) = 1/\lambda^2$. Hence for a simple birth process starting with one individual,

$$
\begin{aligned}
E(W_n) &= E(T_1 + T_2 + \cdots + T_n) \\
&= E(T_1) + E(T_2) + \cdots + E(T_n) \\
&= \frac{1}{\beta} + \frac{1}{2\beta} + \cdots + \frac{1}{n\beta} \\
&= \frac{1}{\beta}\left(1 + \frac{1}{2} + \cdots + \frac{1}{n}\right).
\end{aligned}
$$

Since $T_1, T_2, \ldots, T_n$ are independent,

$$
\begin{aligned}
V(W_n) &= V(T_1) + V(T_2) + \cdots + V(T_n) \\
&= \frac{1}{\beta^2} + \frac{1}{(2\beta)^2} + \cdots + \frac{1}{(n\beta)^2} \\
&= \frac{1}{\beta^2}\left(1 + \frac{1}{2^2} + \cdots + \frac{1}{n^2}\right).
\end{aligned}
$$

Activity 1.1   *Waiting for the eighth birth*

For a simple birth process with birth rate $\beta = 2$, find the mean and variance of W_8, the waiting time to the eighth birth, assuming that initially there is one individual alive.

Example 1.1   Two individuals at the start

Suppose that a simple birth process with birth rate β is initiated by two individuals.

When there are x individuals alive, the waiting time until the next birth has an exponential distribution with parameter βx. Therefore, if there are two individuals at the start, then the distribution of T_1, the time to the first birth, is $M(2\beta)$, and hence

$$E(T_1) = \frac{1}{2\beta}, \quad V(T_1) = \frac{1}{4\beta^2}.$$

If W is the time until there are five individuals, that is, until the third birth, then

$$W = T_1 + T_2 + T_3,$$

where $T_2 \sim M(3\beta)$ and $T_3 \sim M(4\beta)$. Hence

$$E(W) = \frac{1}{2\beta} + \frac{1}{3\beta} + \frac{1}{4\beta} = \frac{13}{12\beta} \simeq \frac{1.083}{\beta},$$

$$V(W) = \frac{1}{4\beta^2} + \frac{1}{9\beta^2} + \frac{1}{16\beta^2} \simeq \frac{0.424}{\beta^2}. \quad \blacklozenge$$

Activity 1.2   More waiting times

Suppose that a simple birth process with birth rate β is initiated by three individuals.

(a) State the distribution of the waiting time until the first birth, and hence write down the mean and variance of this waiting time.

(b) Find in terms of β the mean and standard deviation of the waiting time until the population size reaches 7 (that is, until the fourth birth).

The distributions of the waiting times between births have been found using results for the Poisson process and properties of the exponential distribution. In order to find the distribution of $X(t)$ for a simple birth process, postulates for the process are required. The postulates are given below, and the problem of finding the distribution of $X(t)$ is discussed in Section 2.

If, at some stage, the population has reached size x, then all x members are independently capable of giving birth at the same rate β, so the **overall birth rate** is βx. Therefore, if the size of the population is x at time t, then the probability that a birth will occur in the small interval $[t, t + \delta t]$ is equal to $\beta x \, \delta t + o(\delta t)$.

The postulates for the simple birth process are given in the following box.

The simple birth process

A simple birth process with birth rate β is specified by three postulates.

I   If the size of the population is x at time t, then the probability that (exactly) one birth will occur during the small time interval $[t, t + \delta t]$ is equal to $\beta x \, \delta t + o(\delta t)$.

II   The probability that more than one birth will occur during any small time interval $[t, t + \delta t]$ is equal to $o(\delta t)$.

III   For any individual alive at time t, the incidence of births after time t is independent of the incidence of births before time t.

1.3   The pure death process

The pure death process is a model for a population in which there are no arrivals or births, but in which deaths do occur. Observation starts at time 0 with several individuals present. Independently of each other, these individuals die, and eventually the population dies out. For the **pure death process**, the lifetime of an individual is assumed to be exponentially distributed. The parameter ν of the lifetime distribution is the (**individual**) **death rate** of the process.

Suppose that in a pure death process with death rate ν, the size of the population at time t is equal to x. Then the waiting time until the next death is the minimum of x independent exponential variates each having parameter ν, and hence is exponentially distributed with parameter νx. It follows that the probability that a death occurs in the small time interval $[t, t + \delta t]$ is $\nu x \, \delta t + o(\delta t)$.

The postulates for the pure death process are given in the following box.

The pure death process

A pure death process with death rate ν is specified by three postulates.

I   If the size of the population at time t is equal to x, then the probability that (exactly) one death will occur during the small time interval $[t, t + \delta t]$ is equal to $\nu x \, \delta t + o(\delta t)$.

II   The probability that more than one death will occur during any small time interval $[t, t + \delta t]$ is equal to $o(\delta t)$.

III The occurrence of deaths before any time t and the occurrence of deaths after time t are independent.

For all the random processes discussed in Part I, $X(t)$ denotes the size of the population at time t, T_1 is the time until the first 'event', T_n is the time between the $(n-1)$th and nth events, and W_n is the time at which the nth event occurs. For a pure death process, an 'event' is a death. Since there are no arrivals or births, the population size decreases by 1 as each death occurs, and eventually the population will die out. The time at which extinction occurs is denoted W.

For the pure death process, questions about the size of the population at time t and the waiting time until the size falls to a specified level can be answered using only the distribution of the times between successive deaths. No complicated mathematics is required. Try Activities 1.3 to 1.5.

Activity 1.3   Waiting times

Suppose that there are n individuals alive at time 0 in a pure death process with death rate ν.

(a) State the distribution of the waiting time until the first death, and the distribution of the waiting time between the first death and the second death.

(b) Write down the distribution of the time between the penultimate death and the last death.

(c) Find expressions for the mean and variance of W, the total time until the population dies out.

Activity 1.4   More waiting times

Suppose that there are initially 10 individuals alive in a pure death process with death rate ν.

(a) Find in terms of ν the mean and standard deviation of the waiting time until there are only seven survivors.

(b) Find in terms of ν the expected waiting time until the population dies out.

Activity 1.5   The population size at time t

Suppose that there are initially n individuals alive in a pure death process with death rate ν.

(a) Find the probability that a particular individual alive at time 0 will still be alive at time t.

(b) Hence write down the distribution of the total number of individuals still alive at time t out of the n individuals initially alive.

(c) Find the probability that exactly two individuals are still alive at time t.

(d) Write down the probability that there are no individuals still alive at time t.

The distribution of $X(t)$ can be used to find the c.d.f. of W, the time to the last death, as follows.

The last death occurs at or before time t if and only if the population size is 0 at time t. That is, the events $[W \leq t]$ and $[X(t) = 0]$ are equivalent. Therefore

$$P(W \leq t) = P(X(t) = 0).$$

But, from part (d) of Activity 1.5,

$$P(X(t) = 0) = (1 - e^{-\nu t})^n,$$

so the c.d.f. of W is given by

$$P(W \leq t) = (1 - e^{-\nu t})^n.$$

This result can be used to calculate probabilities for the time to extinction in a pure death process.

The main results obtained in this subsection are summarised in the following box.

> **The pure death process**
>
> For a pure death process with death rate ν, let $X(t)$ be the number of individuals alive at time t and let W be the time until the population dies out.
>
> ◇   If $X(t) = x$, then the distribution of the time until the next death is $M(\nu x)$.
>
> ◇   If $X(0) = n$, then $X(t) \sim B(n, e^{-\nu t})$. $\hspace{2cm}$ (1.1)
>
> ◇   For all $t > 0$,
> $$P(W \leq t) = P(X(t) = 0).$$
>
> ◇   If $X(0) = n$, then the c.d.f. of W is given by
> $$P(W \leq t) = (1 - e^{-\nu t})^n, \quad t > 0.$$ $\hspace{1cm}$ (1.2)

15

1.4   Markov processes

Roughly speaking, a Markov process is a process with the property that future behaviour patterns depend only on the present state of the process and are independent of its past history. This property of a process is called the Markov property.

A discrete-valued random process $\{X_n; n = 0, 1, \ldots\}$ in discrete time is said to have the Markov property if it satisfies the following condition. For each $n \geq 1$, if A is an event depending only on a subset of $\{X_{n-1}, X_{n-2}, \ldots, X_0\}$, then for any states i and j,

$$P(X_{n+1} = j \mid X_n = i \text{ and } A) = P(X_{n+1} = j \mid X_n = i).$$

That is, a process has the Markov property if the probability of any future behaviour of the process, when its current state is known, is not altered by any additional information about its past behaviour.

A discrete-valued random process $\{X(t); t \geq 0\}$ in continuous time is said to have the **Markov property** if, for any sequence of times $t_1, t_2, \ldots, t_n, u, t$, where $0 < t_1 < t_2 < \cdots < t_n < u < t$, and for all states $i_1, i_2, \ldots, i_n, i, j$ in the state space,

$$P(X(t) = j \mid X(u) = i, \ X(t_1) = i_1, \ X(t_2) = i_2, \ \ldots, \ X(t_n) = i_n)$$
$$= P(X(t) = j \mid X(u) = i).$$

A random process in continuous time that satisfies this condition is a **Markov process**. That is, for a Markov process, if the state of the process is known at some time u, then any additional information about the behaviour of the process before time u does not affect the probability of any future behaviour pattern.

This definition is given in Book 3.

Example 1.2   The Poisson process

Suppose that in a Poisson process $\{X(t); t \geq 0\}$, the number of events that have occurred by time u is known, $X(u) = x$ (say). By Postulate III, the occurrence of events after time u is independent of the occurrence of events before time u. Therefore, given $X(u) = x$, if the precise times at which the x events occurred were known, this would not make any difference to the calculation of probabilities about events after time u. So this postulate is an expression of the Markov property for the Poisson process.

The Poisson process is the simplest example of a Markov process in continuous time.   ◆

Example 1.3   The simple birth process

For a simple birth process, if the size of the population is known to be x at time t, so that $X(t) = x$, then the probability of a birth in the interval $[t, t + \delta t]$ is $\beta x \, \delta t + o(\delta t)$. This depends only on x, the state of the process at time t, not on the behaviour of the process before time t, so the simple birth process has the Markov property, and hence it is a Markov process.   ◆

Example 1.4   Regularly spaced events

Consider a process in which events occur regularly with a time interval of length a between events. Suppose that it is known that x events have occurred by time t. If the time at which the process started is unknown, then the future behaviour of the process cannot be specified. However, if the time in the interval $[t - a, t]$ at which the last event occurred is known, then the future behaviour of the process is specified precisely. So the probabilities of future behaviour patterns depend on the past history of the process as well as the present state. Therefore this process is not a Markov process.   ◆

Activity 1.6   Markov processes

Decide whether or not each of the following random processes is a Markov process.

(a) A pure death process.

(b) A non-homogeneous Poisson process in which the probability that an event occurs in the interval $[t, t + \delta t]$ is $\lambda(t)\,\delta t + o(\delta t)$.

(c) A point process in which the time interval between events has the uniform distribution $U(1,3)$.

You have seen that the Poisson process, the simple birth process and the pure death process are all Markov processes. In each case, Postulate III for the process is essentially the Markov property for a random process in continuous time. Postulate II says that the probability that more than one event will occur in a small time interval $[t, t + \delta t]$ is negligible. All the processes described in Part I are Markov processes, and from now on Postulates II and III will be assumed. The important information about each process is contained in the first postulate. For instance, for the Poisson process this may be written as

$$P(X(t + \delta t) = x + 1 \mid X(t) = x) = \lambda\,\delta t + o(\delta t).$$

For the simple birth process, it may be written as

$$P(X(t + \delta t) = x + 1 \mid X(t) = x) = \beta x\,\delta t + o(\delta t).$$

And for the pure death process, the first postulate takes the form

$$P(X(t + \delta t) = x - 1 \mid X(t) = x) = \nu x\,\delta t + o(\delta t).$$

In general, a brief statement of this type can be used to describe concisely each of the processes discussed in Part I.

Transition probabilities

The probability $P(X(t) = j \mid X(u) = i)$ is sometimes called a **transition probability**. In general, it depends on i, j, u and t, so to demonstrate this dependence, it is denoted by $p_{i,j}(u, t)$; that is,

$$p_{i,j}(u, t) = P(X(t) = j \mid X(u) = i).$$

However, for many Markov processes, the time-dependence of the transition probabilities relates only to $t - u$, the length of the interval $[u, t]$, so that for any u, t such that $0 < u < t$, and for all states i and j,

$$p_{i,j}(u, t) = p_{i,j}(0, t - u).$$

In this case the Markov process is said to be **homogeneous**.

The Poisson process, the simple birth process and the pure death process are all homogeneous Markov processes. However, although the non-homogeneous Poisson process is a Markov process, it is not homogeneous (as its name implies)!

A homogeneous process is the continuous-time analogue of a discrete-time process with stationary transition probabilities.

Suppose that a Markov process is in state i at time $t = 0$ and that it is still in this state after u minutes. The probability that it will remain in state i for at least a further t minutes is $P(T > u + t \mid T > u)$, where T is the time until the first change of state occurs. For a homogeneous Markov process, the (conditional) probability that the process remains in state i for the interval $[u, u + t]$ is equal to the (unconditional) probability that it remains in state i for an interval of length t. So

$$P(T > u + t \mid T > u) = P(T > t).$$

In other words, the random variable T has the memoryless property. The exponential distribution is the only continuous distribution that has the memoryless property, so T has an exponential distribution. It follows that the times between successive events are exponentially distributed. This is a fundamental property of a Markov process. In general, if the probability that an event occurs in a small time interval $[t, t + \delta t]$ is equal to $h(x)\,\delta t + o(\delta t)$, where

$h(x)$ may depend on x but is independent of t, then the times between successive events are exponentially distributed with parameter $h(x)$. You have already seen that this is the case for the Poisson process ($h(x) = \lambda$), the simple birth process ($h(x) = \beta x$), and the pure death process ($h(x) = \nu x$).

The main ideas introduced in this subsection are summarised in the following box.

Markov processes

A random process in continuous time is a **Markov process** if the future behaviour of the process, when its current state is known, is independent of its past.

A Markov process is **homogeneous** if, for any states i and j, and any u and t such that $0 < u < t$, the transition probability $P(X(t) = j \,|\, X(u) = i)$ depends on $t - u$, the length of the interval $[u, t]$, but not on u.

The times between successive events in a homogeneous Markov process in continuous time are exponentially distributed. If the probability that an event occurs in any small interval of length δt is $h(x)\,\delta t + o(\delta t)$, then the times between successive events are exponentially distributed with parameter $h(x)$.

Activity 1.7   Arrivals and births

Consider a population in which arrivals occur at rate λ, and suppose that members of the population give birth independently with rate β. Then the process $\{X(t); t \geq 0\}$, where $X(t)$ is the size of the population at time t, is an **immigration–birth process**.

If $X(t) = x$, then the instantaneous birth rate is βx. Independently of this, arrivals occur at rate λ. Hence the process is characterised by the statement

$$P(X(t + \delta t) = x + 1 \,|\, X(t) = x) = (\lambda + \beta x)\,\delta t + o(\delta t).$$

(a)   Given $X(t) = x$, write down the distribution of the waiting time until the next event (arrival or birth). State the mean and variance of this waiting time.

Suppose that initially there is no one in the population; that is, $X(0) = 0$.

(b)   Write down the distributions of the following waiting times: T_1, the time until the first event; T_2, the time from the first event to the second event; T_3, the time from the second event to the third event; T_n, the time from the $(n-1)$th event to the nth event.

(c)   Write down expressions for the mean and variance of W_n, the waiting time from the start of observation until the population size reaches n.

Summary of Section 1

In this section, the Poisson process has been reviewed, and the simple birth process and the pure death process have been introduced. The waiting times between events in these random processes have been studied. Markov processes and the Markov property have been discussed briefly, and you have seen that the Poisson process, the simple birth process and the pure death process are homogeneous Markov processes.

Exercises on Section 1

Suppose that a simple birth process with birth rate β is initiated by five individuals.

(a) State the distribution of the waiting time until the first birth, and hence write down the mean and variance of this waiting time.

(b) Find in terms of β the mean and standard deviation of the waiting time until the population size reaches 10 (that is, until the fifth birth).

Suppose that in a pure death process with death rate ν, there are initially five individuals alive in the population.

(a) Find in terms of ν the mean and variance of the time until the population dies out.

(b) Find the probability that exactly three individuals will be alive at time t.

(c) Find the probability that the population will not yet have died out at time t.

2   The distribution of $X(t)$

In *Book 2*, the distribution of $X(t)$, the number of events that have occurred by time t in a Poisson process, was found by obtaining a set of differential equations for the probabilities

$$p_x(t) = P(X(t) = x), \quad x = 0, 1, \ldots.$$

These equations were solved recursively until a pattern emerged, and the distribution of $X(t)$ was identified. In Subsection 2.1, a similar set of differential equations is obtained for the simple birth process.

When solving a set of differential equations recursively, considerable work is involved, and there is no guarantee that a pattern will emerge. So a different approach to solving the differential equations is adopted in this section. This involves the probability generating function of $X(t)$. This p.g.f. is a function of two variables. Functions of two variables are discussed briefly in Subsection 2.2.

In Subsection 2.3, a partial differential equation for the p.g.f. of $X(t)$ is obtained for each of the three random processes discussed in Section 1. These differential equations are compared in Subsection 2.4, and similarities in the form they take are noted.

2.1 Differential–difference equations

You will not be expected to reproduce the derivations contained in this subsection. However, you should work through them, and try to follow the arguments, in order to familiarise yourself with the ideas and notation that are introduced.

Example 2.1   The Poisson process

For the Poisson process, the probability mass function (p.m.f.) of $X(t)$ is denoted $p_x(t)$; that is, $p_x(t) = P(X(t) = x)$. (More precisely, $p_x(t) = P(X(t) = x \mid X(0) = 0)$. However, it is common practice to leave the information about $X(0)$ – the initial condition – as an implicit condition rather than an explicit one.)

In *Book 2*, the postulates for the Poisson process were used to establish the following set of differential equations:

$$\frac{d}{dt}\, p_0(t) = -\lambda\, p_0(t), \tag{2.1}$$

$$\frac{d}{dt}\, p_x(t) = -\lambda\, p_x(t) + \lambda\, p_{x-1}(t), \quad x = 1, 2, \ldots. \tag{2.2}$$

These equations are called the **differential–difference equations** for the Poisson process: *differential* because the equations involve derivatives, *difference* because they express the probability $p_x(t)$ in terms of the probability $p_{x-1}(t)$. ◆

Example 2.2   The simple birth process

For the simple birth process, $X(t)$ is the size of the population at time t. Conditional on the value of $X(0)$, the population size at the start, the p.m.f. of $X(t)$ is denoted $p_x(t)$; that is, $p_x(t) = P(X(t) = x)$. As for the Poisson process, the dependence on $X(0)$ is not expressed explicitly.

The simple birth process may be characterised by the statement

$$P(X(t + \delta t) = x + 1 \mid X(t) = x) = \beta x\, \delta t + o(\delta t).$$

This is a statement of Postulate I for the simple birth process.

The population must start with at least one member. Otherwise, there would be nobody to give birth to anybody else, and the population size would remain 0 forever. Therefore the possibility $X(t + \delta t) = 0$ need not be considered.

The probability that there is one individual present at time $t + \delta t$ is $p_1(t + \delta t)$. By the Theorem of Total Probability,

$$p_1(t + \delta t) = P(X(t + \delta t) = 1)$$
$$= \sum_{k=0}^{\infty} P(X(t + \delta t) = 1 \mid X(t) = k)\, P(X(t) = k).$$

The event $[X(t + \delta t) = 1]$ can happen only if there is a single individual present at time t and this individual has no offspring in the time interval $[t, t + \delta t]$, so

$$p_1(t + \delta t) = p_1(t)\, (1 - \beta\, \delta t + o(\delta t)).$$

This equation can be rewritten as

$$\frac{p_1(t + \delta t) - p_1(t)}{\delta t} = -\beta\, p_1(t) + \frac{o(\delta t)}{\delta t}.$$

Taking the limit as $\delta t \to 0$ gives the first differential–difference equation for the simple birth process:

$$\frac{d}{dt}\, p_1(t) = -\beta\, p_1(t). \tag{2.3}$$

The probability that there are x individuals in the population at time t is $p_x(t + \delta t)$. By the Theorem of Total Probability,

$$p_x(t + \delta t) = P(X(t + \delta t) = x)$$
$$= \sum_{k=0}^{\infty} P(X(t + \delta t) = x \mid X(t) = k)\, P(X(t) = k).$$

If there are x individuals alive at time t, then the probability that there is no birth in the interval $[t, t + \delta t]$ is $1 - \beta x\, \delta t + o(\delta t)$. If, on the other hand, there are $x - 1$ individuals present at time t, then the probability of one birth in the interval $[t, t + \delta t]$, bringing the population size up to x at time $t + \delta t$, is $\beta(x - 1)\, \delta t + o(\delta t)$. Since, by Postulate II, all other possibilities have probability $o(\delta t)$, these are, essentially, the only two ways in which there can be x individuals alive at time $t + \delta t$. Therefore for $x = 2, 3, \ldots,$

$$p_x(t + \delta t) = p_x(t)\,(1 - \beta x\, \delta t + o(\delta t)) + p_{x-1}(t)\,(\beta(x-1)\,\delta t + o(\delta t)) + o(\delta t).$$

Rearranging this equation, and taking the limit as $\delta t \to 0$, gives, for $x = 2, 3, \ldots,$

$$\frac{d}{dt}\, p_x(t) = -\beta x\, p_x(t) + \beta(x - 1)\, p_{x-1}(t). \tag{2.4}$$

If x is set equal to 1, then the second term on the right-hand side of (2.4) vanishes and the equation reduces to (2.3). So Equations (2.3) and (2.4) can be written as a single family of equations:

$$\frac{d}{dt}\, p_x(t) = -\beta x\, p_x(t) + \beta(x - 1)\, p_{x-1}(t), \quad x = 1, 2, \ldots. \tag{2.5}$$

Equations (2.5) are the differential–difference equations for the simple birth process. $\blacklozenge$

To help fix ideas, try Activity 2.1, in which you are asked to obtain the differential–difference equations for the pure death process.

Activity 2.1 The pure death process

The pure death process with death rate ν may be characterised by the following statement:

$$P(X(t + \delta t) = x - 1 \mid X(t) = x) = \nu x\, \delta t + o(\delta t).$$

Here $X(t)$ is the size of the population at time t. Let $p_x(t) = P(X(t) = x)$, $x = 0, 1, \ldots$. Use the postulates of the process to obtain an expression for $p_x(t + \delta t)$, and hence derive the differential–difference equations for the process.

In *Book 2*, the differential–difference equations for the Poisson process, which are given in (2.1) and (2.2), were solved recursively. First, $p_0(t)$ was found using (2.1), then $p_1(t)$, $p_2(t)$, ... were obtained using (2.2). Eventually, a pattern became clear, and the distribution of $X(t)$ was deduced: $X(t) \sim \text{Poisson}(\lambda t)$.

This approach involves the solution of a conceptually infinite number of differential equations, and for any given set of equations, there is the risk that no 'pattern' will become evident. A procedure that does not have this drawback is discussed in Subsection 2.3. The approach involves the probability generating function of the random variable $X(t)$, which is defined to be

$$\sum_{x=0}^{\infty} P(X(t) = x)\, s^x = \sum_{x=0}^{\infty} p_x(t)\, s^x.$$

This p.g.f. is a function involving both s and t, so to emphasise the functional dependence on two variables, it is denoted by $\Pi(s, t)$. That is,

$$\Pi(s, t) = \sum_{x=0}^{\infty} p_x(t)\, s^x.$$

In Subsection 2.3, the set of differential–difference equations for a random process will be replaced by a single equation whose solution is the p.g.f. $\Pi(s, t)$.

2.2   Functions of two variables

A summary of what you need to know about functions of two variables is contained in this subsection. Examples that do not relate to chance phenomena are used to illustrate the ideas discussed.

The function $f(x) = 2.54x$ $(x \geq 0)$ is a function of one variable. It converts measurements in inches to measurements in centimetres. There are many other simple functions: for example, $g(t) = \log(2 + t)$ and $h(y) = 1 - e^{-\lambda y}$. These functions can be evaluated at particular values of the argument: for example, $g(1.2) \simeq 1.16$, $h(2) = 1 - e^{-2\lambda}$.

A function of two variables is described in Example 2.3.

Example 2.3   Car insurance premiums

A motor insurance company decides that it will determine the annual premium that a motorist must pay for comprehensive cover on his or her car as a function of a, the motorist's age, and c, the rated capacity (in cubic centimetres) of the car engine. Since the premium (in £) depends on the two variables a and c, it can be written as $f(a, c)$. Suppose that the formula adopted, for $a \geq 17$ and $c > 0$, is

$$f(a, c) = 0.8 \, e^{-0.05a} \, c^{1.1}.$$

Then, for instance, a 20-year-old driving a 1.4-litre car will pay an annual premium (in £) of

$$f(20, 1400) = 0.8 \, e^{-1}(1400)^{1.1} \simeq 850.23,$$

and a 50-year-old driving a 2-litre car will pay

$$f(50, 2000) = 0.8 \, e^{-2.5}(2000)^{1.1} \simeq 280.86.$$

1 litre = 1000 cubic centimetres.

The premium is higher for young drivers than it is for older ones, and higher for larger cars: it decreases with increasing a, but increases with c.   ◆

Example 2.4   Representing a function of two variables

A function of a single variable can be represented by a curve drawn in two dimensions. A function $f(x, y)$ of two variables, x and y, can be represented by a surface in three dimensions. For example, the function $f(x, y) = x^2 + y^2 + 1$, $(x, y) \in \mathbb{R}^2$, is represented by the surface shown in Figure 2.1. Setting $x = 1$ and $y = 2$, for instance, gives $f(1, 2) = 1^2 + 2^2 + 1 = 6$, so the surface is 6 units high above the point $(1, 2)$.   ◆

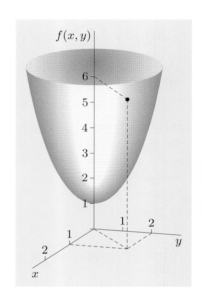

Figure 2.1   The graph of $f(x, y) = x^2 + y^2 + 1$, $(x, y) \in \mathbb{R}^2$

When dealing with a function of a single variable, notions of 'steepness' are quantified through the operation of differentiation. For the function $f(x)$, successive differentiation with respect to x is denoted by the sequence of derivatives $\dfrac{df}{dx}, \dfrac{d^2f}{dx^2}, \dfrac{d^3f}{dx^3}, \ldots$.

When dealing with a function of the form $f(x, y)$, a different notation is used. In general, the **first partial derivative of f with respect to x** is denoted $\dfrac{\partial f}{\partial x}$, and is defined by

$$\frac{\partial f}{\partial x} = \lim_{\delta x \to 0} \frac{f(x + \delta x, y) - f(x, y)}{\delta x},$$

provided that this limit exists. The **first partial derivative of f with respect to y** is denoted $\dfrac{\partial f}{\partial y}$, and is defined by

$$\frac{\partial f}{\partial y} = \lim_{\delta y \to 0} \frac{f(x, y + \delta y) - f(x, y)}{\delta y},$$

provided that this limit exists.

$\dfrac{\partial f}{\partial x}$ is read 'partial d f by d x'.

Notice how the partial d is written.

$\dfrac{\partial f}{\partial y}$ is read 'partial d f by d y'.

The process of calculating partial derivatives is called **partial differentiation**. The first partial derivative of f with respect to x is found by differentiating the function $f(x, y)$ with respect to the variable x while regarding the second variable y as a constant. The first partial derivative of f with respect to y is found by differentiating $f(x, y)$ with respect to y while regarding x as a constant.

Example 2.5   Partial differentiation

The function $f(x, y)$ is defined for all real x and y, and is given by the formula

$$f(x, y) = x^3 + y^2 - xe^y.$$

The first partial derivative of f with respect to x is found by differentiating f with respect to x while regarding y as a constant, so

$$\frac{\partial f}{\partial x} = 3x^2 - e^y.$$

The first partial derivative of f with respect to y is found by differentiating f with respect to y while regarding x as a constant, so

$$\frac{\partial f}{\partial y} = 2y - xe^y. \quad \blacklozenge$$

Activity 2.2   Partial differentiation

For each of the following functions, find the first partial derivative with respect to x and the first partial derivative with respect to y.

(a) $f(x, y) = 2xy^2 + 3x^2y$, $(x, y) \in \mathbb{R}^2$.

(b) $g(x, y) = xe^y + x^2y$, $(x, y) \in \mathbb{R}^2$.

(c) $h(x, y) = \log(x^2 + y)$, $x > 0$, $y > 0$.

Second- and higher-order partial derivatives are found in a similar way. For instance, the **second partial derivative of f with respect to x** is

$$\frac{\partial^2 f}{\partial x^2} = \frac{\partial}{\partial x}\left(\frac{\partial f}{\partial x}\right).$$

When differentiating both with respect to x and with respect to y, the order of differentiation does not matter: whether differentiating first with respect to x then with respect to y, or first with respect to y then with respect to x, the result is the same. So the **mixed derivative** is defined to be

This is true for the functions that you will meet in M343.

$$\frac{\partial^2 f}{\partial x \, \partial y} = \frac{\partial}{\partial x}\left(\frac{\partial f}{\partial y}\right) = \frac{\partial}{\partial y}\left(\frac{\partial f}{\partial x}\right) = \frac{\partial^2 f}{\partial y \, \partial x}.$$

Example 2.6   Second-order partial derivatives

For the function $f(x, y) = x^3 + y^2 - xe^y$, introduced in Example 2.5, the second partial derivative with respect to x is

$$\frac{\partial^2 f}{\partial x^2} = \frac{\partial}{\partial x}\left(\frac{\partial f}{\partial x}\right) = \frac{\partial}{\partial x}(3x^2 - e^y) = 6x.$$

The second partial derivative with respect to y is

$$\frac{\partial^2 f}{\partial y^2} = \frac{\partial}{\partial y}\left(\frac{\partial f}{\partial y}\right) = \frac{\partial}{\partial y}(2y - xe^y) = 2 - xe^y.$$

The mixed derivative is found either by differentiating first with respect to y and then with respect to x, giving

$$\frac{\partial^2 f}{\partial x \, \partial y} = \frac{\partial}{\partial x}\left(\frac{\partial f}{\partial y}\right) = \frac{\partial}{\partial x}(2y - xe^y) = -e^y,$$

or by differentiating first with respect to x and then with respect to y, giving

$$\frac{\partial^2 f}{\partial y \, \partial x} = \frac{\partial}{\partial y}\left(\frac{\partial f}{\partial x}\right) = \frac{\partial}{\partial y}(3x^2 - e^y) = -e^y. \quad \blacklozenge$$

Activity 2.3   Second-order partial derivatives

Find the second partial derivatives and the mixed derivative for each of the functions in Activity 2.2.

2.3   Probability generating function approach

The set of differential–difference equations for a discrete-valued random process $\{X(t); t \geq 0\}$ can be replaced by a single equation whose solution is the probability generating function of $X(t)$. In this subsection, this is done for the Poisson process and the simple birth process. Although you will not be expected to reproduce the derivations, you should work through them and try to follow the arguments.

For all the random processes discussed in Parts I and II, the p.m.f. of $X(t)$, conditional on information about $X(0)$, is denoted $p_x(t)$:

$$p_x(t) = P(X(t) = x), \quad x = 0, 1, \ldots.$$

As already mentioned, the dependence on $X(0)$ is implicit, and is not expressed explicitly. The p.g.f. of $X(t)$ is denoted $\Pi(s, t)$. It is a function of the two variables s and t, and is defined by

$$\Pi(s, t) = \sum_{x=0}^{\infty} p_x(t) \, s^x.$$

Example 2.7   The Poisson process

The differential–difference equations (2.1) and (2.2) for the Poisson process with rate λ are reproduced below:

$$\frac{d}{dt} p_0(t) = -\lambda \, p_0(t), \tag{2.6}$$

$$\frac{d}{dt} p_x(t) = -\lambda \, p_x(t) + \lambda \, p_{x-1}(t), \quad x = 1, 2, \ldots. \tag{2.7}$$

In order to obtain an equation for $\Pi(s, t)$, Equations (2.7) are first multiplied by s^x to give

$$\frac{d}{dt} p_x(t) \, s^x = -\lambda \, p_x(t) \, s^x + \lambda \, p_{x-1}(t) \, s^x, \quad x = 1, 2, \ldots. \tag{2.8}$$

Adding Equation (2.6) and all of Equations (2.8) (one for each value of x) gives

$$\frac{d}{dt} p_0(t) + \sum_{x=1}^{\infty} \frac{d}{dt} p_x(t) \, s^x = -\lambda \, p_0(t) - \lambda \sum_{x=1}^{\infty} p_x(t) \, s^x + \lambda \sum_{x=1}^{\infty} p_{x-1}(t) \, s^x. \tag{2.9}$$

The left-hand side of (2.9) is

$$\sum_{x=0}^{\infty} \frac{d}{dt}\, p_x(t)\, s^x = \frac{\partial}{\partial t}\left(\sum_{x=0}^{\infty} p_x(t)\, s^x\right) = \frac{\partial}{\partial t}\, \Pi(s,t).$$

It has been assumed that the derivative of the sum is equal to the sum of the derivatives.

This can be written simply as $\dfrac{\partial \Pi}{\partial t}$.

There are two sums on the right-hand side of (2.9). The first sum is

$$-\lambda\, p_0(t) - \lambda \sum_{x=1}^{\infty} p_x(t)\, s^x = -\lambda \sum_{x=0}^{\infty} p_x(t)\, s^x = -\lambda\, \Pi(s,t).$$

The second sum is

$$\sum_{x=1}^{\infty} \lambda\, p_{x-1}(t)\, s^x = \lambda s \sum_{x=1}^{\infty} p_{x-1}(t)\, s^{x-1}.$$

Writing $j = x - 1$, this becomes

$$\lambda s \sum_{j=0}^{\infty} p_j(t)\, s^j = \lambda s\, \Pi(s,t).$$

Therefore (2.9) can be written as

$$\frac{\partial \Pi}{\partial t} = -\lambda(1 - s)\Pi. \tag{2.10}$$

This is a **partial differential equation** for $\Pi(s,t)$, the p.g.f. of $X(t)$, the total number of events that occur by time t in a Poisson process. It is effectively a summary of the differential–difference equations (2.1) and (2.2). ♦

Example 2.8   The simple birth process

The differential–difference equations (2.5) for the simple birth process with birth rate β are reproduced below:

$$\frac{d}{dt}\, p_x(t) = -\beta x\, p_x(t) + \beta(x - 1)\, p_{x-1}(t), \quad x = 1, 2, \ldots. \tag{2.11}$$

For a simple birth process, $p_0(t) = 0$ for all t.

Multiplying Equations (2.11) by s^x and summing gives

$$\sum_{x=1}^{\infty} \frac{d}{dt}\, p_x(t)\, s^x = -\beta \sum_{x=1}^{\infty} x\, p_x(t)\, s^x + \beta \sum_{x=1}^{\infty} (x - 1)\, p_{x-1}(t)\, s^x. \tag{2.12}$$

The left-hand side of (2.12) is $\dfrac{\partial \Pi}{\partial t}$.

Making the change of variable $j = x - 1$, the second term on the right-hand side of (2.12) is

$$\beta \sum_{x=1}^{\infty} (x - 1)\, p_{x-1}(t)\, s^x = \beta s \sum_{j=0}^{\infty} j\, p_j(t)\, s^j = \beta s \sum_{j=1}^{\infty} j\, p_j(t)\, s^j.$$

Hence the right-hand side of (2.12) can be written as

$$-\beta \sum_{x=1}^{\infty} x\, p_x(t)\, s^x + \beta s \sum_{j=1}^{\infty} j\, p_j(t)\, s^j = -\beta(1 - s) \sum_{x=1}^{\infty} x\, p_x(t)\, s^x.$$

Note that the first partial derivative of $\Pi(s,t)$ with respect to s is

$$\frac{\partial \Pi}{\partial s} = \sum_{x=0}^{\infty} p_x(t)\, x s^{x-1} = \sum_{x=1}^{\infty} x\, p_x(t)\, s^{x-1}.$$

Multiplying this by s gives

$$s\, \frac{\partial \Pi}{\partial s} = \sum_{x=1}^{\infty} x\, p_x(t)\, s^x.$$

Therefore the right-hand side of (2.12) is equal to

$$-\beta s(1-s)\frac{\partial \Pi}{\partial s}.$$

Hence (2.12) can be written as

$$\frac{\partial \Pi}{\partial t} = -\beta s(1-s)\frac{\partial \Pi}{\partial s}. \tag{2.13}$$

This is a partial differential equation for $\Pi(s,t)$, the p.g.f. of the population size at time t in a simple birth process with birth rate β. Notice that it contains the first partial derivative of Π with respect to s and the first partial derivative of Π with respect to t. ♦

Activity 2.4   The pure death process

In Activity 2.1, you obtained the differential–difference equations for the pure death process with death rate ν. Use these equations to show that $\Pi(s,t)$, the p.g.f. of $X(t)$, the population size at time t, satisfies the partial differential equation

$$\frac{\partial \Pi}{\partial t} = \nu(1-s)\frac{\partial \Pi}{\partial s}.$$

2.4   Lagrange's equation

In Subsection 2.3, partial differential equations have been found for $\Pi(s,t)$, the p.g.f. of $X(t)$, for the Poisson process, the simple birth process and the pure death process. These equations are reproduced below.

Poisson process:

$$\frac{\partial \Pi}{\partial t} = -\lambda(1-s)\Pi.$$

Simple birth process:

$$\frac{\partial \Pi}{\partial t} = -\beta s(1-s)\frac{\partial \Pi}{\partial s}.$$

Pure death process:

$$\frac{\partial \Pi}{\partial t} = \nu(1-s)\frac{\partial \Pi}{\partial s}.$$

These equations are first-order partial differential equations; that is, they contain first-order partial derivatives, but not any higher-order partial derivatives. They are also linear in the partial derivatives. They are special cases of the following partial differential equation, which is called **Lagrange's equation**:

J.L. Lagrange (1736–1813)

$$f(s,t,\Pi)\frac{\partial \Pi}{\partial s} + g(s,t,\Pi)\frac{\partial \Pi}{\partial t} = h(s,t,\Pi).$$

The functions f, g and h are functions of the variables s, t and Π. A method for solving partial differential equations of this type is described in Section 3.

Summary of Section 2

In this section, the differential–difference equations for the Poisson process, the simple birth process and the pure death process have been discussed. You have seen that for each of these random processes, the set of differential–difference equations can be summarised as a partial differential equation for $\Pi(s,t)$, the p.g.f. of $X(t)$, and that these equations are special cases of a type of partial differential equation called Lagrange's equation.

3 Solving Lagrange's equation

Lagrange's equation was introduced in Subsection 2.4. In this section, a method for solving partial differential equations of this type is described. The method, which was given by Lagrange in 1779 and proved by him in 1785, is referred to in M343 as **Lagrange's method**. The method involves first finding the general solution of an equation, and then finding the particular solution that satisfies some initial condition. Finding the general solution is described in Subsection 3.1, and finding particular solutions is discussed in Subsection 3.2. Further practice at applying Lagrange's method is provided in Subsection 3.3.

No explanation will be given of why the method works.

Throughout this section, the notation s, t and Π is used, but the method described is of general application, and the function Π need not necessarily be the p.g.f. of an integer-valued random variable with a continuous time variable. In most of the examples used to illustrate the method in this section, the function $\Pi = \Pi(s, t)$ is not a p.g.f.

3.1 The general solution

The first step in Lagrange's method for solving Lagrange's equation is stated in the following box.

Lagrange's method: Step 1

Given a partial differential equation in which the first partial derivatives $\dfrac{\partial \Pi}{\partial s}$ and $\dfrac{\partial \Pi}{\partial t}$ occur only linearly (if at all), and in which higher-order derivatives do not feature, rewrite it in Lagrange form

$$f \frac{\partial \Pi}{\partial s} + g \frac{\partial \Pi}{\partial t} = h,$$

where f, g and h are functions of s, t and Π, and identify the functions f, g and h.

Example 3.1 Lagrange form

The following partial differential equation will be used to illustrate Lagrange's method:

$$(2 + t) \frac{\partial \Pi}{\partial s} = s\Pi - s \frac{\partial \Pi}{\partial t}.$$

When an equation is written in Lagrange form, the terms involving the partial derivatives are on the left-hand side of the equation. So in Lagrange form, the equation is

$$(2 + t) \frac{\partial \Pi}{\partial s} + s \frac{\partial \Pi}{\partial t} = s\Pi. \tag{3.1}$$

Therefore, for this equation,

$$f = 2 + t, \quad g = s, \quad h = s\Pi. \quad \blacklozenge$$

Activity 3.1   Step 1

Rewrite the following partial differential equation in Lagrange form, and identify the functions f, g and h:

$$s\frac{\partial \Pi}{\partial s} = \frac{\partial \Pi}{\partial t} + 2s^2\Pi. \tag{3.2}$$

The second step in Lagrange's method is to write down a trio of simultaneous ordinary differential equations called the **auxiliary equations** for the partial differential equation. These equations are usually written in the concise form given in the following box.

Lagrange's method: Step 2

Write down the auxiliary equations

$$\frac{ds}{f} = \frac{dt}{g} = \frac{d\Pi}{h}. \tag{3.3}$$

The form in which the auxiliary equations are written in (3.3) is simply a convenient way of writing down three ordinary differential equations associated with the partial differential equation. For example,

$$\frac{ds}{f} = \frac{dt}{g}$$

represents the ordinary differential equation

$$\frac{ds}{dt} = \frac{f}{g},$$

where $\dfrac{ds}{dt}$ is the derivative of s with respect to t. Equations (3.3) are also referred to as differential equations.

Example 3.2   Auxiliary equations

For the partial differential equation (3.1) of Example 3.1,

$$f = 2+t, \quad g = s, \quad h = s\Pi.$$

Therefore the auxiliary equations are

$$\frac{ds}{2+t} = \frac{dt}{s} = \frac{d\Pi}{s\Pi}. \quad \blacklozenge$$

Activity 3.2   Step 2

Write down the auxiliary equations for the partial differential equation (3.2) of Activity 3.1.

The auxiliary equations involve three different ordinary differential equations:

$$\frac{ds}{f} = \frac{dt}{g}, \quad \frac{ds}{f} = \frac{d\Pi}{h}, \quad \frac{dt}{g} = \frac{d\Pi}{h}.$$

Each equation is obtained by choosing two of the three terms in (3.3). This trio of equations actually involves only two independent equations, so only two of the three equations need to be solved.

The third step in Lagrange's method is to solve two of the equations and write the solutions in a particular form that will be discussed shortly. This step is summarised in the following box.

Lagrange's method: Step 3

Solve the auxiliary equations, writing your two solutions in the form

$$c_1 = \phi_1(s, t, \Pi), \quad c_2 = \phi_2(s, t, \Pi).$$

Example 3.3   Solving the auxiliary equations

For the partial differential equation (3.1), the auxiliary equations are

$$\frac{ds}{2+t} = \frac{dt}{s} = \frac{d\Pi}{s\Pi}.$$

See Examples 3.1 and 3.2.

Two of the following three ordinary differential equations must be solved:

$$\frac{ds}{2+t} = \frac{dt}{s}, \quad \frac{dt}{s} = \frac{d\Pi}{s\Pi}, \quad \frac{ds}{2+t} = \frac{d\Pi}{s\Pi}. \tag{3.4}$$

The best approach is to choose the two equations whose solution is most straightforward. A good strategy is to identify those for which the variables are separable. For instance, the first equation in (3.4) can be written as

$$s \, ds = (2+t) \, dt. \tag{3.5}$$

That is,

$$s \frac{ds}{dt} = 2 + t.$$

This equation may be integrated with respect to t:

$$\int s \frac{ds}{dt} \, dt = \int (2+t) \, dt,$$

or

$$\int s \, ds = \int (2+t) \, dt. \tag{3.6}$$

Notice that this equation is just (3.5) with the addition of integral signs. Since the variables have been separated, (3.6) can be written down immediately. This is what will be done from now on.

From (3.6), it follows that

$$\tfrac{1}{2} s^2 = 2t + \tfrac{1}{2} t^2 + \text{constant}.$$

This is one solution of the auxiliary equations. A second solution can be obtained by taking the second equation in (3.4):

$$\frac{dt}{s} = \frac{d\Pi}{s\Pi}.$$

This equation involves s, t and Π, but s vanishes on cancellation to give an equation in which the variables t and Π are separate. Thus

$$\int 1 \, dt = \int \frac{1}{\Pi} \, d\Pi.$$

This has the solution

$$t = \log \Pi + \text{constant}.$$

The term 'constant' means 'any constant', not 'the same constant as before'.

The third equation in (3.4) involves the three variables s, t and Π in an irreducible form. However, since two of the differential equations in (3.4) have already been solved, this equation may be ignored.

It is usual to end the third step by making the constants of integration the subjects of their respective equations, that is, by writing the equations with the constants standing alone on the left-hand side.

The first of the two solutions obtained can be written as

$$\text{constant} = \tfrac{1}{2}s^2 - 2t - \tfrac{1}{2}t^2,$$

or, multiplying by 2,

$$c_1 = s^2 - 4t - t^2.$$

The second solution can be written as

$$\text{constant} = \log \Pi - t.$$

Taking exponentials gives

$$\text{constant} = e^{\log \Pi - t} = \Pi e^{-t},$$

that is,

$$c_2 = \Pi e^{-t}. \quad \blacklozenge$$

In Example 3.3, it would not be wrong to write the second solution as $c_2 = \log \Pi - t$. This would lead to the same final solution to the partial differential equation. However, if for no other reason than to make it easy for you to follow the examples in this book, it is useful to have a convention. So when it is possible to rewrite a solution as a product involving the exponential function rather than as a sum involving the logarithmic function, this will be done.

Activity 3.3   Step 3

Obtain two solutions of the auxiliary equations for the partial differential equation (3.2) of Activities 3.1 and 3.2, and write them in the form $c_1 = \phi_1(s, t, \Pi)$, $c_2 = \phi_2(s, t, \Pi)$.

The fourth step in Lagrange's method is to write down the general solution of the original partial differential equation; this is the solution before any initial conditions are taken into account. Whereas the general solution of a first-order differential equation features an arbitrary constant, the general solution of a first-order partial differential equation involves an *arbitrary function*. This is illustrated in Example 3.4.

Example 3.4   Arbitrary functions

(a) It will be shown that for any differentiable function ψ, $\Pi(s, t) = \psi(s - t)$ is a solution of the partial differential equation

$$\frac{\partial \Pi}{\partial s} + \frac{\partial \Pi}{\partial t} = 0.$$

Since

$$\frac{\partial \Pi}{\partial s} = \psi'(s - t) \times \frac{\partial}{\partial s}(s - t) = \psi'(s - t) \times (+1)$$

and

$$\frac{\partial \Pi}{\partial t} = \psi'(s - t) \times \frac{\partial}{\partial t}(s - t) = \psi'(s - t) \times (-1),$$

it follows that

$$\frac{\partial \Pi}{\partial s} + \frac{\partial \Pi}{\partial t} = \psi'(s - t) - \psi'(s - t) = 0.$$

(b) The general solution of the partial differential equation

$$\frac{\partial \Pi}{\partial s} = s$$

is

$$\Pi(s, t) = \tfrac{1}{2}s^2 + \psi(t),$$

where ψ is an arbitrary function. This is so because, when obtaining the first partial derivative $\dfrac{\partial \Pi}{\partial s}$, t, and therefore the function $\psi(t)$, is regarded as a constant.

(c) It can be shown that for any differentiable function ψ,

$$\Pi(s, t) = 2 - e^{-s}\psi(s + t)$$

is the general solution of the partial differential equation

$$\frac{\partial \Pi}{\partial s} - \frac{\partial \Pi}{\partial t} + \Pi = 2.$$

The first partial derivatives of Π with respect to s and t are

$$\frac{\partial \Pi}{\partial s} = e^{-s}\psi(s + t) - e^{-s}\psi'(s + t),$$

$$\frac{\partial \Pi}{\partial t} = -e^{-s}\psi'(s + t).$$

When these expressions and the given expression for Π are substituted in the left-hand side of the partial differential equation, most of the terms cancel and the left-hand side simplifies to 2. Hence the given expression for Π is a solution of the equation. Any differentiable function ψ gives a solution. For instance, setting the function $\psi(x)$ equal to e^x gives $\Pi(s, t) = 2 - e^t$ as a particular solution; and setting $\psi(x) = x$ gives $\Pi(s, t) = 2 - (s + t)e^{-s}$ as another particular solution. However, the general solution contains an arbitrary function ψ. ◆

In Example 3.3, the solutions of the auxiliary equations were rearranged to yield c_1 and c_2 on the left-hand sides of equations that have expressions involving s, t and Π on the right-hand sides. In fact, the general solution of the original partial differential equation involves these expressions and is given by

$$c_2 = \psi(c_1),$$

where ψ is an arbitrary function.

Example 3.5   The general solution

For the partial differential equation (3.1) of Example 3.1, the two solutions of the auxiliary equations found in Example 3.3 are

$$c_1 = s^2 - 4t - t^2, \quad c_2 = \Pi e^{-t}.$$

The general solution of the partial differential equation is given by $c_2 = \psi(c_1)$, that is,

$$\Pi e^{-t} = \psi(s^2 - 4t - t^2),$$

or

$$\Pi(s, t) = e^t\,\psi(s^2 - 4t - t^2),$$

where ψ is an arbitrary differentiable function. ◆

In Example 3.5, the general solution was found from the equation $c_2 = \psi(c_1)$. But suppose that the second solution of the auxiliary equations had been obtained first, and written $c_1 = \Pi e^{-t}$. In that case, the general solution would have been given by $c_1 = \psi(c_2)$. This possibility is included in the statement of Step 4 of Lagrange's method given in the following box.

Lagrange's method: Step 4

Write down the arbitrary functional equation

$$c_2 = \psi(c_1)$$

(or $c_1 = \psi(c_2)$), and rewrite it to give the function $\Pi = \Pi(s,t)$ standing alone on the left-hand side of an equation involving s, t and the arbitrary function ψ on the right-hand side.

If the expression for c_1 includes Π, then the general solution is given by $c_1 = \psi(c_2)$.

Activity 3.4 Step 4

Find the general solution of the partial differential equation (3.2) of Activities 3.1, 3.2 and 3.3.

Example 3.6 The Poisson process

For the Poisson process, the partial differential equation for $\Pi(s,t)$ is

$$\frac{\partial \Pi}{\partial t} = -\lambda(1-s)\Pi. \tag{3.7}$$

In Lagrange form, it is written as

$$0 \times \frac{\partial \Pi}{\partial s} + 1 \times \frac{\partial \Pi}{\partial t} = -\lambda(1-s)\Pi,$$

so

$$f = 0, \quad g = 1, \quad h = -\lambda(1-s)\Pi.$$

The auxiliary equations are

$$\frac{ds}{0} = \frac{dt}{1} = \frac{d\Pi}{-\lambda(1-s)\Pi}.$$

Taking the first and second expressions together and cross-multiplying gives

$$\int 1\,ds = \int 0\,dt.$$

So one solution of the auxiliary equations is

$$s = \text{constant.}$$

or

$$c_1 = s.$$

At first sight, the equation obtained by taking the second and third expressions together appears to involve all three variables:

$$\frac{dt}{1} = \frac{d\Pi}{-\lambda(1-s)\Pi}.$$

However, from the first solution, s may be regarded as a constant, so this equation can be solved by treating s as a constant. Rewriting the equation gives

$$\int -\lambda(1-s)\,dt = \int \frac{1}{\Pi}\,d\Pi.$$

Remember, this is just a convenient way of writing down the auxiliary equations: we are not actually dividing by 0.

This result would also follow from the first and third expressions taken together. If you find an expression of the form $dx/0$ featuring in the auxiliary equations, you can write down the solution $x = \text{constant}$ immediately.

Remember that the auxiliary equations are simultaneous equations, so the solution for one can always be substituted into another.

If s is a constant, this has the solution

$$-\lambda(1-s)t = \log \Pi + \text{constant},$$

or

$$\text{constant} = \lambda(1-s)t + \log \Pi.$$

Taking exponentials gives

$$\text{constant} = \Pi\, e^{\lambda(1-s)t}.$$

It is this form, where the constant is expressed as a product rather than a sum, that is to be preferred. Thus the second solution is

$$c_2 = \Pi\, e^{\lambda(1-s)t}.$$

Since c_2 involves Π, the general solution of the partial differential equation is

$$c_2 = \psi(c_1).$$

Substituting for the constants c_1 and c_2 gives

$$\Pi\, e^{\lambda(1-s)t} = \psi(s).$$

So the general solution is

$$\Pi = \Pi(s,t) = \psi(s)\, e^{-\lambda(1-s)t},$$

where ψ is an arbitrary differentiable function. ◆

Activity 3.5   Steps 1 to 4

Obtain the general solution of the partial differential equation

$$t\,\frac{\partial \Pi}{\partial s} = s\,\frac{\partial \Pi}{\partial t}. \tag{3.8}$$

Activity 3.6   Further practice

Obtain the general solution of the partial differential equation

$$(s+t)\,\frac{\partial \Pi}{\partial t} = s + \Pi. \tag{3.9}$$

3.2   Particular solutions

The final step in Lagrange's method is to identify the arbitrary function in the general solution that corresponds to a given initial condition, and hence find the particular solution for this initial condition. This step is summarised in the following box.

Lagrange's method: Step 5

Find the particular solution for a given initial condition by identifying the function ψ using the initial condition, and then substituting for ψ in the general solution.

Example 3.7   Finding a particular solution

The general solution of the partial differential equation (3.1), which was found in Example 3.5, is

$$\Pi(s,t) = e^t\,\psi(s^2 - 4t - t^2). \tag{3.10}$$

Suppose that the given initial condition is that at time $t = 0$, the function $\Pi(s,t)$ is equal to s; that is,

$$\Pi(s,0) = s.$$

Setting $t = 0$ in (3.10) gives

$$\Pi(s,0) = \psi(s^2).$$

Therefore, using the given initial condition,

$$\psi(s^2) = s.$$

The function ψ can be identified in this case by writing $x = s^2$, so that $s = \sqrt{x}$. This gives

$$\psi(x) = \sqrt{x}.$$

The particular solution for $\Pi(s,t)$ is found by substituting for ψ in (3.10):

$$\Pi(s,t) = e^t\sqrt{s^2 - 4t - t^2}.$$

This is the solution of the partial differential equation (3.1) satisfying the initial condition $\Pi(s,0) = s$.   ◆

Recall that $\psi(s^2 - 4t - t^2)$ is found by replacing x with $s^2 - 4t - t^2$ in the formula for $\psi(x)$.

Example 3.8   The Poisson process

In Example 3.6, you saw that the general solution of the partial differential equation for a Poisson process with rate λ is

$$\Pi(s,t) = \psi(s)\,e^{-\lambda(1-s)t}. \tag{3.11}$$

The initial condition is $X(0) = 0$. Since $\Pi(s,0)$ is the p.g.f. of $X(0)$, a degenerate random variable that takes the value 0 with probability 1,

$$\Pi(s,0) = s^0 = 1.$$

Setting $t = 0$ in (3.11) gives

$$\Pi(s,0) = \psi(s).$$

Therefore $\psi(s) = 1$, and hence for the Poisson process,

$$\Pi(s,t) = e^{-\lambda(1-s)t}.   ◆$$

Activity 3.7   Step 5

Find the particular solution of the partial differential equation (3.2), given that at time 0, $\Pi(s,0) = 2s\exp(s^2)$.

You found the general solution in Activity 3.4.

Activity 3.8   More practice

Find the particular solution of the partial differential equation (3.8) of Activity 3.5, given that at time 0, $\Pi(s,0) = 1/s^2$.

Activity 3.9   Different initial conditions

Find the particular solution of the partial differential equation (3.9) of Activity 3.6 for each of the following initial conditions.

(a) $\Pi(s,0) = 1$ (b) $\Pi(s,0) = s^2$

3.3   Lagrange's method

The five steps involved in finding a particular solution of Lagrange's equation satisfying a given initial condition are summarised in the following box.

Procedure for solving Lagrange's equation

Step 1   Given a partial differential equation in which the first partial derivatives $\dfrac{\partial \Pi}{\partial s}$ and $\dfrac{\partial \Pi}{\partial t}$ occur only linearly (if at all), and in which higher-order derivatives do not feature, rewrite it in Lagrange form

$$f \frac{\partial \Pi}{\partial s} + g \frac{\partial \Pi}{\partial t} = h,$$

where f, g and h are functions of s, t and Π, and identify the functions f, g and h.

Step 2   Write down the auxiliary equations

$$\frac{ds}{f} = \frac{dt}{g} = \frac{d\Pi}{h}.$$

Step 3   Solve the auxiliary equations, writing your two solutions in the form

$$c_1 = \phi_1(s,t,\Pi), \quad c_2 = \phi_2(s,t,\Pi).$$

Step 4   Write down the arbitrary functional equation

$$c_2 = \psi(c_1)$$

(or $c_1 = \psi(c_2)$), and rewrite it to give the function $\Pi = \Pi(s,t)$ standing alone on the left-hand side of an equation involving s, t and the arbitrary function ψ on the right-hand side.

Step 5   Find the particular solution for a given initial condition by identifying the function ψ using the initial condition, and then substituting for ψ in the general solution.

Example 3.9   Lagrange's method

The procedure will be illustrated by finding the particular solution of the partial differential equation below for the initial condition $\Pi(s, 0) = 1$:

$$s \frac{\partial \Pi}{\partial s} = \frac{\partial \Pi}{\partial t} + s \frac{\partial}{\partial s}(s\Pi).$$

Step 1 is to rewrite this equation in Lagrange form, and identify the functions f, g and h. Expanding the last term on the right-hand side (using the product rule for differentiation) gives

$$s \frac{\partial \Pi}{\partial s} = \frac{\partial \Pi}{\partial t} + s\Pi + s^2 \frac{\partial \Pi}{\partial s}.$$

In Lagrange form, this equation is

$$s(1 - s) \frac{\partial \Pi}{\partial s} - \frac{\partial \Pi}{\partial t} = s\Pi.$$

Therefore

$$f = s(1 - s), \quad g = -1, \quad h = s\Pi.$$

The auxiliary equations are

Step 2.

$$\frac{ds}{s(1 - s)} = \frac{dt}{-1} = \frac{d\Pi}{s\Pi}.$$

Taking the first and third expressions together and cancelling s gives

$$\int \frac{1}{1 - s} \, ds = \int \frac{1}{\Pi} \, d\Pi,$$

so

$$-\log(1 - s) = \log \Pi + \text{constant}.$$

This may be written as

$$\text{constant} = \log(1 - s) + \log \Pi$$

or, taking exponentials,

$$c_1 = (1 - s)\Pi.$$

The second solution may be found by taking the first and second expressions together to give

$$\frac{ds}{s(1 - s)} = \frac{dt}{-1}.$$

This may be rewritten as

$$\int \left(\frac{1}{s} + \frac{1}{1 - s} \right) ds = -\int 1 \, dt,$$

$$\frac{1}{s(1 - s)} = \frac{1}{s} + \frac{1}{1 - s}$$

so

$$\log s - \log(1 - s) = -t + \text{constant},$$

or

$$\text{constant} = \log s - \log(1 - s) + t.$$

Taking exponentials gives

$$c_2 = \frac{s}{1 - s} e^t.$$

This completes Step 3.

Since c_1 includes Π, the general solution is given by $c_1 = \psi(c_2)$, that is,

Step 4.

$$(1 - s)\Pi = \psi \left(\frac{s}{1 - s} e^t \right),$$

so

$$\Pi(s, t) = \frac{1}{1 - s} \psi \left(\frac{s}{1 - s} e^t \right).$$

The given initial condition is $\Pi(s,0) = 1$, and setting $t = 0$ in the general solution gives

$$\Pi(s,0) = \frac{1}{1-s}\,\psi\left(\frac{s}{1-s}\right),$$

so

$$\frac{1}{1-s}\,\psi\left(\frac{s}{1-s}\right) = 1,$$

and hence

$$\psi\left(\frac{s}{1-s}\right) = 1 - s.$$

Writing $x = s/(1-s)$, so that $s = x/(1+x)$, gives

$$\psi(x) = 1 - \frac{x}{1+x} = \frac{1}{1+x}.$$

Therefore the particular solution is

$$\begin{aligned}
\Pi(s,t) &= \frac{1}{1-s}\,\psi\left(\frac{s}{1-s}\,e^t\right)\\
&= \frac{1}{1-s} \times \frac{1}{1 + \dfrac{s}{1-s}\,e^t}\\
&= \frac{1}{1 - s + se^t}. \quad \blacklozenge
\end{aligned}$$

To find $\psi\left(\dfrac{s}{1-s}\,e^t\right)$, x is replaced by $\dfrac{s}{1-s}\,e^t$ in the formula for $\psi(x)$.

This completes Step 5.

Activity 3.10   Using Lagrange's method

Given that at time 0, $\Pi(s,t)$ is equal to s, solve the partial differential equation

$$t\,\frac{\partial \Pi}{\partial s} = s\,\frac{\partial \Pi}{\partial t} + s\,\frac{\partial}{\partial s}(st\Pi).$$

Summary of Section 3

In this section, a procedure for solving a particular type of first-order partial differential equation has been described. You have learned how to find the general solution of an equation, and how to find the particular solution corresponding to a given initial condition.

Exercises on Section 3

Exercise 3.1   Practice at using Lagrange's method

Given that at time 0, $\Pi(s,t)$ is equal to s^3, solve the partial differential equation

$$2st\,\frac{\partial \Pi}{\partial s} - s\,\frac{\partial \Pi}{\partial t} = 2t\Pi.$$

Exercise 3.2   More practice

Given that at time 0, $\Pi(s,t)$ is equal to s, solve the partial differential equation

$$\frac{\partial \Pi}{\partial t} = 1 + s\Pi.$$

4 Two growing populations

Two simple models for increasing populations are discussed in this section – the simple birth process in Subsection 4.1, and the immigration–birth process in Subsection 4.2. In each case, Lagrange's method is used to find the p.g.f. of $X(t)$, the size of the population at time t, and the distribution of $X(t)$ is identified.

4.1 The simple birth process

The simple birth process was introduced in Subsection 1.2. It is a model for a population in which each individual independently gives birth to new individuals according to a Poisson process. The rate at which an individual gives birth to new individuals is denoted β; this is the (**individual**) **birth rate** of the process. There are no arrivals from outside the population, and there are no deaths.

If $X(t)$ denotes the size of the population at time t, then the simple birth process $\{X(t); t \geq 0\}$ is characterised by the probability statement

$$P(X(t + \delta t) = x + 1 \mid X(t) = x) = \beta x \, \delta t + o(\delta t).$$

In Section 2, you saw that $\Pi(s, t)$, the p.g.f. of $X(t)$, satisfies the partial differential equation

$$\frac{\partial \Pi}{\partial t} = -\beta s(1 - s) \frac{\partial \Pi}{\partial s}. \tag{4.1}$$

See Example 2.8.

Activity 4.1 The general solution

Use Lagrange's method to show that the general solution of the partial differential equation (4.1) for a simple birth process with birth rate β is

$$\Pi(s, t) = \psi \left(\frac{s}{1 - s} e^{-\beta t} \right). \tag{4.2}$$

Example 4.1 One individual at the start

Suppose that a simple birth process with birth rate β starts with one individual at time 0, that is, $X(0) = 1$. Since the p.g.f. of a degenerate random variable that takes the value 1 with probability 1 is s,

$$\Pi(s, 0) = s.$$

A degenerate random variable that takes the value n with probability 1 has p.g.f. s^n.

Setting $t = 0$ in the general solution (4.2) gives

$$\Pi(s, 0) = \psi \left(\frac{s}{1 - s} \right).$$

Therefore

$$\psi \left(\frac{s}{1 - s} \right) = s.$$

Writing $s/(1 - s) = x$ gives $s = x/(1 + x)$, so

$$\psi(x) = \frac{x}{1 + x}.$$

Therefore the particular solution corresponding to a population of size 1 at time 0 is

$$\Pi(s,t) = \psi\left(\frac{s}{1-s}e^{-\beta t}\right)$$

$$= \frac{\dfrac{s}{1-s}e^{-\beta t}}{1+\dfrac{s}{1-s}e^{-\beta t}}$$

$$= \frac{se^{-\beta t}}{1-(1-e^{-\beta t})s}.$$

This is the p.g.f. of a geometric random variable starting at 1 with parameter $e^{-\beta t}$, so $X(t) \sim G_1(e^{-\beta t})$. So the p.m.f. of $X(t)$ is

$$p_x(t) = P(X(t) = x) = e^{-\beta t}(1-e^{-\beta t})^{x-1}, \quad x = 1, 2, \ldots.$$

These probabilities are all implicitly conditional on the event $[X(0) = 1]$.

Thus, for instance, the probability that there are three individuals in the population at time t is given by

$$P(X(t) = 3) = e^{-\beta t}(1-e^{-\beta t})^2.$$

The probability that there are more than three individuals in the population at time t is given by

$$P(X(t) > 3) = (1-e^{-\beta t})^3.$$

The expected size of the population at time t is given by

$$E[X(t)] = \frac{1}{e^{-\beta t}} = e^{\beta t}. \quad \blacklozenge$$

From Table 8 in the *Handbook*, if $X \sim G_1(p)$, then
$$\Pi_X(s) = \frac{ps}{1-qs},$$
where $q = 1 - p$.

If $X \sim G_1(p)$, then
$$P(X > x) = q^x,$$
where $q = 1 - p$.

If $X \sim G_1(p)$, then $E(X) = 1/p$.

Activity 4.2   More than one at the start

Suppose that a simple birth process with birth rate β starts with three individuals at time 0.

(a) Find the particular solution of the partial differential equation (4.1) in this case.

(b) Hence identify the distribution of $X(t)$ in this case, and find $E[X(t)]$.

(c) Write down an expression for $P(X(t) = 5)$.

More generally, if a simple birth process is initiated by n individuals (so that $X(0) = n$, and $\Pi(s,0) = s^n$), then applying Step 5 leads to

$$\Pi(s,t) = \left(\frac{se^{-\beta t}}{1-(1-e^{-\beta t})s}\right)^n. \tag{4.3}$$

You may like to check this for yourself.

This is the p.g.f. of a negative binomial distribution. So in a simple birth process initiated by n individuals, the number of individuals alive at time t has a negative binomial distribution with parameters n and $e^{-\beta t}$, and range $\{n, n+1, \ldots\}$.

Alternatively, note that the individuals in the population at time 0 generate independent family trees, so the total number of individuals alive at time t is the sum of n independent identically distributed geometric variates, each with p.g.f.

$$\frac{se^{-\beta t}}{1-(1-e^{-\beta t})s}.$$

It follows that the p.g.f. of $X(t)$ is given by (4.3).

Waiting times

In Subsection 1.2, you learned how to find the mean and variance of W_n, the waiting time to the nth birth in a simple birth process with birth rate β. The c.d.f. of W_n can be obtained from the distribution of $X(t)$, as follows.

Suppose that a simple birth process starts with one individual at time 0. The nth birth brings the population size up to $n + 1$, so if this occurs at or before time t, that is, if $W_n \leq t$, then the population size at time t will be at least $n + 1$. That is, $X(t) \geq n + 1$ or equivalently $X(t) > n$. Similarly, if $X(t) \geq n + 1$, then the nth birth must have occurred at or before time t; that is, $W_n \leq t$. So the events $X(t) \geq n + 1$ and $W_n \leq t$ are equivalent, and hence

$$P(W_n \leq t) = P(X(t) \geq n + 1).$$

In Example 4.1, it was shown that $X(t) \sim G_1(e^{-\beta t})$, so

$$P(X(t) \geq n + 1) = P(X(t) > n) = (1 - e^{-\beta t})^n.$$

Therefore the c.d.f. of W_n is given by

$$P(W_n \leq t) = (1 - e^{-\beta t})^n. \tag{4.4}$$

If $X \sim G_1(p)$, then
$$P(X > x) = q^x,$$
where $q = 1 - p$.

Activity 4.3   Waiting times

Suppose that a simple birth process with birth rate β starts with one individual at time 0.

(a) Write down the c.d.f. of W_4, the waiting time to the fourth birth.

(b) Find the median waiting time to the fourth birth.

Activity 4.4   Another waiting time

In Activity 4.2, you found the distribution of $X(t)$ for a simple birth process with birth rate β that starts with three individuals at time 0.

If W_2 is the waiting time to the second birth, then which of the following statements is equivalent to the statement $W_2 \leq t$?

$$X(t) \geq 2, \quad X(t) \geq 3, \quad X(t) \geq 4, \quad X(t) \geq 5.$$

Hence write down the c.d.f. of W_2.

4.2   The immigration–birth process

The immigration–birth process was introduced in Activity 1.7. Suppose that $X(t)$ is the size of a population at time t. If arrivals join the population at rate λ (as in a Poisson process) and individuals in the population give birth independently at rate β (as in a simple birth process), then the random process $\{X(t); t \geq 0\}$ is an immigration–birth process.

The immigration–birth process is characterised by the statement

$$P(X(t + \delta t) = x + 1 \mid X(t) = x) = (\lambda + \beta x)\,\delta t + o(\delta t).$$

This is Postulate I for the process.

The p.m.f. of $X(t)$, conditional on $X(0)$, is denoted $p_x(t)$; that is, $p_x(t) = P(X(t) = x)$. The dependence on $X(0)$ is not expressed explicitly. The differential–difference equations for the process can be derived using the postulates for the process; the partial differential equation for $\Pi(s,t)$, the p.g.f. of $X(t)$, can be obtained using the methods described in Section 2 for the Poisson process and the simple birth process.

The details will not be given here.

The partial differential equation for the immigration–birth process is

$$\beta s(1-s)\frac{\partial \Pi}{\partial s} + \frac{\partial \Pi}{\partial t} = -\lambda(1-s)\Pi. \tag{4.5}$$

You will not be expected to derive this equation. However, you should be able to solve the equation using Lagrange's method. You are asked to find the general solution of (4.5) in Activity 4.5. Particular solutions are the subject of Activities 4.6 and 4.7.

Activity 4.5   The general solution

Use Lagrange's method to show that the general solution of the partial differential equation (4.5) for an immigration–birth process may be written as

$$\Pi(s,t) = s^{-\lambda/\beta}\,\psi\left(\frac{s}{1-s}\,e^{-\beta t}\right). \tag{4.6}$$

Activity 4.6   No one at the start

Suppose that in an immigration–birth process there is no one in the population at time 0; that is, $X(0) = 0$.

(a) Find the particular solution for $\Pi(s,t)$ in this case.

(b) Hence identify the distribution of $X(t)$.

Activity 4.7   Several individuals at the start

Suppose that in an immigration–birth process there are n individuals in the population at time 0; that is, $X(0) = n$.

(a) Find the particular solution for $\Pi(s,t)$ in this case.

(b) Write $\Pi(s,t)$ as the product of the p.g.f.s of two negative binomial distributions.

(c) Since $\Pi(s,t)$ is the product of two p.g.f.s, $X(t)$ is the sum of two independent random variables. Identify the distributions of these two random variables.

In Activity 4.7, you saw that $X(t)$, the population size at time t in an immigration–birth process, is the sum of two random variables, each with a negative binomial distribution. The first random variable, with p.g.f. of the form $(q/(1-ps))^{\lambda/\beta}$, represents the arrivals after time 0 and their offspring. The second random variable, with p.g.f. of the form $(ps/(1-qs))^n$, represents those who were there at the start, if any, and their offspring; the p.g.f. is the same as that for the number alive in a simple birth process initiated by n individuals.

So far in M343, any negative binomial variates that you have met have arisen as the sum of independent geometric variates. However, λ/β is not necessarily an integer, so the first negative binomial variate cannot be regarded as a sum of geometric variates. Nevertheless, the formulas in Table 8 in the *Handbook* apply. In particular, if X has p.m.f.

$$\Pi_X(s) = \left(\frac{q}{1-ps}\right)^\alpha,$$

where α is not necessarily an integer, then the p.m.f. is given by

$$P(X=0) = q^\alpha,$$

$$P(X=x) = \binom{\alpha+x-1}{x} q^\alpha p^x, \quad x = 1, 2, \ldots.$$

Whether or not α is an integer,

$$\binom{\alpha+x-1}{x} = \frac{(\alpha+x-1)(\alpha+x-2)\cdots\alpha}{x!}.$$

Example 4.2   Another initial condition

Suppose that when observation of an immigration–birth process starts, the size of the population is not known but is itself a random variable.

For example, consider a process in which $\lambda = \beta$, and suppose that $X(0) \sim G_0(0.5)$. Then the p.g.f. of $X(0)$ is

$$\Pi(s,0) = \frac{0.5}{1-0.5s} = \frac{1}{2-s}.$$

Setting $\lambda = \beta$ and $t = 0$ in the general solution (4.6) gives

$$\Pi(s,0) = s^{-1}\,\psi\left(\frac{s}{1-s}\right).$$

Therefore

$$s^{-1}\,\psi\left(\frac{s}{1-s}\right) = \frac{1}{2-s},$$

and hence

$$\psi\left(\frac{s}{1-s}\right) = \frac{s}{2-s}.$$

Writing $x = s/(1-s)$ gives $s = x/(1+x)$, so

$$\psi(x) = \frac{x}{1+x} \left/ \left(2 - \frac{x}{1+x}\right)\right. = \frac{x}{2+x}.$$

Therefore, in this case, the particular solution of (4.5) is

$$\Pi(s,t) = s^{-1}\,\psi\left(\frac{s}{1-s}e^{-\beta t}\right)$$

$$= s^{-1}\,\frac{\dfrac{s}{1-s}e^{-\beta t}}{2 + \dfrac{s}{1-s}e^{-\beta t}}$$

$$= \frac{e^{-\beta t}}{2 - (2 - e^{-\beta t})s}$$

$$= \frac{\tfrac{1}{2}e^{-\beta t}}{1 - (1 - \tfrac{1}{2}e^{-\beta t})s}.$$

This is the p.g.f. of a geometric random variable starting at 0:

$$X(t) \sim G_0(1 - \tfrac{1}{2}e^{-\beta t}). \quad \blacklozenge$$

Activity 4.8   Yet another initial condition

Suppose that in an immigration–birth process with $\lambda = 2\beta$, the number of individuals in the population at time 0 has a negative binomial distribution with range $\{0, 1, \ldots\}$ and parameters $r = 2$ and $p = \frac{2}{3}$.

Find the particular solution of the partial differential equation (4.5) in this case, and identify the distribution of $X(t)$.

Summary of Section 4

In this section, you have used Lagrange's method to solve the partial differential equations for the simple birth process and the immigration–birth process, for several different initial conditions. You have also learned how to find the c.d.f. of the waiting time to the nth birth in a simple birth process given the population size at time 0.

Exercises on Section 4

Exercise 4.1   Waiting for the second birth

Suppose that a simple birth process with birth rate β starts with two individuals.

(a) Find the p.g.f. of $X(t)$, and hence identify the distribution of $X(t)$.

(b) Find the probabilities $P(X(t) = 2)$ and $P(X(t) = 3)$.

(c) Find the c.d.f. of W_2, the waiting time to the second birth.

Exercise 4.2   An immigration–birth process

Suppose that $X(t)$ is the number of individuals alive at time t in an immigration–birth process, and that $\Pi(s, t)$ is the p.g.f. of $X(t)$. In Activity 4.5, you showed that the general solution of the partial differential equation (4.5) for $\Pi(s, t)$ is

$$\Pi(s, t) = s^{-\lambda/\beta} \, \psi\left(\frac{s}{1 - s} \, e^{-\beta t} \right).$$

Suppose that $\lambda = 3\beta$ and $X(0)$, the number of individuals alive at time 0, is a random variable, and that $X(0)$ has a negative binomial distribution with range $\{0, 1, \ldots\}$ and parameters $r = 3$ and $p = \frac{3}{4}$.

(a) Find the particular solution corresponding to this case.

(b) Identify the probability distribution of $X(t)$ in this case, and find its mean.

5 Birth and death processes

Four models have been discussed so far in this book – the Poisson process, the simple birth process, the immigration–birth process and the pure death process. These are all Markov processes, which are reviewed briefly in Subsection 5.1. They also belong to a class of processes known as birth and death processes, which are discussed briefly in Subsection 5.2. A particular birth and death process, the immigration–birth–death process, is described in Subsection 5.3. This is a model for a population in which there is immigration (arrivals), and in which individuals give birth independently to new individuals (as in the simple birth process) and have exponential lifetimes (as in the pure death process).

5.1 Markov processes

A random process is a Markov process if it has the Markov property, that is, if the future behaviour of the process, when its current state is known, is independent of its past. Notation for the transition probabilities of a Markov process was introduced in Subsection 1.4: for any states i and j, and for $u < t$,

$$p_{i,j}(u, t) = P(X(t) = j \mid X(u) = i).$$

For any time v such that $u < v < t$, applying the Theorem of Total Probability, conditioning on the state k occupied at time v, and using the Markov property, a set of equations known as the Chapman–Kolmogorov equations can be derived. These are stated in the following box.

> **The Chapman–Kolmogorov equations**
>
> For a Markov process in continuous time with a discrete state space, for $u < v < t$ and any states i and j,
>
> $$p_{i,j}(u, t) = \sum_{k} p_{i,k}(u, v)\, p_{k,j}(v, t), \tag{5.1}$$
>
> where the summation is over all states k in the state space. These equations are known as the **Chapman–Kolmogorov equations**.

The Chapman–Kolmogorov equations for a Markov chain were derived in *Book 3*.

The first step in obtaining the differential–difference equations for a Markov process involves applying the Chapman–Kolmogorov equations (5.1) with 0, t and $t + \delta t$ replacing u, v and t, respectively. This was done in Section 2, without stating the equations explicitly, when deriving the differential–difference equations for the simple birth process, and in *Book 2*, when deriving the differential–difference equations for the Poisson process. The equations will be used in this way in Subsection 5.2.

5.2 Birth and death processes

In the Poisson process, the simple birth process and the immigration–birth process, the only change possible in a small interval of time is an increase of 1. In the pure death process, the only change possible is a decrease of 1. Markov processes in which the only change possible in a small interval of time is either an increase of 1 or a decrease of 1 are known as **birth and death processes**.

In a birth and death process, the random variable $X(t)$ represents the size of some population at time t. If $X(t) = x$, then the possible changes in the interval $[t, t + \delta t]$ are an increase of 1, increasing the population size to $x + 1$ at time $t + \delta t$, and a decrease of 1, reducing the size to $x - 1$ at time $t + \delta t$; these have probabilities $p_{x,x+1}(t, t + \delta t)$ and $p_{x,x-1}(t, t + \delta t)$. Since the process is a Markov process, these probabilities depend only on x, t and δt, hence they may be written as

$$p_{x,x+1}(t, t + \delta t) = \beta_x \, \delta t + o(\delta t), \tag{5.2}$$
$$p_{x,x-1}(t, t + \delta t) = \nu_x \, \delta t + o(\delta t), \tag{5.3}$$

where β_x and ν_x are functions of x and t. The quantity β_x is called the **overall birth rate** of the process, and ν_x is the **overall death rate**. The population size must be a non-negative integer, so the death rate ν_0 is defined to be 0, and (5.2) and (5.3) hold for $x = 0, 1, \dots$. The probability that two or more events occur in the interval $[t, t + \delta t]$ is $o(\delta t)$, so the probability that no change occurs in $[t, t + \delta t]$ is given by

β_x and ν_x may be functions of x only, or of t only, or of both x and t.

$$p_{x,x}(t, t + \delta t) = 1 - \beta_x \, \delta t - \nu_x \, \delta t + o(\delta t). \tag{5.4}$$

Note that if an increase and a decrease both occur in $[t, t + \delta t]$, then the population size returns to x at the end of the interval. However, the probability that two events occur is $o(\delta t)$, so the probability of this happening is included in (5.4).

The main points concerning birth and death processes that have been discussed are summarised in the following box.

Birth and death processes

A **birth and death process** is a Markov process $\{X(t); t \geq 0\}$ in which $X(t)$ takes non-negative integer values, and the only changes possible in any small interval $[t, t + \delta t]$ are an increase of 1 and a decrease of 1. For $x = 0, 1, \dots$, these changes have probabilities

$$p_{x,x+1}(t, t + \delta t) = \beta_x \, \delta t + o(\delta t),$$
$$p_{x,x-1}(t, t + \delta t) = \nu_x \, \delta t + o(\delta t),$$

where β_x, the **overall birth rate**, and ν_x, the **overall death rate**, are functions of x and t, and ν_0 is defined to be 0. The probability that two or more events occur in any small interval $[t, t + \delta t]$ is $o(\delta t)$, so for $x = 0, 1, \dots$,

$$p_{x,x}(t, t + \delta t) = 1 - \beta_x \, \delta t - \nu_x \, \delta t + o(\delta t).$$

Example 5.1   The simple birth process

For the simple birth process, if there are x individuals in the population at time t, then the probability of a birth occurring in the interval $[t, t + \delta t]$ is $\beta x \, \delta t + o(\delta t)$. Therefore β_x, the overall birth rate, is equal to βx. No deaths occur in this process, so $\nu_x = 0$. ◆

Activity 5.1   The pure death process

Write down the values of β_x and ν_x for the pure death process.

Activity 5.2   *Overall birth and death rates*

What processes are represented by the following overall birth and death rates?

(a) $\beta_x = \lambda$, $\nu_x = 0$.

(b) $\beta_x = \lambda(t)$, $\nu_x = 0$.

All the birth and death processes that are studied in this book are homogeneous, so β_x and ν_x are independent of time. Moreover, in Parts I and II, the overall birth and death rates take the form of linear functions of x; that is,

$$\beta_x = \beta x + \lambda, \quad \nu_x = \nu x + \varepsilon.$$

The overall birth rate β_x consists of two terms: βx, where β is the individual birth rate – that is, the rate at which each individual gives birth to new individuals – and λ, the immigration rate. The overall death rate ν_x also consists of two terms: νx, where ν is the individual death rate – so that the lifetime of each individual has an exponential distribution with mean $1/\nu$ – and ε, which is known as the **emigration** rate.

All the models discussed in Part I involve one or more of immigration, births and deaths, but they do not involve emigration. Several of the models for queues discussed in Part II are birth and death processes and include emigration.

For a birth and death process $\{X(t); t \geq 0\}$, $X(t)$ is the size of the population at time t. Usually, the size of the population is given at time $t = 0$, so to find the distribution of $X(t)$, the probabilities $p_{i,x}(0, t)$ must be calculated. For simplicity, the zero will be omitted from $p_{i,x}(0, t)$. That is, the probability that the population size is x at time t, given that there were i individuals at the start, will be denoted $p_{i,x}(t)$:

$$p_{i,x}(t) = P(X(t) = x \,|\, X(0) = i).$$

The differential–difference equations for the general birth and death process, which are known as the Kolmogorov forward equations, will now be derived.

Applying the Chapman–Kolmogorov equations (5.1), with 0, t and $t + \delta t$ replacing u, v and t, respectively, gives

$$p_{i,x}(t + \delta t) = \sum_k p_{i,k}(t)\, p_{k,x}(t, t + \delta t). \tag{5.5}$$

The only values of k for which the transition probability $p_{k,x}(t, t + \delta t)$ is non-negligible are $k = x - 1$, $k = x + 1$ and $k = x$. From (5.2), (5.3) and (5.4),

$$p_{x-1,x}(t, t + \delta t) = \beta_{x-1}\, \delta t + o(\delta t),$$
$$p_{x+1,x}(t, t + \delta t) = \nu_{x+1}\, \delta t + o(\delta t),$$
$$p_{x,x}(t, t + \delta t) = 1 - \beta_x\, \delta t - \nu_x\, \delta t + o(\delta t).$$

These are the transition probabilities corresponding to the situations where the population size is $x - 1$ at time t and an increase of 1 occurs in the interval $[t, t + \delta t]$, the size is $x + 1$ at time t and a decrease of 1 occurs, and the size is x at time t and no change occurs.

Substituting these probabilities in (5.5) gives

$$p_{i,x}(t + \delta t) = p_{i,x-1}(t)\, \beta_{x-1}\, \delta t + p_{i,x+1}(t)\, \nu_{x+1}\, \delta t$$
$$+ p_{i,x}(t)(1 - \beta_x\, \delta t - \nu_x\, \delta t) + o(\delta t).$$

Rearranging this equation gives, for $x = 1, 2, \ldots,$

$$\frac{p_{i,x}(t + \delta t) - p_{i,x}(t)}{\delta t}$$
$$= \beta_{x-1}\, p_{i,x-1}(t) + \nu_{x+1}\, p_{i,x+1}(t) - (\beta_x + \nu_x)\, p_{i,x}(t) + \frac{o(\delta t)}{\delta t}. \tag{5.6}$$

By definition, the death rate ν_0 is equal to 0, so provided that β_{-1} and $p_{i,-1}(t)$ are also defined to be 0, this equation also holds for $x = 0$.

Usually i, the size of the population at time $t = 0$, is given and, for simplicity, i is omitted from $p_{i,x}(t)$. Then $p_x(t)$ represents the probability that the population contains x individuals at time t assuming $X(0) = i$, some known value. Writing $p_x(t)$ for $p_{i,x}(t)$ and letting $\delta t \to 0$ in (5.6), leads to the following differential–difference equations:

$$\frac{d}{dt}\, p_x(t) = \beta_{x-1}\, p_{x-1}(t) + \nu_{x+1}\, p_{x+1}(t) - (\beta_x + \nu_x)\, p_x(t), \quad x = 0, 1, \ldots.$$

$p_{-1}(t)$ is defined to be 0.

These are the differential–difference equations for the general birth and death process; they are known as the **Kolmogorov forward equations**. The above result is stated in the following box.

The Kolmogorov forward equations

The differential–difference equations for the general birth and death process, which are known as the **Kolmogorov forward equations**, are as follows. For $x = 0, 1, \ldots$,

$$\frac{d}{dt}\, p_x(t) = \beta_{x-1}\, p_{x-1}(t) + \nu_{x+1}\, p_{x+1}(t) - (\beta_x + \nu_x)\, p_x(t), \tag{5.7}$$

where $p_x(t)$ represents the probability $P(X(t) = x \mid X(0) = i)$ for some known value i, and β_{-1} and $p_{-1}(t)$ are defined to be 0.

By identifying β_x and ν_x, the overall birth and death rates, the Kolmogorov forward equations (5.7) can be used to write down directly the differential–difference equations for any specific birth and death process.

Activity 5.3   *Differential–difference equations*

Use the Kolmogorov forward equations (5.7) to write down the differential–difference equations for each of the following processes.

(a)   The Poisson process

(b)   The simple birth process

5.3   The immigration–birth–death process

The **immigration–birth–death process** is a birth and death process in which arrivals, births and deaths can all occur. The overall birth and death rates are given by

$$\beta_x = \beta x + \lambda, \quad \nu_x = \nu x.$$

Each individual in the population gives birth independently to new individuals at rate β throughout their life, and the lifetimes of individuals are exponentially distributed with parameter ν. Individuals join the population from outside according to a Poisson process with rate λ.

The differential–difference equations for the immigration–birth–death process can be written down using the Kolmogorov forward equations (5.7). Setting $\beta_x = \beta x + \lambda$ and $\nu_x = \nu x$ in (5.7) gives, for $x = 0, 1, \ldots,$

$$\frac{d}{dt}\, p_x(t) = (\beta(x-1) + \lambda)\, p_{x-1}(t) + \nu(x+1)\, p_{x+1}(t)$$
$$- ((\beta + \nu)x + \lambda)\, p_x(t). \tag{5.8}$$

These equations are used to derive the partial differential equation for $\Pi(s,t)$, the p.g.f. of $X(t)$, the population size at time t. The partial differential equation for the immigration–birth–death process is

$$(1 - s)(\nu - \beta s)\, \frac{\partial \Pi}{\partial s} - \frac{\partial \Pi}{\partial t} = \lambda(1 - s)\Pi. \tag{5.9}$$

You will not be expected to derive this equation. The method is similar to that used in Section 2 for the simple birth process.

This equation includes the partial differential equations for all processes involving some combination of birth, death and immigration. If one or two of birth, death and immigration are not included in a model, then β, ν or λ is set equal to 0, as appropriate, in (5.9).

The immigration–birth–death process is the most complex of the models described in Part I. Its analysis is included as an exercise in Section 24. You may wish to use this exercise later to help you to consolidate your understanding of the ideas and techniques discussed in Part I, or for revision.

See Exercise 24.5.

Summary of Section 5

The class of Markov processes known as birth and death processes has been defined in this section. The Kolmogorov forward equations for the general birth and death process have been derived. You have seen that they can be used to write down directly the differential–difference equations for any particular birth and death process. The immigration–birth–death process has been described briefly.

6   The simple birth–death process

The simple birth process and the pure death process were introduced in Section 1. The simple birth–death process, which is discussed in this section, combines features of these two processes: each individual gives birth to new individuals independently as in the simple birth process, and the lifetime of an individual is exponentially distributed as in the pure death process.

The model is appropriate for the development of a colony of simple organisms such as bacteria or yeasts, and it is fairly realistic, at least in the early stages of development. However, it is not suitable for the development of a human or animal population, for several reasons. For instance, individuals give birth independently, one at a time, so the model does not allow for two sexes or for multiple births (twins, triplets, and so on). Also, in any interval $[t, t + \delta t]$, each individual has probability $\beta\, \delta t + o(\delta t)$ of giving birth to a new individual. This probability is independent of the age of the individual, whereas humans and animals cannot give birth when very young or very old. Moreover, the model does not allow for a period of gestation: after an individual gives birth, it immediately becomes able to give birth again.

The distribution of $X(t)$, the size of the population at time t in a simple birth–death process, is discussed in Subsection 6.1. What happens to the population size over time is the subject of Subsection 6.2: is extinction certain to occur eventually, or can the size of the population fluctuate indefinitely? In Subsection 6.3, some results for random walks are used to explore the behaviour of the process.

6.1   The size of the population

A **simple birth–death process** with birth rate β and death rate ν is characterised by the following probability statements:

$$P(X(t + \delta t) = x + 1 \mid X(t) = x) = \beta x\, \delta t + o(\delta t),$$
$$P(X(t + \delta t) = x - 1 \mid X(t) = x) = \nu x\, \delta t + o(\delta t).$$

The process is a birth and death process with overall birth rate $\beta_x = \beta x$ and overall death rate $\nu_x = \nu x$.

If $X(t)$ is the size of the population at time t and $\Pi(s, t)$ is the p.g.f. of $X(t)$, then the partial differential equation for $\Pi(s, t)$ can be written down by setting $\lambda = 0$ in the partial differential equation (5.9) for the immigration–birth–death process. This gives

$$(1 - s)(\nu - \beta s) \frac{\partial \Pi}{\partial s} - \frac{\partial \Pi}{\partial t} = 0. \tag{6.1}$$

Activity 6.1   Different birth and death rates

Suppose that in a simple birth–death process, $\beta \neq \nu$; that is, the birth rate is not equal to the death rate.

(a) Use Lagrange's method to show that the general solution of the partial differential equation (6.1) for the process may be written

$$\Pi(s, t) = \psi\left(\frac{\nu - \beta s}{1 - s} e^{(\nu - \beta)t} \right). \tag{6.2}$$

You may find the following result useful:

$$\frac{-1}{(\nu - \beta s)(1 - s)} = \frac{1}{\beta - \nu}\left(\frac{1}{1 - s} - \frac{\beta}{\nu - \beta s} \right).$$

(b) Show that if there are n individuals in the population at time $t = 0$, then the p.g.f. of $X(t)$ is given by

$$\Pi(s, t) = \left(\frac{\nu(1 - s) - (\nu - \beta s)\, e^{(\nu - \beta)t}}{\beta(1 - s) - (\nu - \beta s)\, e^{(\nu - \beta)t}} \right)^n. \tag{6.3}$$

When the process starts with a single individual and $\beta \neq \nu$, the p.g.f. (6.3) can be rewritten as

$$\Pi(s, t) = \frac{\nu(1 - e^{(\nu - \beta)t}) - s(\nu - \beta e^{(\nu - \beta)t})}{\beta - \nu e^{(\nu - \beta)t} - \beta s(1 - e^{(\nu - \beta)t})}. \tag{6.4}$$

This p.g.f. is of the form $(a - bs)/(c - ds)$, so $X(t)$ has a modified geometric distribution. Therefore the probability that the size is equal to x decreases as x increases, and hence large population sizes are less likely than small ones.

Several results for the modified geometric distribution are given in Table 8 in the *Handbook*. These can be used to calculate probabilities or to find the mean and variance of the population size, for instance.

Activity 6.2   The mean population size

Suppose that a simple birth–death process with $\beta \neq \nu$ starts with a single individual. The p.g.f. of $X(t)$ is given by (6.4), and $X(t)$ has a modified geometric distribution.

(a) Identify the parameters a, b, c and d of the modified geometric distribution.

(b) Find the expected population size at time t.

Use the formula for the mean of a modified geometric distribution given in Table 8 in the *Handbook*.

When a simple birth–death process starts with n individuals at time 0, the p.g.f. of $X(t)$ is given by (6.3). This is the product of n identical terms, each of which is the p.g.f. for a simple birth–death process starting with one individual. So $X(t)$ can be thought of as the sum of n independent variates, each of which represents the size at time t of a simple birth–death process starting with one individual. In other words, there are n processes developing independently of each other. This is a direct result of one of the basic assumptions of the model, that individuals give birth and die independently of each other.

Activity 6.3   The mean population size

Suppose that a simple birth–death process with birth rate β and death rate ν, where $\beta \neq \nu$, starts with n individuals at time 0. What is the expected size of the population at time t?

The analysis corresponding to equal birth and death rates is very similar, and is the subject of Activity 6.4.

Activity 6.4   Equal birth and death rates

Suppose that $X(t)$ is the size of the population at time t in a simple birth–death process with equal birth and death rates ($\beta = \nu$), and that $\Pi(s,t)$ is the p.g.f. of $X(t)$. A partial differential equation for $\Pi(s,t)$ is

$$\frac{\partial \Pi}{\partial t} = \beta(1-s)^2 \frac{\partial \Pi}{\partial s}. \tag{6.5}$$

This equation is obtained by putting $\nu = \beta$ in (6.1).

(a) Show that the general solution of this equation is given by

$$\Pi(s,t) = \psi\left(\beta t + \frac{1}{1-s}\right),$$

where ψ is an arbitrary function.

(b) If there are n individuals in the population at time 0, show that the p.g.f. $\Pi(s,t)$ is given by

$$\Pi(s,t) = \left(\frac{\beta t - s\beta t + s}{\beta t - s\beta t + 1}\right)^n. \tag{6.6}$$

(c) Identify the distribution of $X(t)$ for the case where the process starts with a single individual at time 0. Hence find the expected population size at time t in this case.

(d) Find the expected population size at time t if the process starts with n individuals at time 0.

6.2 Extinction

Some properties of the simple birth–death process are apparent from the model. For example, since both births and deaths can occur, the size of the population may fluctuate. This is different from the simple birth process, where the size of the population can only increase, and the pure death process, where the size only decreases and eventually reaches 0. In the simple birth–death process, the size of the population may decrease to 0, but once there it remains there (if no individuals are present, then no births can occur). But is extinction certain to occur? Or is it possible for the population size to fluctuate indefinitely and remain finite? Or will the population grow without limit?

Questions such as these can be answered by looking at $\Pi(s, t)$, the p.g.f. of $X(t)$. For a simple birth–death process that starts with n individuals, $\Pi(s, t)$ is given by (6.3) when $\beta \neq \nu$.

First, consider $P(X(t) = 0)$, the probability that no individual is alive at time t, and hence that extinction has occurred by time t. By definition,

$$\Pi(s, t) = \sum_{x=0}^{\infty} p_x(t) \, s^x,$$

so setting $s = 0$ gives

$$\Pi(0, t) = p_0(t) = P(X(t) = 0).$$

Setting $s = 0$ in (6.3) gives

$$\Pi(0, t) = \left(\frac{\nu - \nu e^{(\nu - \beta)t}}{\beta - \nu e^{(\nu - \beta)t}} \right)^n. \tag{6.7}$$

When $\beta > \nu$, $e^{(\nu - \beta)t} \to 0$ as $t \to \infty$, and when $\beta < \nu$, $e^{(\nu - \beta)t} \to \infty$ as $t \to \infty$, so letting $t \to \infty$ in (6.7) gives

$$\lim_{t \to \infty} \Pi(0, t) = \begin{cases} \left(\dfrac{\nu}{\beta} \right)^n & \text{when } \beta > \nu, \\ 1 & \text{when } \beta < \nu. \end{cases}$$

Therefore extinction is certain to occur eventually if the death rate is greater than the birth rate. However, if the birth rate is greater than the death rate, then the probability of eventual extinction is $(\nu/\beta)^n$, and hence there is a positive probability that the population will not die out.

If the population does not die out, does its size remain finite or increase without limit? This can be investigated by letting $t \to \infty$ in the p.g.f. in (6.3). The limit is the p.g.f. of X, the population size after the process has been running for a long time. Taking the limit leads to

$$\lim_{t \to \infty} \Pi(s, t) = \begin{cases} \left(\dfrac{\nu}{\beta} \right)^n & \text{when } \beta > \nu, \\ 1 & \text{when } \beta < \nu. \end{cases}$$

Therefore if $\beta < \nu$, the limiting value of $\Pi(s, t)$ is 1 for all s. So $P(X = 0) = 1$ and $P(X = x) = 0$ for $x = 1, 2, \ldots$. This confirms that the population size is certain to be 0 eventually, and hence the population will die out. However, if $\beta > \nu$, the limiting value of $\Pi(s, t)$ is $(\nu/\beta)^n$, so $P(X = 0) = (\nu/\beta)^n < 1$ and $P(X = x) = 0$ for $x = 1, 2, \ldots$. Therefore in this case, there is a positive probability, $1 - (\nu/\beta)^n$, that the population will not die out. However, since the probability of any finite size is 0, if extinction does not occur, then the population size increases without bound.

Activity 6.5   *Equal birth and death rates*

Suppose that a simple birth–death process starts with n individuals at time 0, and has equal birth and death rates.

(a) Find the probability that extinction will have occurred by time t.

(b) Find the probability of eventual extinction.

When $\beta = \nu$, the p.g.f. of $X(t)$ is given by (6.6).

The results concerning the probability of eventual extinction that have been obtained in this subsection are summarised in the following box.

> **Extinction**
>
> Suppose that a simple birth–death process with birth rate β and death rate ν starts with n individuals at time 0.
>
> ◇   When $\beta \leq \nu$, extinction is certain.
>
> ◇   When $\beta > \nu$, the probability of extinction is $(\nu/\beta)^n$.

Activity 6.6   *Extinction*

Suppose that a simple birth–death process starts with five individuals and that the birth rate is twice the death rate, that is, $\beta = 2\nu$.

Calculate the probability that the population will eventually die out.

The time to extinction is a random variable T, and

$$P(T \leq t) = P(\text{population is extinct by time } t)$$
$$= P(X(t) = 0).$$

This probability is equal to $\Pi(0, t)$, so if $F(t)$ is the c.d.f. of T, then

$$F(t) = P(T \leq t) = \Pi(0, t).$$

Therefore when $\beta \neq \nu$, the c.d.f. is given by (6.7), and when $\beta = \nu$, it is given by the formula obtained in the solution to Activity 6.5. Note that since extinction is not certain when $\beta > \nu$, T has an improper distribution in this case (as $t \to \infty$, $F(t) \to (\nu/\beta)^n < 1$). When $\beta \leq \nu$, T has a proper distribution and the c.d.f. can be used, for instance, to calculate probabilities concerning the time to extinction, or the mean or median time to extinction.

Activity 6.7   *The time to extinction*

Suppose that a simple birth–death process starts with n individuals at time 0 and that the birth rate is equal to the death rate.

(a) Write down the c.d.f. of T, the time to extinction.

(b) Find the median time to extinction if the process starts with a single individual at time 0.

6.3   The embedded random walk

Suppose that a simple birth–death process is observed only at those instants when a birth or a death actually occurs. At each of these times, the size of the population changes by 1. If the instants at which changes occur are labelled $n = 0, 1, 2, 3, \ldots$, and the size of the population immediately after the instant of the nth change is denoted X_n, then $\{X_n; n = 0, 1, \ldots\}$ is a random process in discrete time. This process is said to be **embedded** in the original one, and it is referred to as an **embedded process**. The random variable X_n is the size of the embedded process at time n.

A realisation of a simple birth–death process starting with three individuals is shown in Figure 6.1, and the same realisation as an embedded process is shown in Figure 6.2.

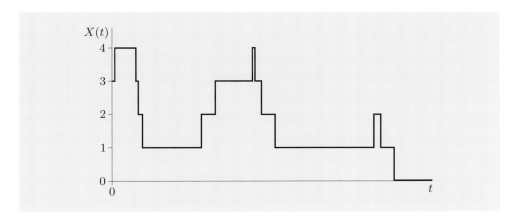

Figure 6.1   A realisation of a simple birth–death process

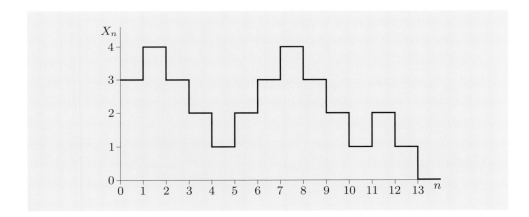

Figure 6.2   A realisation of the embedded process

In the realisation of Figure 6.2, $X_0 = 3$, $X_1 = 4$, $X_2 = 3$, and so on.

The embedded process has many of the properties of the original process. For example, the value of X_n can only increase by 1 or decrease by 1 at each change, and the probability that the next change is an increase (or a decrease) is the same as for the simple birth–death process. Also, the population will become extinct or its size will increase indefinitely, and it will attain the same maximum or minimum size. However, results involving real time for the original process are not relevant to the embedded process.

Suppose that the population contains x individuals at time t. Then in the interval $[t, t + \delta t]$, the probability that a birth occurs is $\beta x\, \delta t + o(\delta t)$, and the probability that a death occurs is $\nu x\, \delta t + o(\delta t)$. Hence the probability that an event occurs is $(\beta + \nu)x\, \delta t + o(\delta t)$. So if an event occurs, the conditional probability that it is a birth is

$$P(\text{a birth occurs in } [t, t + \delta t] \mid \text{an event occurs in } [t, t + \delta t])$$

$$= \frac{P(\text{a birth occurs in } [t, t + \delta t])}{P(\text{an event occurs in } [t, t + \delta t])}$$

$$= \frac{\beta x\, \delta t + o(\delta t)}{(\beta + \nu)x\, \delta t + o(\delta t)}$$

$$= \frac{\beta + o(\delta t)/\delta t}{\beta + \nu + o(\delta t)/\delta t}$$

$$\to \frac{\beta}{\beta + \nu} \quad \text{as } \delta t \to 0.$$

By definition, $o(\delta t)/\delta t \to 0$ as $\delta t \to 0$.

So if an event occurs, then the probability that it is a birth is $\beta/(\beta + \nu)$ and the probability that it is a death is $1 - \beta/(\beta + \nu) = \nu/(\beta + \nu)$. These probabilities are independent of the time t at which the event occurs and the size of the population at that time. Thus if the probability that the next event in a simple birth process is a birth is denoted p_b and the probability that the next event is a death is denoted p_d, then

$$p_b = \frac{\beta}{\beta + \nu}, \quad p_d = \frac{\nu}{\beta + \nu}.$$

Therefore for the embedded process $\{X_n; n = 0, 1, \ldots\}$,

$$P(X_{n+1} = x + 1 \mid X_n = x) = \frac{\beta}{\beta + \nu}, \quad x = 1, 2, \ldots,$$

$$P(X_{n+1} = x - 1 \mid X_n = x) = \frac{\nu}{\beta + \nu}, \quad x = 1, 2, \ldots.$$

If the population size is ever 0, it remains 0 thereafter, so 0 is an absorbing state, and hence 0 acts as an absorbing barrier for the embedded process. Therefore the embedded process is a simple random walk with an absorbing barrier at 0, in which $p = \beta/(\beta + \nu)$ and $q = \nu/(\beta + \nu)$. Hence results derived in *Book 3* for gambling against an opponent with unlimited resources (gambling against a casino) can be applied to the random walk embedded in a simple birth–death process. Also, as you will see in Example 6.1, results for the gambler's ruin can be used to calculate the probability that the size of the population will ever reach any particular value.

Example 6.1   *Using the embedded random walk*

Suppose that a simple birth–death process starts with four individuals and that $\beta = \frac{3}{2}\nu$. Then

$$p_b = \frac{\beta}{\beta + \nu} = 0.6, \quad p_d = \frac{\nu}{\beta + \nu} = 0.4.$$

The probability that the population will die out is equal to the probability of ruin for a gambler who starts with £4 and has probability 0.6 of winning each £1 bet when gambling against a casino. That is, the required probability is q_4 when $p = 0.6$ and $q = 0.4$.

The probability of ruin when starting with £j is given by

$$q_j = \begin{cases} 1 & \text{when } p \leq q, \\ \left(\dfrac{q}{p}\right)^j & \text{when } p > q. \end{cases}$$

This result is in the *Handbook*.

In this case, $p > q$, so the probability that the population will eventually die out is

$$q_4 = \left(\frac{0.4}{0.6}\right)^4 = \frac{16}{81} \simeq 0.198.$$

The probability that the size of the population will ever reach 10 can be calculated using the formula for the probability of ruin in the gambler's ruin, as follows. The required probability is the probability that the 'particle' in the embedded random walk visits 10 before 0. This is equal to the probability of winning when $p = 0.6$, $q = 0.4$, $a = 10$ and $j = 4$ (see Figure 6.3).

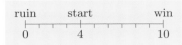

Figure 6.3   The embedded random walk

In the gambler's ruin problem, q_j, the probability of ruin when starting with £j and making £1 bets, is given by

$$q_j = \begin{cases} \dfrac{(q/p)^j - (q/p)^a}{1 - (q/p)^a} & \text{when } p \neq q, \\ 1 - \dfrac{j}{a} & \text{when } p = q. \end{cases}$$

This result is in the *Handbook*.

In this case, $a = 10$, $j = 4$, $p = 0.6$ and $q = 0.4$, so the probability required is

$$1 - q_4 = 1 - \frac{\left(\frac{2}{3}\right)^4 - \left(\frac{2}{3}\right)^{10}}{1 - \left(\frac{2}{3}\right)^{10}} \simeq 0.817. \quad \blacklozenge$$

Activity 6.8   Another embedded random walk

Suppose that a simple birth–death process starts with three individuals and that $\beta = \frac{2}{3}\nu$.

(a) Calculate the probability that at any time the next event will be a birth.

(b) Calculate the probability that the population will eventually die out.

(c) Calculate the probability that the size of the population will ever reach 8.

Activity 6.9   General results for extinction

Suppose that a simple birth–death process with birth rate β and death rate ν starts with n individuals. Use the embedded random walk to find the probability that the population will eventually die out in each of the following cases.

(a) $\beta < \nu$ (b) $\beta = \nu$ (c) $\beta > \nu$

Check that your answers confirm the results obtained in Subsection 6.2 using the p.g.f. of $X(t)$.

Summary of Section 6

The simple birth–death process has been discussed in this section. Given the initial population size, Lagrange's method has been used to find the p.g.f. of $X(t)$, the size of the population at time t, and the distribution of $X(t)$ has been identified. The probability that the population will eventually die out has been found using the p.g.f. of $X(t)$ and using the random walk embedded in the process. The embedded random walk has also been used to find the probability that the population size will ever reach any particular value.

Exercises on Section 6

Exercise 6.1   The population size

A simple birth–death process with $\beta = \nu = 1$ is initiated by a single individual at time 0.

(a) Write down the p.g.f. $\Pi(s,t)$ of $X(t)$, the number of individuals in the population at time t, and identify the distribution of $X(t)$.

(b) Calculate the probability that at time $t = 1$, the population size is

    (i) 0,   (ii) 1,   (iii) 2.

(c) Calculate the probability that at time $t = 3$, the population contains more than one individual.

Exercise 6.2   The embedded random walk

A simple birth–death process with $\nu = \frac{3}{5}\beta$ is initiated by four individuals.

(a) Write down the probability that the first two changes in population size are due to births and the third is due to a death.

(b) Calculate the probability that the population eventually dies out.

(c) Calculate the probability that the process dies out without the population size ever reaching 10.

(d) Calculate the probability that the population size ever reaches 10.

7   The immigration–death process

In the immigration–death process, individuals arrive and join the population according to a Poisson process, and once in the population they may die at any time, the lifetime of each individual having an exponential distribution. There are no births: individuals in the population do not give birth to new individuals.

This model provides a fairly realistic representation of many practical situations. For example, the population might consist of the dust particles or the molecules of a gas in a given volume. New particles may enter the volume at any time, and the Poisson process provides a reasonable model for their arrival pattern. Once inside, any particle may leave at any time, and the exponential distribution provides a reasonable model for the time spent inside the volume.

This process can also be used to model the number of people in a shop, or the number of cars in a car park, provided that the shop or car park is large enough to accommodate all individuals that may arrive. It also arises as the model for a queueing system in which customers arrive according to a Poisson process, there are (theoretically) infinitely many servers, and the service time of each customer is exponentially distributed. The theoretically infinite number of servers means that, in practice, there are sufficient servers for each customer to be served immediately on arrival. This might be an appropriate model for a telephone system with sufficient lines to accommodate all callers, and where the 'service' is the conversation and it can be assumed that the rate of incoming calls is constant. However, in practice, the rate would probably vary over a period of several hours, so the model would apply only for the period during which the rate is constant.

Other models for queues are studied in Part II.

A detailed discussion of the immigration–death process has been included for two reasons: to help you to consolidate some of the material discussed so far in this book, and to introduce some ideas that are essential for the queueing models in Part II.

The distribution of $X(t)$, the size of the population at time t in an immigration–death process, is discussed in Subsection 7.1, and the behaviour of the process is studied in Subsection 7.2.

7.1 The size of the population

Suppose that individuals join the population in an immigration–death process according to a Poisson process with rate λ, and that the lifetimes of individuals in the population are exponentially distributed with parameter ν. Then the immigration–death process is characterised by the following probability statements:

$$P(X(t+\delta t) = x + 1 \mid X(t) = x) = \lambda\,\delta t + o(\delta t),$$
$$P(X(t+\delta t) = x - 1 \mid X(t) = x) = \nu x\,\delta t + o(\delta t).$$

The process is a birth and death process with overall birth rate $\beta_x = \lambda$ and overall death rate $\nu_x = \nu x$.

If $X(t)$ is the size of the population at time t and $\Pi(s,t)$ is the p.g.f. of $X(t)$, then the partial differential equation for $\Pi(s,t)$ can be written down by setting $\beta = 0$ in the partial differential equation (5.9) for the immigration–birth–death process. This gives

$$\nu(1-s)\,\frac{\partial \Pi}{\partial s} - \frac{\partial \Pi}{\partial t} = \lambda(1-s)\Pi. \tag{7.1}$$

Activity 7.1   *The distribution of $X(t)$*

Suppose that the size of the population in an immigration–death process is 0 at time 0.

(a) Use Lagrange's method to show that the general solution of the partial differential equation (7.1) may be written

$$\Pi(s,t) = e^{\lambda s/\nu}\,\psi\left((1-s)e^{-\nu t}\right).$$

(b) Find the particular solution in this case, and hence identify the distribution of $X(t)$.

Now suppose that there are n individuals alive at time 0. The distribution of $X(t)$ can be found by finding the particular solution of (7.1) satisfying this condition. Alternatively, it can be identified by noting that the n individuals alive at the start will die as in a pure death process with death rate ν; they will not be affected by arrivals. An immigration–death process starting with 0 individuals at time 0 will take place independently. Therefore $X(t)$, the total population size at time t, can be written as $X_1(t) + X_2(t)$, where $X_1(t)$ is the number alive at time t in a pure death process starting with n individuals, and $X_2(t)$ is the number alive at time t in an immigration–death process starting with 0 individuals. From Subsection 1.3,

$$X_1(t) \sim B(n, e^{-\nu t});$$

This is result (1.1).

and from the solution to Activity 7.1,

$$X_2(t) \sim \text{Poisson}\left(\frac{\lambda}{\nu}(1 - e^{-\nu t})\right).$$

Therefore

$$X(t) = X_1(t) + X_2(t),$$

where $X_1(t) \sim B(n, e^{-\nu t})$ and $X_2(t) \sim \text{Poisson}\left(\frac{\lambda}{\nu}(1 - e^{-\nu t})\right)$.

7.2 What happens in the long run?

How will the size of the population change over time? Clearly, it will fluctuate as immigrants arrive and individuals die. Suppose that the population dies out at some time. Eventually an immigrant will arrive, so permanent extinction will not occur. So what will happen to the population size in the long run? Will it eventually increase without bound? Or will the distribution of $X(t)$, the population size at time t, approach a limiting distribution as t increases? And if it does, will this happen however large or small the immigration rate is?

Two methods of investigating the long-run behaviour of the process are described in this subsection. The first method, which was used in Section 6 for the simple birth–death process, involves taking the limit as t tends to infinity of $\Pi(s, t)$, the p.g.f. of $X(t)$.

Suppose that there are no individuals in the population at time $t = 0$. Then, from the solution to Activity 7.1, the p.g.f. of $X(t)$ is given by

$$\Pi(s, t) = \exp\left(-\frac{\lambda}{\nu}(1 - s)(1 - e^{-\nu t})\right).$$

Since $\nu > 0$, $e^{-\nu t} \to 0$ as $t \to \infty$, so

$$\lim_{t \to \infty} \Pi(s, t) = \exp\left(-\frac{\lambda}{\nu}(1 - s)\right).$$

This is the p.g.f. of a Poisson distribution with parameter λ/ν. So a **limiting distribution** for the population size exists, and it is Poisson(λ/ν).

Limiting distributions for discrete-time random processes were discussed in *Book 3*.

Note that if there are n individuals in the population at the start of an immigration–death process, then these individuals will all eventually die (as in a pure death process), and hence the limiting distribution will be the same as when there are no individuals at the start. Since the limiting distribution is independent of the initial population size, it is usually referred to as the **equilibrium distribution** of the process.

If the equilibrium distribution is denoted $\{p_x\}$, then p_x is the probability that after a long time, the population size will be equal to x, or equivalently, p_x is the proportion of the time in the long run that the population size is equal to x.

The second method of investigating the long-run behaviour of a random process uses the differential–difference equations for the process. The differential–difference equations for the immigration–death process can be obtained by setting $\beta = 0$ in the differential–difference equations (5.8) for the immigration–birth–death process. This gives

$$\frac{d}{dt}p_0(t) = \nu p_1(t) - \lambda p_0(t), \qquad (7.2)$$

$$\frac{d}{dt}p_x(t) = \lambda p_{x-1}(t) + \nu(x+1)p_{x+1}(t) - (\lambda + \nu x)p_x(t), \quad x = 1, 2, \ldots. \qquad (7.3)$$

If a limiting distribution exists, then for $x = 0, 1, \ldots$, $p_x(t) \to p_x$ as $t \to \infty$, and hence

$$\lim_{t\to\infty} \frac{d}{dt}p_x(t) = 0, \quad x = 0, 1, \ldots.$$

Therefore letting $t \to \infty$ in (7.2) gives

$$\nu p_1 - \lambda p_0 = 0,$$

so

$$p_1 = \frac{\lambda}{\nu}p_0.$$

For $x = 1$, letting $t \to \infty$ in (7.3) gives

$$\lambda p_0 + 2\nu p_2 - (\lambda + \nu)p_1 = 0.$$

Since $\nu p_1 = \lambda p_0$, this simplifies to

$$2\nu p_2 - \lambda p_1 = 0,$$

so

$$p_2 = \frac{\lambda}{2\nu}p_1 = \frac{\lambda^2}{2\nu^2}p_0.$$

Activity 7.2 The limiting distribution

(a) By letting $t \to \infty$ in (7.3) with $x = 2$, find an expression for p_3 in terms of p_0.

(b) By inspecting the pattern in the expressions for p_1, p_2, p_3, deduce an expression for p_x in terms of p_0, for $x = 1, 2, \ldots$.

(c) Use the fact that the sum of the probabilities $p_0, p_1, p_2, \ldots$ is equal to 1 for a proper probability distribution to show that $p_0 = e^{-\lambda/\nu}$. Hence find p_x for $x = 1, 2, \ldots$, and confirm that the limiting distribution is Poisson(λ/ν).

If a birth and death process has an equilibrium distribution, then it can be found from the differential–difference equations for the process by the method just described. This method is important because it can be used for a wider range of processes than the first method, and not just when a partial differential equation for $\Pi(s, t)$ can be obtained and solved. This method is used in Part II where several models for queues are discussed.

Activity 7.3 An immigration–death process

In an immigration–death process, the immigration rate and the death rate are given by $\lambda = 3$ and $\nu = 2$.

(a) In the long run, what is the expected number of individuals alive at any time?

(b) Calculate the proportion of time in the long run that the population contains

    (i) 0 individuals,   (ii) 3 individuals.

Summary of Section 7

The immigration–death process has been discussed in this section. Lagrange's method has been used to find the p.g.f. of $X(t)$, the size of the population at time t, and the distribution of $X(t)$ has been identified. You have seen that permanent extinction cannot take place, and that the process has an equilibrium distribution. Two methods of finding the equilibrium distribution have been described.

Exercise on Section 7

Exercise 7.1   An immigration–death process

In an immigration–death process, the immigration rate is $\lambda = 0.4$ and the death rate is $\nu = 0.5$.

(a) Suppose that the population contains 0 individuals at time $t = 0$.

    (i)   Find the expected number of individuals in the population at time t.

    (ii)   Calculate the probability that the population will contain two individuals at time $t = 1$.

(b) Calculate the proportion of the time in the long run that the population contains two individuals.

8   Deterministic models

The mathematics required to analyse a random process such as the Poisson process is quite straightforward, and the probability distributions of all random variables of interest can be obtained. However, even for processes that seem fairly simple, the mathematics can become extremely difficult, or even impossible, to handle analytically. In such cases, it is difficult to identify the fundamental properties of a process and the extent to which the behaviour of the process depends on the values of the parameters involved.

One useful approach is to carry out simulations, which will certainly give a good indication of likely and unlikely realisations.

Another approach is to study the **deterministic** version of the model, which ignores random fluctuations and investigates only the 'average' behaviour. When a population is large, a deterministic model provides a good approximation to the stochastic behaviour, though it is not much help in describing the behaviour of a small population subject to random variation. In this section, deterministic models are developed from some simple random processes in continuous time.

Deterministic analogues for discrete-time random processes are not considered in M343.

Example 8.1   The Poisson process

Figure 8.1 shows three realisations of the random process $\{X(t); t \geq 0\}$, where $X(t)$ is the number of events that have occurred by time t in a Poisson process with rate $\lambda = \frac{1}{2}$.

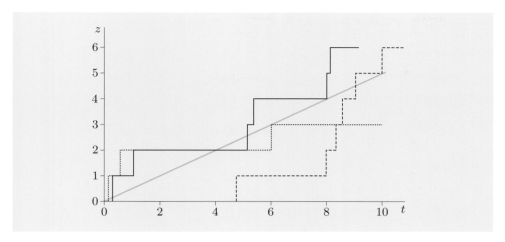

Figure 8.1   Three realisations of a Poisson process $\{X(t); t \geq 0\}$ with rate $\lambda = \frac{1}{2}$

Since $X(t) \sim \text{Poisson}(\lambda t)$ and $\lambda = \frac{1}{2}$,

$$E[X(t)] = \lambda t = \tfrac{1}{2}t.$$

Hence the expected number of events that have occurred by time t in these realisations is $\frac{1}{2}t$. The line $z = \frac{1}{2}t$ is also included in Figure 8.1. This line represents some kind of 'trend' or average. It could not be a realisation, as realisations are all step functions, incorporating jumps of size 1 at random times.   ◆

Here z is just a convenient label for the vertical axis in Figure 8.1.

Example 8.2   The simple birth process

Figure 8.2 shows four realisations of a simple birth process $\{X(t); t \geq 0\}$ with birth rate $\beta = 1$, starting with one individual at time $t = 0$.

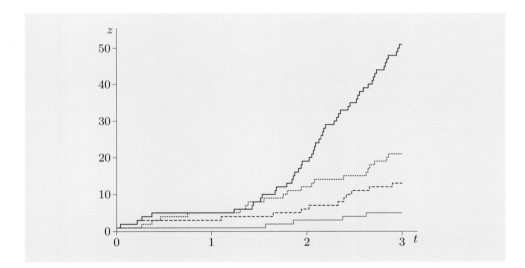

Figure 8.2   Four realisations of a simple birth process $\{X(t); t \geq 0\}$ with birth rate $\beta = 1$

At time $t = 3$, when simulation ceased, the size of the population had increased to 51 in one realisation, but to only 5 in another. Although the four realisations are very different, in all cases the overall birth rate, or rate of change of $X(t)$, appears to increase with time. It looks as if no straight line could provide an 'average' of the behaviour; a curve with increasing slope would be more appropriate.   ◆

Example 8.3   A deterministic model for the Poisson process

By the first postulate for the Poisson process,

$$P(\text{one event occurs in } [t, t + \delta t]) = \lambda \, \delta t + o(\delta t).$$

Since multiple events have probability $o(\delta t)$,

$$P(\text{no event occurs in } [t, t + \delta t]) = 1 - (\lambda \, \delta t + o(\delta t)) - o(\delta t)$$
$$= 1 - \lambda \, \delta t + o(\delta t).$$

Hence the number of events expected to occur in $[t, t + \delta t]$ is

$$1 \times (\lambda \, \delta t + o(\delta t)) + 0 \times (1 - \lambda \, \delta t + o(\delta t)) = \lambda \, \delta t + o(\delta t).$$

In the deterministic model for the Poisson process, random fluctuations are ignored and it is assumed that in any small interval $[t, t + \delta t]$, the number of events that occur is exactly equal to $\lambda \, \delta t + o(\delta t)$. Let $z = z(t)$ denote the total number of events that have occurred by time t in the deterministic model. Then

Note that in the deterministic model, z is a function of time.

$$z(t + \delta t) = z(t) + \lambda \, \delta t + o(\delta t),$$

and hence

$$\frac{z(t + \delta t) - z(t)}{\delta t} = \lambda + \frac{o(\delta t)}{\delta t}.$$

Since $o(\delta t)/\delta t \to 0$ as $\delta t \to 0$, taking the limit as $\delta t \to 0$ gives

$$\frac{dz(t)}{dt} = \lambda.$$

So in this model, the rate at which events occur is a constant, λ. Solving this differential equation gives $z(t) = \lambda t + c$. Since no events have occurred when the process starts at time $t = 0$, $z(0) = 0$ and hence $c = 0$. Therefore the deterministic solution is

$$z(t) = \lambda t.$$

This gives the number of events that occur by time t in the deterministic analogue of a Poisson process. In this case, the deterministic solution is equal to the mean of the random variable $X(t)$. The deterministic solution is said to be equal to the mean of the random process. ◆

Activity 8.1   The deterministic analogue of the simple birth process

A simple birth process has birth rate β.

(a) Suppose that the population size is x at time t. Use the postulates for the simple birth process to find the expected number of births in any small interval $[t, t + \delta t]$.

(b) Derive a differential equation satisfied by $z(t)$, the size of the population at time t in the deterministic model in which it is assumed that the number of births in $[t, t + \delta t]$ is equal to the expected number that you found in part (a).

(c) Solve this differential equation, given that the process starts with one individual at time $t = 0$.

In the solution to Activity 8.1, you found that for a simple birth process starting with one individual, the solution to the deterministic analogue is the exponential curve $z(t) = e^{\beta t}$. When $\beta = 1$, this gives $z(t) = e^t$. In Figure 8.3, this curve is superimposed on the four realisations of Figure 8.2.

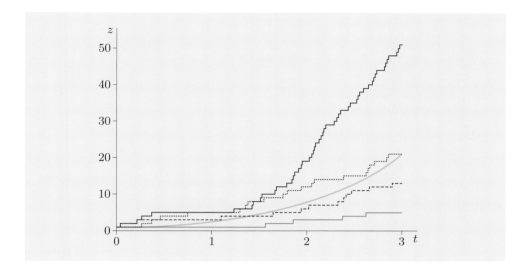

Figure 8.3 Realisations of a simple birth process and the deterministic curve

Notice that the curve does indeed provide an 'average' of the developing process, though it gives no indication of the amount of possible variability.

The method used to derive the deterministic analogue of a random process in Example 8.3 and Activity 8.1 generalises to any random process $\{X(t); t \geq 0\}$ in which an 'event' corresponds to an increase of 1 in the size of the population being counted. Suppose that the random process $\{X(t); t \geq 0\}$ is characterised by the probability statement

$$P(X(t + \delta t) = x + 1 \mid X(t) = x) = h(x, t)\,\delta t + o(\delta t). \tag{8.1}$$

Then, using an argument similar to that in Example 8.3, the expected number of events in $[t, t + \delta t]$ is $h(x, t)\,\delta t + o(\delta t)$. If $z(t)$ denotes the size of the population at time t in the deterministic analogue, then

$$z(t + \delta t) = z(t) + h(z, t)\,\delta t + o(\delta t).$$

Rearranging this, and letting $\delta t \to 0$, leads to the differential equation

$$\frac{dz(t)}{dt} = h(z, t). \tag{8.2}$$

The differential equation (8.2) constitutes the deterministic formulation of the model characterised by (8.1). The solution of this differential equation is called the **deterministic approximation to the stochastic process** $\{X(t); t \geq 0\}$. It can be shown that if $h(z, t)$ is a linear function of z, that is, if $h(z, t) = h_0(t) + z\,h_1(t)$ for some functions $h_0(t)$ and $h_1(t)$, then the deterministic approximation is equal to the mean of the stochastic process.

The proof of this result will not be given.

For example, for the Poisson process, $h(z, t) = \lambda$, which is linear in z ($h_1(t) = 0$), and the deterministic solution $z(t) = \lambda t$ is equal to the mean of the random process ($X(t) \sim \text{Poisson}(\lambda t)$, so $E[X(t)] = \lambda t$). For the simple birth process starting with one individual at time 0, $X(t) \sim G_1(e^{-\beta t})$, so $E[X(t)] = 1/e^{-\beta t} = e^{\beta t}$. For this process, $h(z, t) = \beta z$, which is a linear function of z, and the deterministic solution is $z(t) = e^{\beta t}$ (see Activity 8.1), so the deterministic approximation is equal to the mean of the random process.

If $h(z, t)$ is not of the form $h_0(t) + z\,h_1(t)$, then the deterministic approximation still gives a useful indication of trend, but it is not equal to the mean of the random process. However, in such cases, analysing the stochastic model is often difficult, so the deterministic approach is a useful one.

Part III includes examples of this type.

Activity 8.2   The immigration–birth process

The immigration–birth process is characterised by the probability statement

$$P(X(t + \delta t) = x + 1 \mid X(t) = x) = (\lambda + \beta x) \, \delta t + o(\delta t).$$

(a) Use (8.2) to write down a differential equation for $z(t)$, the deterministic approximation to the process.

(b) Solve the ordinary differential equation, assuming that the population size is 0 at time $t = 0$.

(c) More generally, if the population size is z_0 at time 0, show that the corresponding particular solution of the differential equation is

$$z = z_0 e^{\beta t} + \frac{\lambda}{\beta}(e^{\beta t} - 1).$$

When an increase of 1 and a decrease of 1 in population size are both possible, a stochastic model is based on a pair of equations:

$$P(X(t + \delta t) = x + 1 \mid X(t) = x) = h_1(x, t) \, \delta t + o(\delta t),$$
$$P(X(t + \delta t) = x - 1 \mid X(t) = x) = h_{-1}(x, t) \, \delta t + o(\delta t).$$

Then the expected change in population size during the time interval $[t, t + \delta t]$, given that $X(t) = x$, is

$$1 \times (h_1(x, t) \, \delta t + o(\delta t)) + (-1) \times (h_{-1}(x, t) \, \delta t + o(\delta t))$$
$$+ 0 \times (1 - (h_1(x, t) \, \delta t + h_{-1}(x, t) \, \delta t) + o(\delta t))$$
$$= (h_1(x, t) - h_{-1}(x, t)) \, \delta t + o(\delta t).$$

The deterministic analogue is the solution of the differential equation

$$\frac{dz}{dt} = h_1(z, t) - h_{-1}(z, t).$$

This result is stated in the following box.

Deterministic models

Suppose that a random process $\{X(t); t \geq 0\}$ is characterised by a pair of probability statements of the form

$$P(X(t + \delta t) = x + 1 \mid X(t) = x) = h_1(x, t) \, \delta t + o(\delta t),$$
$$P(X(t + \delta t) = x - 1 \mid X(t) = x) = h_{-1}(x, t) \, \delta t + o(\delta t).$$

Then the deterministic approximation to the random process is the solution of the differential equation

$$\frac{dz}{dt} = h_1(z, t) - h_{-1}(z, t). \tag{8.3}$$

Example 8.4   The pure death process

The pure death process is characterised by the probability statement

$$P(X(t + \delta t) = x - 1 \mid X(t) = x) = \nu x \, \delta t + o(\delta t).$$

Increases in the population size are not possible, so

$$h_1(x, t) = 0, \quad h_{-1}(x, t) = \nu x.$$

Therefore, using (8.3), the deterministic analogue of the pure death process is the solution of the differential equation

$$\frac{dz}{dt} = -\nu z. \quad \blacklozenge$$

Activity 8.3   The deterministic analogue

Suppose that the population in a pure death process with death rate ν contains n individuals at time 0.

(a) Solve the differential equation for the deterministic analogue, which was obtained in Example 8.4.

(b) According to the deterministic model, at what time are only half of the original population still alive? When does the population die out?

Activity 8.4   The simple birth–death process

The simple birth–death process is characterised by the probability statements
$$P(X(t + \delta t) = x + 1 \mid X(t) = x) = \beta x\, \delta t + o(\delta t),$$
$$P(X(t + \delta t) = x - 1 \mid X(t) = x) = \nu x\, \delta t + o(\delta t).$$

(a) Write down the differential equation for the deterministic analogue of the simple birth–death process.

(b) Show that for a population whose size is n at time $t = 0$, the population size at time t in the deterministic analogue is given by
$$z = ne^{(\beta - \nu)t}.$$

(c) Briefly compare the behaviour of the stochastic model and that of the deterministic model for the simple birth–death process.

Summary of Section 8

In this section, the idea of the deterministic analogue of a random process has been introduced. A deterministic model ignores the randomness inherent in a random process and demonstrates instead its 'average' development with passing time. Deterministic analogues of several random processes have been derived.

Exercise on Section 8

Exercise 8.1   The immigration–death process

(a) Write down the differential equation satisfied by the deterministic approximation to the immigration–death process with immigration rate λ and death rate ν.

(b) Solve this differential equation given that the population size is 0 at time 0.

Part II   Queues

Introduction to Part II

Most of us are familiar with queueing for service in one form or another. Examples include waiting in a line at a supermarket checkout, circling in a jet over Heathrow airport waiting to land, and waiting for a hospital bed to become available.

There are many features that could be included in a queueing model, and some very sophisticated models have been developed. However, every model must include the *arrival mechanism*, the *service time* (the time it takes a server to serve a customer) and the *number of servers*. In addition, it is usually necessary to specify the *queue discipline*, which deals with the manner in which customers reach the service point. For all the models discussed in this book, it is assumed that customers are served in the order in which they arrive. This means that if there is more than one server, then a central queueing system is in operation: arrivals join a single central queue, and when a server becomes free, the person at the front of the queue moves forward to be served. It is also assumed that arrivals occur one at a time, rather than in groups.

In Section 9, some standard notation used to characterise queueing models is introduced. The model discussed in Section 10 is a model for a single-server queue, and is arguably the simplest queueing model. It is known as the *simple queue*. The only difference between the model described in Section 11 and the simple queue is that instead of a single server, there are several. A useful general result for single-server queues in which arrivals occur at random is discussed in Section 12.

Exact results for the size of a queue at time t are often difficult to derive and complicated in form. Equilibrium results are generally easier to obtain and apply. Most of the results derived in Part II are for queues in equilibrium.

9   Models and notation

A neat way of characterising a queue has been developed to express concisely its arrival mechanism, the service time and the number of servers.

First, the inter-arrival time distribution is specified. For example, if the inter-arrival time has a uniform distribution, this is written U, and if it has a gamma distribution, this is written Γ, and so on. If arrivals occur at random, then arrivals can be modelled as a Poisson process, and hence the time between arrivals has an exponential distribution. This is written M. For a fixed-interval appointment system, the inter-arrival time is constant, so it is deterministic. This is written D. If no assumption is made about the inter-arrival time distribution, this is written G.

G stands for 'general'.

Next, the service time distribution is specified using the same notation: M for exponential service times, D for constant service times, and so on. Finally, the number of servers is specified.

For example, for the queueing system described in Section 10, arrivals occur according to a Poisson process (M), the time taken to serve an individual customer is exponentially distributed (M), and there is one server (1). The specification of this model is written $M/M/1$. The specification of the queueing model discussed in Section 11 is $M/M/n$: arrivals occur as in a Poisson process (M), the service times are exponentially distributed (M), and n servers are on duty ($n > 1$).

Example 9.1   Queue notation

For a queue with the specification $D/U/4$, arrivals join the queue at regular intervals (constant inter-arrival times), the service time has a uniform distribution, and there are four servers.   ◆

Activity 9.1   Interpreting queue specifications

Interpret each of the following queue specifications.

(a) $M/U/6$ (b) $D/D/2$

Example 9.2   Using the queue notation

A bank branch has two cash dispensers outside, neither of which has ever been known to break down. A customer who arrives to find either one free uses it immediately. Otherwise, a convention seems to have developed that customers arriving to find both machines busy form a central queue by an adjacent litter bin, moving forward to the first machine to become available. It always takes the same amount of time to use the machine, and customers arrive at random.

Customers arrive at random, so the inter-arrival distribution is exponential: M. The service time is constant: D. There is a central queue for two 'servers'. The queue is denoted $M/D/2$.   ◆

Activity 9.2   Characterising queues

Write down the specification of each of the following queues.

(a) Customers arrive at random at a post office where there are always three assistants on duty, and join a central queue. The time taken to serve each customer is equally likely to be anything between two and five minutes.

(b) Patients arrive every ten minutes at a doctor's surgery, where one doctor is on duty. The time spent with each patient has an exponential distribution with mean eight minutes.

Summary of Section 9

In this section, the standard notation used to characterise queues has been introduced. This notation includes information on the distributions of the time between arrivals and the service time, and the number of servers.

Exercises on Section 9

Exercise 9.1   Interpreting queue specifications

Interpret each of the following queue specifications.

(a) $M/\Gamma/3$

(b) $D/G/1$

Exercise 9.2   Characterising queues

Write down the specification of each of the following queues.

(a) Patients arrive at random at a drop-in chest X-ray clinic where there are two X-ray machines in operation. Patients are seen in the order in which they arrive, and a patient is seen by the technician operating the machine that becomes available first. The time spent with each patient is constant.

(b) People arrive by appointment every fifteen minutes at a tax office where there is one inspector on duty. The time spent with each person is exponentially distributed with mean ten minutes.

10   The simple queue

In the queueing model discussed in this section, customers arrive singly, independently of one another and at random (as in a Poisson process), the time taken to serve a customer has an exponential distribution, and there is one server. This model is known as the **simple queue**, and its specification is $M/M/1$.

The service time distribution is probably the least representative element of the model. It really is rather difficult to conceive of a situation where the service time can be regarded as memoryless: if on arrival at a queue at a post office, say, you discover that the person at the front of the queue has already been there for ten minutes, you might reasonably incline to the view that he cannot be there much longer. Also, the exponential distribution is very skewed, and a more symmetric service time distribution would be more representative in most situations.

In this book, the use of the pronoun 'he' should be interpreted as relating to either a male or a female.

Suppose that customers arrive at random at rate λ. Also suppose that the service time has an exponential distribution with parameter ε. This means that (except for those periods of time where the server is free, or 'idle') customers not only arrive according to a Poisson process, but also exit according to a Poisson process. Therefore the simple queue is a particular instance of a birth and death process: it is an **immigration–emigration process** with immigration rate λ and emigration rate ε. The parameter ε is the **service rate for the queue**: it is the rate at which a server deals with customers (when there are customers in the queue). If the service time is denoted T, then $T \sim M(\varepsilon)$ and the mean service time is $E(T) = 1/\varepsilon$.

This is the first time in M343 that emigration has been included in a model.

Since the simple queue is a birth and death process, it would seem sensible to attempt to use the methods of Part I to find the distribution of $X(t)$, the length of the queue at time t. In Subsection 10.1, you will see that a problem arises when this approach is adopted. However, it is relatively straightforward to obtain properties of a queue when it has been in operation for a long time. Therefore the long-run behaviour of the simple queue is explored in the rest of this section. A formula for the equilibrium distribution, when it exists, is derived in Subsection 10.2, and a condition for its existence is obtained. The time that an individual spends in the queue is discussed in Subsection 10.3, and the lengths of idle periods and busy periods experienced by the server in Subsection 10.4.

10.1   Queue size

The length of the queue is normally referred to as the **queue size**. The queue size at time t is denoted $X(t)$. It is of particular interest to an arrival at time t, since it has a bearing on the time he will have to spend waiting for service. The queue size $X(t)$ includes the customer (if any) who is currently at the head of the queue and being served.

The probability that the queue contains exactly x customers at time t is denoted $p_x(t)$; that is,

$$p_x(t) = P(X(t) = x).$$

This notation was used for the birth and death processes of Part I.

Strictly speaking, if there are x_0 individuals in the queue at the start of observation, then $p_x(t)$ denotes the conditional probability $P(X(t) = x \,|\, X(0) = x_0)$. However, as in Part I, the initial condition is not explicit in the notation $p_x(t)$.

The differential–difference equations for a birth and death process are given by (5.7). They take the form

$$\frac{d}{dt} p_x(t) = \beta_{x-1}\, p_{x-1}(t) + \nu_{x+1}\, p_{x+1}(t) - (\beta_x + \nu_x)\, p_x(t), \quad x = 0, 1, \ldots,$$

where $\beta_{-1} = p_{-1}(t) = 0$ (by definition).

For the simple queue, the arrival rate is constant, so $\beta_x = \lambda$ for $x = 0, 1, \ldots$. If there is nobody in the queue, then there is nobody there to depart having received service, so $\nu_0 = 0$. When there are customers in the queue, the server attends to them at rate ε, so $\nu_x = \varepsilon$ for $x = 1, 2, \ldots$. Therefore the differential–difference equations for the simple queue are

$$\left.\begin{aligned}
\frac{d}{dt} p_x(t) &= \lambda\, p_{x-1}(t) + \varepsilon\, p_{x+1}(t) - (\lambda + \varepsilon)\, p_x(t), \quad x = 1, 2, \ldots, \\
\frac{d}{dt} p_0(t) &= \varepsilon\, p_1(t) - \lambda\, p_0(t).
\end{aligned}\right\} \tag{10.1}$$

Using the method of Part I, the differential–difference equations (10.1) can be used to establish the following partial differential equation for $\Pi(s, t)$, the probability generating function of $X(t)$:

$$\frac{\partial \Pi}{\partial t} = -(1 - s) \left[\left(\lambda - \frac{\varepsilon}{s} \right) \Pi + \frac{\varepsilon}{s}\, p_0(t) \right]. \tag{10.2}$$

The details of the derivation have been omitted.

The partial differential equations for the birth and death processes studied in Part I could all be written in the Lagrange form

$$f \frac{\partial \Pi}{\partial s} + g \frac{\partial \Pi}{\partial t} = h,$$

where f, g and h are functions of s, t and Π. The equation for the simple queue in (10.2) does not take this form because it contains the term $p_0(t)$. This probability is not known, so the partial differential equation cannot be solved using Lagrange's method.

It is possible to find the probability distribution of $X(t)$, but the derivation is neither simple nor quick. Moreover, the exact probability distribution for the queue size at time t in the $M/M/1$ queue is given by a quite complicated formula. Therefore the exact distribution of $X(t)$ will not be pursued further. Instead, the long-run behaviour of the queue will be explored.

10.2   The equilibrium queue size

After the queue has been operating for a long time, one of two things will have happened. Either the server is coping, or customers will be arriving at a rate too fast for the server to attend to them. In the former case, the queue is said to have attained **steady state**, or to be **in equilibrium**. In the latter case, the queue will tend to get longer and longer, overwhelming the server. In this subsection, the conditions under which the two types of long-run behaviour occur are studied, and the distribution of the equilibrium queue size (when it exists) is derived.

The steady-state or equilibrium distribution of the queue size, assuming that it exists, is obtained by setting the derivatives $dp_x(t)/dt$ equal to 0 in the differential–difference equations (10.1). This represents the notion that the probabilities $p_x = \lim_{t \to \infty} p_x(t)$ are invariant with respect to time, which is what is meant by the term **steady state**. This gives

$$0 = \lambda p_{x-1} + \varepsilon p_{x+1} - (\lambda + \varepsilon) p_x, \quad x = 1, 2, \ldots, \tag{10.3}$$
$$0 = \varepsilon p_1 - \lambda p_0. \tag{10.4}$$

From (10.4), it follows that $p_1 = \rho p_0$, where $\rho = \lambda/\varepsilon$. The quantity ρ, which is the ratio of arrival rate to service rate, is known as the **traffic intensity** of the queue.

By definition, $\rho \geq 0$.

For $x = 1, 2, \ldots$, Equation (10.3) can be rewritten as

$$\begin{aligned} p_{x+1} &= \left(1 + \frac{\lambda}{\varepsilon}\right) p_x - \frac{\lambda}{\varepsilon} p_{x-1} \\ &= (1 + \rho) p_x - \rho p_{x-1}. \end{aligned} \tag{10.5}$$

Since $p_1 = \rho p_0$, setting $x = 1$ in (10.5) gives

$$\begin{aligned} p_2 &= (1 + \rho) p_1 - \rho p_0 \\ &= (1 + \rho) \rho p_0 - \rho p_0 \\ &= \rho^2 p_0. \end{aligned}$$

Setting $x = 2$ in (10.5) leads to

$$\begin{aligned} p_3 &= (1 + \rho) p_2 - \rho p_1 \\ &= (1 + \rho) \rho^2 p_0 - \rho^2 p_0 \\ &= \rho^3 p_0. \end{aligned}$$

A pattern is emerging here: this suggests that

$$p_x = \rho^x p_0, \quad x = 0, 1, \ldots. \tag{10.6}$$

This result can be verified by substituting for p_{x+1}, p_x and p_{x-1} in (10.5) using the formula in (10.6).

The equilibrium distribution exists if the sum of the probabilities in (10.6) is equal to 1. The sum is

$$p_0 + p_1 + p_2 + \cdots = p_0(1 + \rho + \rho^2 + \cdots).$$

This converges only if $0 \leq \rho < 1$, so the equilibrium distribution exists only if $0 \leq \rho < 1$. When this condition is satisfied, the sum of the probabilities is $p_0/(1 - \rho)$. Since the sum is equal to 1, it follows that $p_0 = 1 - \rho$ and hence

$$p_x = (1 - \rho)\rho^x, \quad x = 0, 1, \ldots. $$

For $0 \leq |x| < 1$,
$$1 + x + x^2 + \cdots = \frac{1}{1 - x}.$$

This is the p.m.f. of a geometric distribution starting at 0 with parameter ρ. Therefore if X is a random variable representing the queue size in equilibrium, then $X \sim G_0(\rho)$.

The results obtained so far in this section are summarised in the following box.

The simple queue

In the simple queue, arrivals are assumed to occur at random at rate λ, there is one server, and the service time has an exponential distribution with parameter ε. The parameter ε is the service rate for the queue.

◇   The specification of the queue is $M/M/1$.

◇   The traffic intensity of the queue is $\rho = \lambda/\varepsilon$.

◇   If $\rho < 1$, then the equilibrium queue size distribution exists.

◇   If X is a random variable representing the equilibrium queue size, then $X \sim G_0(\rho)$.

Example 10.1   *Traffic intensity*

The arrivals and departures of customers at a village post office may be modelled as a simple queue. On average, a customer arrives every 12 minutes, and the mean service time is 8 minutes.

The arrival rate is

$$\lambda = \tfrac{1}{12} \text{ per minute} = 5 \text{ per hour.}$$

Since the service time is exponentially distributed with parameter ε, the mean service time is $1/\varepsilon$. That is,

$$\frac{1}{\varepsilon} = 8 \text{ minutes,}$$

so

$$\varepsilon = \tfrac{1}{8} \text{ per minute} = 7.5 \text{ per hour.}$$

The traffic intensity is

$$\rho = \lambda/\varepsilon = \tfrac{1}{12} / \tfrac{1}{8} = \tfrac{2}{3}.$$

Alternatively,

$$\rho = \lambda/\varepsilon = 5/7.5 = \tfrac{2}{3}.$$

Note the importance of using the same units of time for λ and ε.   ◆

Activity 10.1   *Traffic intensity*

Suppose that during off-peak hours, the queue at the only ticket window at a railway station may be modelled as an $M/M/1$ queue. Calculate the traffic intensity of the queue if customers arrive at the rate of three every ten minutes, and the mean service time is three minutes.

Activity 10.2   *Another queue*

Suppose that the queue in a shoe repairer's shop may be modelled as an $M/M/1$ queue. Calculate the traffic intensity of the queue if customers arrive once every five minutes on average, and the mean service time is two minutes.

Example 10.2   *A simple queue*

For the simple queue of Example 10.1, the traffic intensity ρ is $\tfrac{2}{3}$. Since $\rho < 1$, an equilibrium queue size distribution exists.

Suppose that the post office has been open for some time and that, for practical purposes, the queue may be assumed to be in equilibrium. Then X, the queue size, has the geometric distribution $G_0\left(\tfrac{2}{3}\right)$. This distribution can be used to obtain information about the queue. For instance, the mean queue size is

$$E(X) = \frac{\tfrac{2}{3}}{1 - \tfrac{2}{3}} = 2.$$

The mean of $G_0(p)$ is p/q, where $q = 1 - p$.

The proportion of the time that the counter clerk is idle is given by

$$p_0 = 1 - \tfrac{2}{3} = \tfrac{1}{3}.$$

The probability that there will be more than two people already queueing when a customer enters the post office is

$$P(X > 2) = 1 - p_0 - p_1 - p_2$$
$$= 1 - \tfrac{1}{3} - \tfrac{2}{3} \times \tfrac{1}{3} - \left(\tfrac{2}{3}\right)^2 \times \tfrac{1}{3}$$
$$= 1 - \tfrac{1}{3} - \tfrac{2}{9} - \tfrac{4}{27}$$
$$= \tfrac{8}{27}. \quad \blacklozenge$$

Activity 10.3   A queue in equilibrium

Suppose that the queue at the ticket window at a railway station during off-peak hours may be modelled as a simple queue, as in Activity 10.1. You may assume that the queue is in equilibrium.

(a) Calculate the mean length of the queue.

(b) For what proportion of the time are there at least two people in the queue?

Activity 10.4   Another queue in equilibrium

Suppose that the queue described in Activity 10.2 is in equilibrium. Calculate the probability that there will be exactly three people already queueing when a customer arrives.

You have seen that a simple queue settles down to equilibrium only if the traffic intensity is strictly less than 1. What happens when $\rho > 1$ or $\rho = 1$? In fact, in both cases, the queue will eventually grow without bound, and the server will be overwhelmed. This is obvious when the traffic intensity is greater than 1, since customers arrive faster than the server can cope with them ($\lambda > \varepsilon$). However, it is not so obvious when $\rho = 1$. Intuitively, sooner or later the queue will become quite large, and since the mean service time is equal to the mean time between arrivals, the server will be unable to clear the backlog of customers.

10.3   Queueing time

How long does an arriving customer spend in the queue waiting for the server to be free to attend to him? How long is it from his arrival until his service is completed and he can leave? The distribution of this latter time will now be derived.

You will not be expected to reproduce the derivation.

If the server is free, then an arriving customer goes straight to the head of the queue and is served immediately. If the server is busy, then the new customer has to join the end of the queue and wait while earlier customers are served before he can be served.

For a customer who has to wait, the more customers there are preceding him in the queue, the longer this waiting time is likely to be. His actual service time will be a single observation from the service time distribution. The total time spent in the queue from the moment of his arrival to the moment of departure is called the **queueing time**. The queueing time is the sum of the time spent waiting in the queue before his service begins and his service time:

queueing time = waiting time + service time.

The waiting time is the time spent literally waiting in the queue while earlier arrivals receive attention. When the customer reaches the front of the queue, his waiting time ends and his service time begins immediately. Of these two components, the first depends on the size of the queue at arrival, that is, on the number of customers in front of him.

If there are no customers in front, then the arriving customer's waiting time is 0. Otherwise, suppose that the number of customers ahead is exactly x: the probability of this is

$$P(X = x) = p_x = (1 - \rho)\rho^x.$$

His waiting time will consist of the residual service time of the first customer (the new customer might have arrived just after that service commenced, or perhaps very close to the end), plus the complete service times of the remaining $(x - 1)$ customers. The algebra of residual time is usually rather complicated. However, for the simple queueing model, the service time is exponential, and this distribution has the memoryless property. Therefore the distribution of the residual service time for the first customer is the same as the distribution of the service time for subsequent customers. Overall, the waiting time for an individual joining the queue when there are x individuals ahead of him is simply the sum of x independent exponential variates, each with parameter ε. (This includes the case when x is 0.) To find the distribution of a customer's queueing time, his service time must be added to this waiting time. His service time is independent of any preceding service time and also has the distribution $M(\varepsilon)$. Therefore his queueing time is the sum of $(x + 1)$ independent exponential variates $M(\varepsilon)$, which has the gamma distribution $\Gamma(x + 1, \varepsilon)$. Hence the probability density function of his queueing time conditional on there being x customers in the queue when he arrives is

$$f(t \mid X = x) = \frac{\varepsilon^{x+1}t^x e^{-\varepsilon t}}{x!}, \quad t \geq 0.$$

The p.d.f. of the gamma distribution is given in Table 9 in the *Handbook*.

Now suppose that the queue is in equilibrium, so that the distribution of X, the size of the queue, is $G_0(\rho)$. Then by the Theorem of Total Probability,

$$f(t) = \sum_{x=0}^{\infty} f(t \mid X = x)\,P(X = x)$$

This form of the Theorem of Total Probability is in the *Handbook*.

$$= \sum_{x=0}^{\infty} \frac{\varepsilon^{x+1}t^x e^{-\varepsilon t}}{x!}\,(1 - \rho)\rho^x$$

$$= \varepsilon e^{-\varepsilon t}(1 - \rho)\sum_{x=0}^{\infty}(\varepsilon\rho t)^x / x!$$

$$= \varepsilon e^{-\varepsilon t}(1 - \rho)e^{\varepsilon\rho t}$$

$$= (\varepsilon - \lambda)e^{-(\varepsilon - \lambda)t}.$$

$\varepsilon(1 - \rho) = \varepsilon\left(1 - \dfrac{\lambda}{\varepsilon}\right) = \varepsilon - \lambda.$

This is the p.d.f. of an exponential distribution with parameter $\varepsilon - \lambda$. This result is stated in the following box.

Queueing time

For a simple queue with arrival rate λ and service rate ε that is in equilibrium, the total queueing time of an arrival has an exponential distribution with parameter $\varepsilon - \lambda$: queueing time $\sim M(\varepsilon - \lambda)$.

Example 10.3   Queueing time

For the simple queue described in Example 10.1, the arrival rate and the service rate are given by

$\lambda = \frac{1}{12}$ per minute $= 5$ per hour,

$\varepsilon = \frac{1}{8}$ per minute $= 7.5$ per hour.

In equilibrium, the queueing time, W say, has an exponential distribution with parameter $\varepsilon - \lambda$. Working in minutes,

$\varepsilon - \lambda = \frac{1}{8} - \frac{1}{12} = \frac{1}{24}.$

So the mean queueing time of an arrival is

$$E(W) = \frac{1}{\varepsilon - \lambda} = 24 \text{ minutes.}$$

The probability that the total queueing time of an arrival will exceed half an hour is

$$P(W > 30) = e^{-\frac{1}{24} \times 30} = e^{-1.25} \simeq 0.287. \quad \blacklozenge$$

You might like to check that working in hours gives the same result!

Activity 10.5   Queueing time

Suppose that the queue described in Activity 10.1 is in equilibrium.

(a) Calculate the probability that an arriving customer will be in the queue for less than ten minutes.

(b) How long should a customer expect to spend queueing?

Activity 10.6   Another queue

Suppose that the queue described in Activity 10.2 is in equilibrium.

Calculate the probability that an arriving customer will have to queue for more than a quarter of an hour.

10.4   Idle periods and busy periods

An interval when the server is not serving anyone and there is no one waiting to be served is called an **idle period**. A **busy period** is the time spent by the server continuously attending to customers between two successive idle periods.

If $\rho > 1$, then eventually the server will be overwhelmed. Early on, occasional periods of idleness are possible, but not guaranteed. However, sooner or later a busy period will be initiated that never ends.

If $\rho = 1$, then any busy period will eventually come to an end with probability 1, but the expected duration of any busy period is infinite.

You need not worry about how these results are derived.

If $\rho < 1$, then intervals of idleness, alternating with busy periods where the server is serving continuously, are guaranteed. In this case, a consideration of long-run averages (if not exact probabilities) is straightforward. Over a very long period of time, of duration Ω say, the server will be idle for a total time of $p_0\Omega = (1 - \rho)\Omega$. Since an arrival terminates a period of idleness and inter-arrival times have the exponential distribution $M(\lambda)$, which is memoryless, the duration of each period of idleness is an observation from $M(\lambda)$.

Therefore the mean length of an idle period is $1/\lambda$. It follows intuitively that the number of idle intervals over the period of duration Ω has expectation

$$\frac{(1-\rho)\Omega}{1/\lambda} = \lambda(1-\rho)\Omega.$$

Since busy periods alternate with intervals of idleness, the expected number of busy periods is also $\lambda(1-\rho)\Omega$, covering a total time of $\rho\Omega$, so the mean duration of a busy period is

$$\frac{\rho\Omega}{\lambda(1-\rho)\Omega} = \frac{\lambda}{\varepsilon\lambda(1-\lambda/\varepsilon)} = \frac{1}{\varepsilon - \lambda}.$$

How many customers are served during a busy period? Over the long time period of duration Ω, the expected number of arrivals is $\lambda\Omega$. The expected number of busy periods is $\lambda(1-\rho)\Omega$, so the expected number of customers served during a busy period is

> Notice that this is the same as the time a customer would expect to have to spend in the queue.

$$\frac{\lambda\Omega}{\lambda(1-\rho)\Omega} = \frac{1}{1-\rho}.$$

The results just obtained are summarised in the following box.

Idle periods and busy periods

Suppose that the traffic intensity ρ of a simple queue is less than 1.

◇   Idle periods have an exponential distribution with parameter λ.

◇   Over a long period, the expected duration of a busy period is $1/(\varepsilon - \lambda)$.

◇   The expected number of customers served during a busy period is $1/(1-\rho)$.

Example 10.4   The post office queue

For the village post office described in Example 10.1, the arrival rate is $\lambda = \frac{1}{12}$ per minute, the service rate is $\varepsilon = \frac{1}{8}$ per minute, and the traffic intensity ρ is $\frac{2}{3}$.

The mean length of an idle period is

$$\frac{1}{\lambda} = 12 \text{ minutes.}$$

The expected duration of a busy period is

$$\frac{1}{\varepsilon - \lambda} = 24 \text{ minutes.}$$

The expected number of customers served during a busy period is

$$\frac{1}{1-\rho} = 3. \quad \blacklozenge$$

Activity 10.7   Busy periods at the ticket window

Suppose that the ticket window queue described in Activity 10.1 is in equilibrium. How long should the clerk expect to be busy attending to customers between periods of idleness? How many customers should the clerk expect to serve during a busy period?

Activity 10.8   Idle periods and busy periods

Suppose that the queue at the shoe repairer's shop described in Activity 10.2 is in equilibrium. Find the expected lengths of idle periods and busy periods for the shop assistant.

Summary of Section 10

The simple queue has been discussed in this section. You have seen that an equilibrium distribution for the queue size exists when the arrival rate is less than the service rate, and that this is a geometric distribution with parameter ρ, that is, $G_0(\rho)$.

For a simple queue in equilibrium, the distributions of the queueing time and the length of an idle period have been derived, and a formula for the expected duration of a busy period has been obtained.

Exercise on Section 10

Exercise 10.1   Queueing for sweets

The arrivals and departures of customers at a sweet shop may be modelled as a simple queue. The pattern of arrivals and departures may, for practical purposes, be assumed to attain equilibrium shortly after the shop opens each day. On average, two customers arrive every five minutes, and the average time taken to serve a customer is two minutes.

(a) Calculate the traffic intensity ρ of this queue.

(b) At any time, what is the mean number of customers in the shop?

(c) What proportion of customers arriving at the shop receive immediate service?

(d) Calculate the mean time that a customer spends in the shop.

(e) Calculate the probability that a customer will be in the shop for more than a quarter of an hour.

(f) How long should the shopkeeper expect to spend continuously serving customers between periods of idleness?

11 Markov queues

In Section 10, it was observed that the simple queue is a birth and death process. Therefore it is also a Markov process. The queueing models discussed in this section are all Markov processes. In Subsection 11.1, the simple queue is extended to allow for more than one server. Other Markov queues are discussed briefly in Subsection 11.2.

11.1 The $M/M/n$ queue

The model described in this subsection has the queue specification $M/M/n$. This means that, as for the simple queue, arrivals are assumed to occur at random and independently of one another: arrivals are modelled as a Poisson process with rate λ. Also as in the simple queue, the time taken to serve a customer is assumed to be exponentially distributed. Moreover, the service times of the servers are assumed to be independent random variables, identically distributed from server to server, each being exponentially distributed with parameter ε, and hence mean $1/\varepsilon$. There are n servers, where $n > 1$. The queue discipline is first-come-first-served: any customer arriving to find all the servers busy joins a central queue, moving forward as served customers depart. A customer's service commences (but does not necessarily end) in the order of arrival. A customer has no choice about which server attends to him: when he reaches the front of the central queue, he moves forward to whichever server next becomes free.

As for the simple queue, the analysis of the model will be restricted to properties of the queue when it is in equilibrium. First, the differential–difference equations for the distribution of the queue size will be obtained. These will be used to determine a condition for the equilibrium distribution to exist, and to find a formula for this distribution when it exists.

The Kolmogorov forward equations (5.7) can be used to write down the differential–difference equations for the queue size distribution once the overall birth rate β_x and the overall death rate ν_x have been found.

Customers arrive according to a Poisson process with rate λ, so $\beta_x = \lambda$ for $x = 0, 1, \ldots$. When x, the number of customers in the queue, is less than the number of servers (n), there are no delays, and customers leave as fast as the servers can process them, that is, at an overall rate proportional to the number of customers $(x\varepsilon)$. In other words, as long as the queue does not get too long $(x < n)$, the exit process is (mathematically) the same as a death process, and the queueing process looks exactly like the immigration–death process described in Section 7. Therefore setting $\beta_x = \lambda$, $\nu_x = x\varepsilon$ for $x = 0, 1, \ldots, n-1$ in the Kolmogorov forward equations (5.7) gives

$$\frac{d}{dt}\,p_0(t) = \varepsilon\,p_1(t) - \lambda\,p_0(t),$$

$$\frac{d}{dt}\,p_x(t) = \lambda\,p_{x-1}(t) + (x+1)\varepsilon\,p_{x+1}(t) - (\lambda + x\varepsilon)\,p_x(t), \quad x = 1, 2, \ldots, n-1.$$

$p_x(t) = P(X(t) = x)$, where $X(t)$ denotes the queue size at time t.

When the number of customers in the queue is n or more, all n servers are busy, and the exit rate is $n\varepsilon$. Thus $\beta_x = \lambda$, $\nu_x = n\varepsilon$ for $x = n, n+1, \ldots$. Substituting these values in the Kolmogorov forward equations gives

$$\frac{d}{dt}\,p_x(t) = \lambda\,p_{x-1}(t) + n\varepsilon\,p_{x+1}(t) - (\lambda + n\varepsilon)\,p_x(t), \quad x = n, n+1, \ldots.$$

These equations can be solved to find the distribution $\{p_x(t)\}$ of $X(t)$, the queue size at time t. The equilibrium queue size distribution $\{p_x\}$ (if it exists) is found by setting the derivatives on the left-hand sides of the differential–difference equations equal to 0. Doing this and rearranging the resulting equations gives

$$p_1 = \frac{\lambda}{\varepsilon} p_0,$$

$$p_{x+1} = \begin{cases} \dfrac{1}{\varepsilon(x+1)} \left((\lambda + x\varepsilon) p_x - \lambda p_{x-1} \right), & x = 1, 2, \ldots, n-1, \\[3mm] \dfrac{1}{n\varepsilon} \left((\lambda + n\varepsilon) p_x - \lambda p_{x-1} \right), & x = n, n+1, \ldots. \end{cases}$$

$p_x = \lim\limits_{t \to \infty} p_x(t).$

This family of equations has solution

$$p_x = \begin{cases} \dfrac{1}{x!} \left(\dfrac{\lambda}{\varepsilon} \right)^x p_0, & x = 0, 1, \ldots, n-1, \\[3mm] \dfrac{n^n}{n!} \left(\dfrac{\lambda}{n\varepsilon} \right)^x p_0, & x = n, n+1, \ldots. \end{cases}$$

If you wish, you can check this for yourself by substitution.

For $\{p_x\}$ to be a probability distribution, the sum of the terms must be equal to 1. In order to write the distribution in a convenient form (when it exists), the symbol K is defined as

$$K = 1 + \lambda/\varepsilon + \frac{(\lambda/\varepsilon)^2}{2!} + \frac{(\lambda/\varepsilon)^3}{3!} + \cdots + \frac{(\lambda/\varepsilon)^{n-1}}{(n-1)!} + \frac{(\lambda/\varepsilon)^n}{n!} \left(\sum_{j=0}^{\infty} \left(\frac{\lambda}{n\varepsilon} \right)^j \right).$$

Then

$$p_0 + p_1 + p_2 + \cdots = p_0 K.$$

The sequence of terms $p_0, p_1, p_2, \ldots$ defines a probability distribution provided that the series $\sum (\lambda/(n\varepsilon))^j$ converges. Therefore an equilibrium distribution exists only if $\lambda < n\varepsilon$. This means that an $M/M/n$ queue will attain equilibrium only if the arrival rate λ is less than the maximum rate at which the servers can process customers ($n\varepsilon$). The **traffic intensity** ρ of an $M/M/n$ queue is defined to be $\lambda/(n\varepsilon)$. Thus an $M/M/n$ queue will attain equilibrium provided that the traffic intensity ρ is less than 1.

By definition, $\rho \geq 0$.

When $\rho < 1$, the equilibrium queue size distribution exists and

$$p_0 + p_1 + p_2 + \cdots = p_0 K = 1,$$

so

$$p_0 = \frac{1}{K}.$$

Therefore the equilibrium queue size distribution can be written in terms of ρ and K as

$$p_x = \begin{cases} \dfrac{1}{K} \dfrac{n^x}{x!} \rho^x, & x = 0, 1, \ldots, n-1, \\[3mm] \dfrac{1}{K} \dfrac{n^n}{n!} \rho^x, & x = n, n+1, \ldots. \end{cases}$$

Note that K can be written in terms of ρ as

$$K = 1 + n\rho + \frac{(n\rho)^2}{2!} + \cdots + \frac{(n\rho)^{n-1}}{(n-1)!} + \frac{(n\rho)^n}{n!} \sum_{j=0}^{\infty} \rho^j$$

$$= 1 + n\rho + \frac{(n\rho)^2}{2!} + \cdots + \frac{(n\rho)^{n-1}}{(n-1)!} + \frac{(n\rho)^n}{n!(1-\rho)}.$$

The results just obtained are summarised in the following box.

The $M/M/n$ queue

In an $M/M/n$ queue, arrivals occur independently and at random at rate λ, there are n servers, and for all servers the service time has an exponential distribution with parameter ε.

The traffic intensity of the queue is $\rho = \lambda/(n\varepsilon)$. If $\rho < 1$, then the equilibrium queue size distribution exists and its p.m.f. is given by

$$p_x = \frac{1}{K}\frac{n^x}{x!}\rho^x, \quad x = 0, 1, \ldots, n-1, \tag{11.1}$$

$$p_x = \frac{1}{K}\frac{n^n}{n!}\rho^x, \quad x = n, n+1, \ldots, \tag{11.2}$$

where

$$K = 1 + n\rho + \frac{(n\rho)^2}{2!} + \cdots + \frac{(n\rho)^{n-1}}{(n-1)!} + \frac{(n\rho)^n}{n!(1-\rho)}. \tag{11.3}$$

You will not be expected to reproduce the derivation of these results.

Example 11.1   A queue with three servers

Suppose that three cashiers are on duty in a bank where customers may be assumed to arrive independently and at random at the rate of 40 per hour. If a cashier is free, then an arriving customer receives immediate attention; otherwise, a central queue is formed. The service time of each cashier may be assumed to be exponentially distributed with mean three minutes.

The specification of this queue is $M/M/3$.

The arrival rate is

$\lambda = 40$ per hour $= \frac{2}{3}$ per minute.

The service rate is

$\varepsilon = \frac{1}{3}$ per minute $= 20$ per hour.

Therefore the traffic intensity of the queue is

$$\rho = \frac{\lambda}{n\varepsilon} = \frac{40}{3 \times 20} = \frac{2}{3}.$$

Alternatively,
$$\rho = \tfrac{2}{3}\big/\big(3 \times \tfrac{1}{3}\big) = \tfrac{2}{3}.$$

Since $\rho < 1$, an equilibrium queue size distribution exists. Setting $n = 3$ and $\rho = \frac{2}{3}$ in (11.3) gives

$$K = 1 + 3\rho + \frac{(3\rho)^2}{2!} + \frac{(3\rho)^3}{3!(1-\rho)}$$

$$= 1 + 2 + 2 + 4$$

$$= 9.$$

Substituting for K, n and ρ in (11.1) and (11.2) gives

$$p_x = \begin{cases} \dfrac{1}{9}\dfrac{3^x}{x!}\left(\dfrac{2}{3}\right)^x, & x = 0, 1, 2, \\[3mm] \dfrac{1}{9}\dfrac{3^3}{3!}\left(\dfrac{2}{3}\right)^x, & x = 3, 4, \ldots. \end{cases}$$

Thus, for instance, the proportion of the time that all three cashiers are idle is

$$p_0 = \tfrac{1}{9}.$$

An arriving customer receives immediate service if at least one of the cashiers is free, that is, if the queue size is at most 2. Hence the probability that an arriving customer receives immediate service is

$$p_0 + p_1 + p_2 = \tfrac{1}{9} + \tfrac{2}{9} + \tfrac{2}{9} = \tfrac{5}{9}. \quad \blacklozenge$$

The queue includes any customers currently being served as well as those waiting to be served.

Activity 11.1   A bank queue: more probabilities

Suppose that the bank queue in Example 11.1 is in equilibrium.

(a) What proportion of the time are all three cashiers busy?

(b) Calculate the probability that when a customer enters the bank, all three cashiers are busy and two customers are waiting in the central queue.

(c) When Tom enters the bank, all the cashiers are busy, but no one is waiting to be served. Calculate the probability that he will have to wait for more than 30 seconds for a cashier to be free to serve him.

Activity 11.2   Two servers

Two advisers are on duty at a tax enquiry office. Members of the public may be assumed to arrive independently and at random at the rate of 16 per hour. If an adviser is free, then an arriving enquirer is seen immediately; otherwise, a central queue is formed. The time spent by either adviser with an enquirer is exponentially distributed with mean six minutes.

(a) Write down the specification of this queue, and calculate the traffic intensity ρ.

Assume that the queue is in equilibrium.

(b) What proportion of the time are both advisers idle?

(c) What proportion of enquirers are seen immediately?

(d) Calculate the probability that when I enter the office, both advisers are busy and three people are waiting to be seen.

(e) When Helen enters the office, both advisers are busy, but no one is waiting to be seen. Calculate the probability that she will have to wait more than five minutes before an adviser is free to see her.

Example 11.2   The mean equilibrium queue size

The equilibrium queue size distribution for the bank queue of Example 11.1 can be used to find the mean length of the queue in equilibrium. By definition, the mean queue size is given by

$$E(X) = \sum_{x=0}^{\infty} x p_x.$$

Instead of evaluating this sum directly, the mean queue size can be calculated by first finding $\Pi(s)$, the p.g.f. of X. Then

$$E(X) = \Pi'(1).$$

The advantage of this method is that the algebra involved is generally more straightforward, so this approach will be used here.

For the bank queue of Example 11.1, the p.g.f. of X is

$$\Pi(s) = p_0 + p_1 s + p_2 s^2 + p_3 s^3 + \cdots$$

$$= \tfrac{1}{9} + \tfrac{2}{9}s + \tfrac{2}{9}s^2 + \sum_{x=3}^{\infty} \tfrac{1}{9}\tfrac{3^3}{3!}\left(\tfrac{2}{3}\right)^x s^x$$

$$= \tfrac{1}{9}\left(1 + 2s + 2s^2 + \tfrac{9}{2}\sum_{x=3}^{\infty}\left(\tfrac{2}{3}s\right)^x\right).$$

The last term in the brackets involves the sum of a geometric series:

$$\tfrac{9}{2} \times \left(\tfrac{2}{3}s\right)^3 \times \sum_{j=0}^{\infty}\left(\tfrac{2}{3}s\right)^j = \tfrac{4}{3}s^3\sum_{j=0}^{\infty}\left(\tfrac{2}{3}s\right)^j$$

$$= \tfrac{4}{3}s^3 \times \frac{1}{1-\tfrac{2}{3}s}$$

$$= \frac{4s^3}{3-2s}.$$

For $-1 < x < 1$,
$$1 + x + x^2 + \cdots = \frac{1}{1-x}.$$

Hence

$$\Pi(s) = \tfrac{1}{9}\left(1 + 2s + 2s^2 + \frac{4s^3}{3-2s}\right).$$

Differentiating $\Pi(s)$ with respect to s gives

$$\Pi'(s) = \tfrac{1}{9}\left(2 + 4s + \frac{12s^2(3-2s) + 8s^3}{(3-2s)^2}\right).$$

Therefore the mean equilibrium queue size is

$$E(X) = \Pi'(1) = \tfrac{1}{9}(2 + 4 + 20)$$

$$= 2\tfrac{8}{9}$$

$$\simeq 2.89. \quad \blacklozenge$$

Activity 11.3   Two servers

The queue at a tax enquiry office was described in Activity 11.2. Show that $\Pi(s)$, the p.g.f. of X, the equilibrium queue size, is given by

$$\Pi(s) = \tfrac{1}{45}\left(5 + 8s + \frac{32s^2}{5-4s}\right).$$

Hence calculate the mean equilibrium queue size.

The $M/M/\infty$ queue

If the number of servers can be assumed to be infinite, then no customer ever has to wait, as there is always somebody available to give immediate attention. This queue is sometimes called 'a queue with ample servers'. This utopian situation could not be realised in practice, but something very close to it could happen when the number of servers is very large. The $M/M/\infty$ queue is simply an immigration–death process with immigration rate λ and death rate ε. In Section 7, the exact distribution of the population size $X(t)$ was obtained: if the population size is 0 initially, then $X(t) \sim \text{Poisson}(\lambda(1 - e^{\varepsilon t})/\varepsilon)$. The limiting distribution is $\text{Poisson}(\lambda/\varepsilon)$.

See Activity 7.1.

11.2   Other Markov queues

The $M/M/1$ queue and the $M/M/n$ queue are variations on the general theme of (Markov) birth and death processes. Such processes can be characterised by statements of the form

$$P(X(t + \delta t) = x + 1 \mid X(t) = x) = \beta_x \, \delta t + o(\delta t),$$
$$P(X(t + \delta t) = x - 1 \mid X(t) = x) = \nu_x \, \delta t + o(\delta t).$$

For the $M/M/1$ queue,

$$\beta_x = \lambda, \quad \nu_x = \varepsilon, \quad x = 0, 1, \dots.$$

For the $M/M/n$ queue,

$$\beta_x = \lambda, \quad x = 0, 1, \dots,$$
$$\nu_x = \begin{cases} x\varepsilon, & x = 1, 2, \dots, n - 1, \\ n\varepsilon, & x = n, n + 1, \dots. \end{cases}$$

The method that has been used to find the equilibrium queue size distribution for the $M/M/1$ and $M/M/n$ queues can be applied to any Markov queueing model. In general, the equilibrium distribution is given by

$$p_x = \frac{1}{K} \rho_x, \quad x = 0, 1, \dots, \tag{11.4}$$

where $\rho_0 = 1$ and

$$\rho_x = \frac{\beta_0 \, \beta_1 \, \beta_2 \cdots \beta_{x-1}}{\nu_1 \, \nu_2 \, \nu_3 \cdots \nu_x}, \quad x = 1, 2, \dots, \tag{11.5}$$

and

$$K = 1 + \rho_1 + \rho_2 + \cdots. \tag{11.6}$$

You will not be expected to use this general result to find an equilibrium queue size distribution.

The formula for the p.m.f. of the equilibrium queue size distribution of a general Markov queue given by (11.4), (11.5) and (11.6) can be applied to any queueing situation where the parameters β_x and ν_x are functions of x but not of t. You may like to check that using them leads to the results obtained previously for the $M/M/1$ queue and the $M/M/n$ queue. Two further examples of Markov queueing models are given in Examples 11.3 and 11.4.

Example 11.3   Queues with discouragement

We have all suffered the experience of arriving at a service point only to discover that the queue is very long indeed. Sometimes it is so long that we simply turn away. Suppose that the sight of a queue already containing x persons is such that the probability that a new arrival stays to queue is only $1/(x + 1)$. Then

$$\beta_x = \frac{\lambda}{x + 1}, \quad x = 0, 1, \dots,$$
$$\nu_x = \varepsilon, \quad x = 1, 2, \dots. \quad \blacklozenge$$

Example 11.4   Finite waiting room

Sometimes people cannot wait because there is no room to do so. If the waiting room is of finite capacity 10, say, so that the queue can accommodate at most 11 individuals (one being served and 10 sitting waiting), then

$$\beta_x = \begin{cases} \lambda, & x = 0, 1, \dots, 10, \\ 0, & x = 11, 12, \dots, \end{cases}$$
$$\nu_x = \varepsilon, \quad x = 1, 2, \dots. \quad \blacklozenge$$

Markov queues will not be discussed further, but if you are interested, then you will find an example of the use of (11.4), (11.5) and (11.6) in the section 'Exercises on Book 4'.

See Exercise 24.17.

Summary of Section 11

The $M/M/n$ queue has been discussed in this section. This model is an extension of the $M/M/1$ queue that allows for more than one server. You have seen that an equilibrium distribution for the queue size exists when the arrival rate is less than the maximum throughput of the servers, that is, when the traffic intensity $\rho = \lambda/(n\varepsilon)$ is less than 1. You have used the equilibrium distribution to calculate probabilities and solve problems for an $M/M/n$ queue. Other Markov queues have been discussed briefly.

Exercise on Section 11

Exercise 11.1   Queueing for advice

Members of the public arrive independently and at random at an advice bureau where there are five advisers on duty. If an adviser is free, then a person entering the bureau receives immediate attention. Otherwise, a central queue is formed. The time that an adviser spends with a member of the public is exponentially distributed with mean ten minutes and is the same for all the advisers. On average, three members of the public arrive every ten minutes.

(a) Write down the specification of this queue, and calculate the traffic intensity ρ.

Assume that the queue is in equilibrium.

(b) Calculate the proportion of the time that all five advisers are free.

(c) What proportion of the time are exactly three advisers busy?

(d) Calculate the probability that when I arrive at the bureau, all the advisers will be busy and one person will be waiting for advice.

(e) Sam arrives to find that all five advisers are busy but no one is waiting for advice. Calculate the probability that he will have to wait for at least five minutes for an adviser to be free to attend to him.

12   General service times

Possibly the least representative element of the $M/M/1$ and $M/M/n$ queues discussed in Sections 10 and 11 is the assumption that the service time distribution is exponential. The results discussed in this section can be applied whether or not the service time distribution is exponential and are valid for any service time distribution. The specification of a single-server queue with random arrivals and general service time distribution is $M/G/1$. A formula for the mean equilibrium queue size of an $M/G/1$ queue is given in Subsection 12.1. Queues with a general service time distribution and more than one server are discussed very briefly in Subsection 12.2.

This point was discussed briefly at the beginning of Section 10.

12.1   The $M/G/1$ *queue*

Suppose that customers arrive independently and at random at a single-server queue with service time T. If the distribution of T is not exponential, then it does not have the memoryless property, and the queue is not a Markov process. This means that at any time t, the future behaviour of the queue depends on the time for which the customer at the service point at time t has been receiving service. Consequently, although general results can be derived for the $M/G/1$ queue, in practice they are not particularly easy to use. Therefore in this subsection, the discussion will be restricted to a single general result that holds for any $M/G/1$ queue in equilibrium.

Essentially, all that is required for a queue to attain equilibrium is that 'customers should not arrive too often', or equivalently that 'service should not be too slow'. The **traffic intensity** of an $M/G/1$ queue with arrival rate λ and service time T is defined as

$$\rho = \lambda\, E(T). \tag{12.1}$$

In Section 10, the traffic intensity of an $M/M/1$ queue was defined to be λ/ε, where ε is the service rate. For an $M/M/1$ queue, $T \sim M(\varepsilon)$, so $E(T) = 1/\varepsilon$, and hence (12.1) reduces to λ/ε. Thus the definition in (12.1) for the traffic intensity of an $M/G/1$ queue is consistent with that given in Section 10 for an $M/M/1$ queue.

It can be shown that, as for an $M/M/1$ queue, an $M/G/1$ queue will attain equilibrium if the traffic intensity is less than 1. An important result for the mean equilibrium queue size of an $M/G/1$ queue, known as **Pollaczek's formula**, is stated in the following box.

Pollaczek's formula

Suppose that customers arrive at an $M/G/1$ queue at rate λ, and that the service time T has mean $E(T)$ and variance $V(T)$.

If the traffic intensity satisfies $\rho = \lambda\, E(T) < 1$, then the equilibrium queue size distribution exists and its mean is given by **Pollaczek's formula**:

$$E(X) = \frac{\rho - \tfrac{1}{2}\rho^2 + \tfrac{1}{2}\lambda^2\, V(T)}{1 - \rho}. \tag{12.2}$$

A proof of this result will not be given.

This result demonstrates that in equilibrium the mean queue length depends not only on the mean service time but also on the variability in service time. If the mean service time is unchanged, but the variability is reduced, then the mean queue length gets shorter: from the customer's point of view, the most efficient server is one whose service time is constant.

Example 12.1   *Uniform service times*

Suppose that customers arrive at random every 90 seconds on average at a railway station ticket office where there is one assistant, and that the service time has a uniform distribution, being anything between 30 seconds and 90 seconds.

Working in seconds, the arrival rate is

$$\lambda = \tfrac{1}{90} \text{ per second.}$$

The distribution of the service time T is $U(30, 90)$, so

$$E(T) = 60,$$

$$V(T) = \frac{(90 - 30)^2}{12} = 300.$$

Hence the traffic intensity is

$$\rho = \lambda\,E(T)$$
$$= \tfrac{1}{90} \text{ per second} \times 60 \text{ seconds}$$
$$= \tfrac{2}{3}.$$

Since $\rho < 1$, the equilibrium queue size distribution exists and its mean is given by Pollaczek's formula:

$$E(X) = \frac{\tfrac{2}{3} - \tfrac{1}{2} \times \left(\tfrac{2}{3}\right)^2 + \tfrac{1}{2} \times \left(\tfrac{1}{90}\right)^2 \times 300}{1 - \tfrac{2}{3}}$$
$$= \tfrac{25}{18}$$
$$\simeq 1.39.$$

Alternatively, working in minutes, $\lambda = \tfrac{2}{3}$ per minute, $E(T) = 1$ and $V(T) = \left(1\tfrac{1}{2} - \tfrac{1}{2}\right)^2 \big/ 12 = \tfrac{1}{12}$, so $\rho = \lambda\,E(T) = \tfrac{2}{3}$ and

$$E(X) = \frac{\tfrac{2}{3} - \tfrac{1}{2} \times \left(\tfrac{2}{3}\right)^2 + \tfrac{1}{2} \times \left(\tfrac{2}{3}\right)^2 \times \tfrac{1}{12}}{1 - \tfrac{2}{3}} \simeq 1.39. \quad \blacklozenge$$

Activity 12.1   Constant service time

Clients arrive independently and at random every 25 minutes on average at an advice centre where there is one adviser. The adviser spends 20 minutes with each client.

(a) Calculate the traffic intensity of the queue.

(b) Calculate the mean number of clients in the centre, either receiving advice or waiting for advice, when the queue is in equilibrium.

Activity 12.2   Gamma service time

Suppose that customers join a single-server queue independently and at random at the rate of 24 per hour, and that the service time T (in minutes) has the gamma distribution $\Gamma(3, 2)$.

(a) Calculate the traffic intensity of the queue.

(b) Calculate the mean queue length when the queue is in equilibrium.

Activity 12.3   Another queue in equilibrium

Suppose that customers join a single-server queue independently and at random at the rate of 6 per hour, and that the service time T (in minutes) has the chi-squared distribution with 7 degrees of freedom.

(a) Calculate the traffic intensity of the queue.

(b) Calculate the mean equilibrium queue size.

12.2   More than one server

The $M/G/n$ queue where several servers are on hand but the service time is arbitrary has a complex structure, and will not be discussed.

The $M/G/\infty$ queue where customers are always served immediately is of some interest, particularly once it has attained equilibrium. If customers arrive according to a Poisson process with rate λ and the random arrival times are written $t_1, t_2, t_3, \ldots$, then the exit times can be written $t_1 + g_1, t_2 + g_2, t_3 + g_3, \ldots$, where g_i is the service time of the customer who arrived at time t_i. The customers will not necessarily leave in the order in which they arrived, but it is interesting that after some time the departure process is indistinguishable from a Poisson process, also with rate λ. This means that if these departing customers go on to a subsequent service point, then the input there may also be regarded as random.

There are many applications where the 'point process' $\{t_1 + g_1, t_2 + g_2, t_3 + g_3, \ldots\}$ arises, and to be able to regard this as 'approximately' a Poisson process almost always results in a considerable simplification of the analysis. For instance, consider the following situation. Cars pass an observer standing by the side of a road according to a Poisson process in time. They are travelling at constant – but different – speeds, and when they pass a second observer a kilometre further up the road, their order might have changed. A car passing the first observer at time t_i will pass the second at time $t_i + g_i$, where g_i is the time that the car takes to travel one kilometre. The second observer also sees random traffic flow. (Actually, if starting at time 0 the cars pass the first observer according to a Poisson process in time with rate λ, then they pass the second according to a non-homogeneous Poisson process with rate $\lambda(t) = \lambda\, G(t)$, where G is the c.d.f. of the speed random variable. After some time, $G(t) = 1$, and the result follows.)

Summary of Section 12

Queues with random arrivals and general service time distribution have been discussed in this section. You have learned that an $M/G/1$ queue will attain equilibrium if the traffic intensity is less than 1, and you have used Pollaczek's formula to calculate the mean equilibrium queue size of an $M/G/1$ queue.

Exercise on Section 12

Exercise 12.1   Using Pollaczek's formula

Customers arrive independently and at random at the rate of one every 20 minutes at a shoe shop where there is one salesman.

Calculate the traffic intensity and the mean equilibrium queue size for each of the following service time distributions.

(a) Constant, and equal to 12 minutes.

(b) Uniform, taking anything between 4 minutes and 20 minutes.

Part III Epidemics

Introduction to Part III

Throughout history, epidemics of infectious diseases have not only caused immeasurable human suffering, but often played a decisive role in the destruction of armies and of empires. They have also exercised a profound influence on rates of population growth. Although such diseases as plague, smallpox and typhus fever are no longer the common cause of death that they once were, other diseases have remained, or have become, important as major sources of illness. For example, in the tropics, malaria and schistosomiasis are widespread debilitating diseases. And every few years, a worldwide pandemic of influenza occurs, facilitated by the ever-increasing amount of air travel between the cities of the world.

Two basic models for the spread of an infectious disease are described in Part III: the *simple epidemic model* and the *general epidemic model*. In Section 13, some epidemiological principles relevant to the construction of mathematical models are outlined. For instance, to construct an even roughly competent model, it is necessary to know something of the way in which diseases are passed from one individual to another: when they can be passed on, and when not; when an individual may be regarded as being immune to a disease, or as having recovered from it; and so on. The simple epidemic model is discussed in Section 14. This model applies to a situation where individuals, once they have caught a disease, forever after remain infectious and capable of communicating the disease to anybody who has not yet caught it. If the community is closed, everyone will eventually catch the disease. In the general epidemic model, infected individuals do not remain infectious forever. Eventually, they recover from the disease and can no longer pass it on. They remain in the community, but it is also assumed that once they have caught the disease and have recovered from it, they are thereafter immune from further attacks. Since it is possible to recover from the disease without passing it on, or after passing it on to only a small number of people, the epidemic may die out before every member of the community has been infected. In Section 15, the model is described and the deterministic version of the model is examined. The stochastic model is discussed in Section 16. In Section 17, the question of whether the disease will affect nearly everyone or disappear from the community almost unnoticed is explored. Some situations for which the simple epidemic model and the general epidemic model are not suitable are considered very briefly in Section 18.

13   Modelling the spread of an infectious disease

The stages in the development of a disease after an individual is infected are discussed briefly in this section, and some of the terminology used by epidemiologists is introduced.

An epidemiologist is a scientist concerned with how diseases affect populations.

An individual who does not have the disease, and is not immune to infection, is called a **susceptible**. A person who has the disease and is infectious is referred to as an **infective**. At the start of an epidemic, it is assumed that there is at least one infective. Immediately after an infective communicates the disease to a susceptible, a period called the **latent period** begins. During the latent period, the disease develops within the newly-infected individual, but he (or she) is not capable of passing on the infection. The latent period is followed by an **infectious period**, during which the infected person, who is now an infective, is capable of transmitting the disease. The infectious period ends when the infective once again becomes incapable of passing on the disease. This might be because he has died or, if he has recovered, he might be immune to further attacks of the disease (as is the case for measles). When an individual is first infected, there is also an **incubation period**. This is the period until the first symptoms of the disease appear, and is generally longer than the latent period. These concepts are illustrated in Figure 13.1.

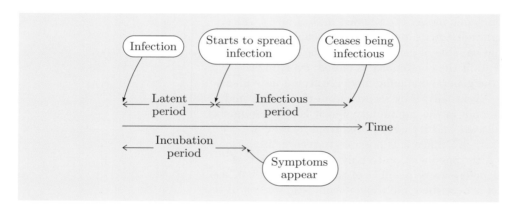

Figure 13.1   Stages in the development of a disease after a susceptible is infected

For some diseases, in some communities, when symptoms appear at the end of the incubation period, the infected individual is isolated so that he can no longer pass on the disease to others. However, even where this occurs, there may be a period between the end of the latent period and the onset of symptoms, during which the infectious person is circulating in the community. Where a sufferer is not isolated, he may continue to transmit the disease until the end of the infectious period, at which time he either recovers or, in the case of fatal diseases, dies. After recovery, he may be at least temporarily immune to the disease. The term **removal** is used to refer to the end of the infectious period, and may cover isolation, recovery or death. After removal, the individual is assumed to play no further part in the spread of the disease.

The salient features for the mathematical modelling of an infectious disease are illustrated in Figure 13.2.

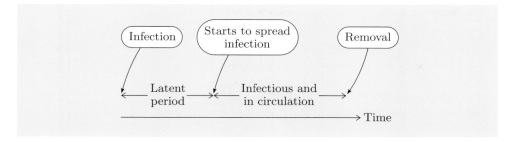

Figure 13.2   Stages relevant to modelling the spread of an infectious disease

One aspect of the modelling process involves specifying the lengths of the latent period and the period during which an individual is infectious and in circulation. These periods may be taken to be of fixed length (in some cases zero), or to have lengths specified by some probability distribution. For the models discussed in Part III, the latent period is assumed to be zero.

When the latent period is taken to have zero length, only three classes of individuals need to be considered (that is, counted):

◇   **susceptibles** – those liable to catch the disease if they meet an infected person;

◇   **infectives** – those capable of passing on the disease;

◇   **removed** – those who have had the disease but who are no longer capable of passing it on.

Any individual who is eventually infected passes through these three stages:

    SUSCEPTIBLE   ⟶   INFECTIVE   ⟶   REMOVED.

These technical terms will be used throughout Part III.

In constructing the models, assumptions also have to be made about the community in which the spread of a disease is being modelled. The size of the community has to be considered. At one extreme, we might be interested in the spread of the disease in a small household: will you catch your spouse's cold? At the other extreme, we might be concerned with a disease spreading through a population consisting of millions of individuals.

In Parts I and II, populations have been modelled that have changed size as individuals are born or die, and as others arrive or depart. Of course, births, deaths and migration are bound to occur in communities where there is disease. However, in the epidemic models considered in Part III, the population is assumed to be **closed**. This means that during the course of the epidemic, no individual either leaves the community or joins it from outside, and no births take place. Moreover, removed individuals are assumed to have recovered from the disease, to be immune from further attacks and to remain in the population. Consequently, the total size of the population remains constant: the sum of the numbers of infectives, susceptibles and removed remains the same throughout the epidemic.

A further assumption of the models that will be discussed deals with the manner in which a disease spreads from infectious individuals to susceptibles. At any given moment, members of the community are free to come into contact with any others. It is assumed that any two individuals are as likely to come into contact as any other two. This is known as **homogeneous mixing**. Some contacts will be between two susceptibles: since neither can transmit the disease, neither will catch it. Other contacts will be between two infectives: since they both already have the disease, there will be no new infections. The disease will be transmitted only when a susceptible comes into contact with an infective. At what rate will contacts between infectives and susceptibles occur?

Suppose that a community contains $n+1$ individuals, and that each member of the community comes into contact with others according to a Poisson process with rate β. This means that a particular member David has contacts with the n other members according to a Poisson process with rate β. Assuming homogeneous mixing, the probability that David has contact with a particular member Gary is $1/n$. Therefore David meets Gary according to a Poisson process with rate β/n.

Now suppose that there are x susceptibles in the community and that David is one of y infectives in the community. Since there are x susceptibles, David will come into contact with susceptibles according to a Poisson process with rate $\beta x/n$. Therefore, since there are y infectives, contacts between susceptibles and infectives will occur according to a Poisson process with rate $\beta xy/n$.

The size of a community is taken to be $n+1$ rather than n as this simplifies some results.

Contacts between groups

Suppose that in a community of size $n+1$, there are x individuals of one type and y individuals of a second type. Assuming homogeneous mixing, if any particular member of the community comes into contact with others according to a Poisson process with rate β, then contacts between the different types occur according to a Poisson process with rate

$$\frac{\beta xy}{n}. \tag{13.1}$$

All of these assumptions may be questioned in the context of a given epidemic. In particular, the assumption of homogeneous mixing is rarely even approximately valid. The idea that contacts occur as a Poisson process with constant rate is also doubtful. However, simplifying assumptions have to be made in order to produce models that can be analysed mathematically, and even simple models can provide valuable insights into the behaviour of epidemics. In addition, although this is not a point that will be developed, various data sets collected from past epidemic outbreaks have been found to be reasonably consistent with the predictions of the simple models that will be described in this book.

Summary of Section 13

The stages in the development of a disease when an individual is infected have been described briefly in this section, and some terminology has been introduced. Some of the assumptions of the epidemic models that will be developed in the next few sections have been discussed.

14 The simple epidemic

The model discussed in this section is known as the **simple epidemic model**. The model is described in Subsection 14.1. Even for this simple model, useful general results for the stochastic model are rare, so in Subsection 14.2, in order to gain some indication of the way in which an epidemic is 'likely' to develop, the deterministic analogue is analysed. The stochastic model is then explored: waiting times between infections and the duration of the epidemic are studied in Subsection 14.3, and the distribution of the number of infectives at time t in Subsection 14.4.

14.1 The model

The assumptions of the simple epidemic model are listed in the following box.

> **Simple epidemic model: assumptions**
> ◇   The community through which the infection is spreading is closed.
> ◇   Any two individuals are as likely to come into contact as any other two (homogeneous mixing).
> ◇   Each individual comes into contact with other individuals according to a Poisson process with rate β.
> ◇   When a susceptible meets an infective, he catches the infection with probability 1.
> ◇   The latent period has length 0.
> ◇   Removals do not occur: an infected individual stays infectious and remains in the community.

The first three assumptions were discussed in Section 13. The last three assumptions together mean that on contact with an infective, each susceptible immediately becomes and then remains an infective. So there are only two stages to the disease:

SUSCEPTIBLE $\longrightarrow$ INFECTIVE.

Let $X(t)$ and $Y(t)$ denote, respectively, the numbers of susceptibles and infectives in the community at time t. Also, let x_0 and y_0 denote the numbers of susceptibles and infectives at time 0; that is, $X(0) = x_0$, $Y(0) = y_0$. Since the community is closed, for all t,

$$X(t) + Y(t) = x_0 + y_0.$$

If the size of the community is $n + 1$, then for all t,

$$X(t) + Y(t) = x_0 + y_0 = n + 1.$$

Therefore $X(t) = n + 1 - Y(t)$ for all t, and hence it is sufficient to work with the single random variable $Y(t)$ in order to monitor the progress of the epidemic. If required, $X(t)$ can be found by subtraction.

Example 14.1   Progress of an epidemic

In a family of six (two parents and four children), one of the children catches a 'bug'. Next day, both parents and one of the other children are also down with the same ailment. Two days later, they all have it.

In this case, $y_0 = 1$, $n = 5$ (and hence $x_0 = 5$). If time is measured in days, then the next information given is that $Y(1) = 4$ (and hence $X(1) = 2$). Finally, $Y(3) = 6$ and $X(3) = 0$: everyone in the family has caught the infection. Note that $X(t) = 6 - Y(t)$ for all t.   ◆

When a susceptible meets an infective, he catches the infection with probability 1. Since the length of the latent period is 0, the number of infectives increases immediately by 1. Moreover, by (13.1), when there are x susceptibles and y infectives, contacts between susceptibles and infectives occur according to a Poisson process with rate $\beta xy/n$. Therefore the random process $\{Y(t); t \geq 0\}$, which describes the number of infectives in the community at time t, is a sort of 'birth' process. Hence the transition probability $P(Y(t + \delta t) = y + 1 \mid Y(t) = y)$ takes the form $\beta_y \, \delta t + o(\delta t)$, where $\beta_y = \beta xy/n$. But $X(t) = n + 1 - Y(t)$ for all t, so $x = n + 1 - y$, and hence the **epidemic rate** β_y is given by

$$\beta_y = \frac{\beta y(n + 1 - y)}{n}. \tag{14.1}$$

Therefore the simple epidemic model can be characterised by a single probability statement as stated in the following box.

The simple epidemic

Let $Y(t)$ denote the number of infectives in a community at time t. Then the stochastic simple epidemic model for the spread of the disease through the community is characterised by the following probability statement:

$$P(Y(t + \delta t) = y + 1 \mid Y(t) = y) = \frac{\beta y(n + 1 - y)}{n} \delta t + o(\delta t). \qquad (14.2)$$

Notice that when $y = 0$, there are no infected individuals from whom to catch the infection, so the epidemic rate β_y is equal to 0. Similarly, when $y = n + 1$, there are no susceptible individuals left to whom it can be transmitted, so $\beta_y = 0$. For intermediate values of y, $\beta_y > 0$.

Activity 14.1   Refining the model

How might you alter the simple epidemic model to represent the notion that when an infective meets a susceptible, the infection is passed on only with probability θ, where $0 < \theta < 1$?

The probability θ could be used to reflect the virulence of the disease, or the resistance to infection of those who have not yet caught it.

14.2   The deterministic model

The stochastic simple epidemic model is characterised by the probability statement (14.2). Hence, using (8.3), the deterministic model for the simple epidemic may be written in the form of the ordinary differential equation

$$\frac{dy}{dt} = \frac{\beta y(n + 1 - y)}{n}. \qquad (14.3)$$

The solution of this differential equation is the deterministic approximation to the stochastic model.

The equation (14.3) could have been written in the form $dz/dt = \beta z(n + 1 - z)/n$, the change of notation intended to emphasise that it is the deterministic version that is being studied (as was done for the models discussed in Section 8). However, in this section, the lower-case letter y corresponding to the random variable $Y(t)$ will be used.

Activity 14.2   The deterministic solution

(a) Use separation of variables to show that the solution y of the differential equation (14.3) satisfies

$$\frac{n}{n + 1} \log \left(\frac{y}{n + 1 - y} \right) = \beta t + \text{constant}.$$

You may find the following identity useful:

$$\frac{1}{y(n + 1 - y)} = \frac{1}{n + 1} \left(\frac{1}{y} + \frac{1}{n + 1 - y} \right).$$

(b) Suppose that there are initially n susceptibles and one infective in a community. Show that in this case, the solution of the differential equation (14.3) is

$$y = \frac{n+1}{n \exp\left(-\left(1 + \dfrac{1}{n}\right)\beta t\right) + 1}. \tag{14.4}$$

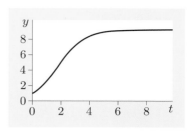

Figure 14.1   Development of the simple epidemic – deterministic model

From (14.4), $y \to n+1$ as $t \to \infty$, so eventually all the original susceptibles will become infected. The graph of the deterministic solution (14.4) is shown in Figure 14.1 for $n = 8$ and $\beta = 1$.

Activity 14.3   Infections

Suppose that at time 0, an inhabitant of a village of total size 112 becomes infected, that the spread of the infection may be modelled as a deterministic simple epidemic, and that the contact rate β is 4 per day.

(a) According to the model, how many villagers will be infected after one day? How many will be infected after two days?

(b) After how long will everyone in the village be infected?

14.3   The stochastic model: waiting times

In the stochastic version of the simple epidemic model, the random variable $Y(t)$ is the number of infectives at time t. The random process $\{Y(t); t \geq 0\}$ is characterised by the probability statement (14.2); that is,

$$P(Y(t + \delta t) = y + 1 \mid Y(t) = y) = \beta_y \, \delta t + o(\delta t),$$

where

$$\beta_y = \frac{\beta y(n + 1 - y)}{n}, \quad y = 1, 2, \ldots, n. \tag{14.5}$$

Therefore when there are y infectives, T_y, the time to the next infection, has an exponential distribution with parameter β_y; that is, $T_y \sim M(\beta_y)$. In particular,

$$E(T_y) = \frac{1}{\beta_y}, \quad V(T_y) = \frac{1}{\beta_y^2}.$$

Since the waiting times between infections are independent random variables, these results can be used to find the mean and variance of the waiting time until any specified number of susceptibles have been infected. This is illustrated in Example 14.2.

Example 14.2   Waiting times

Suppose that in a closed community of total size 7, initially two people are suffering from an infectious disease that is incurable but not serious, and that the spread of the infection through the community is modelled as a stochastic simple epidemic with contact rate $\beta = 0.09$ per day. How long will it be until the first new infection, or until the second new infection? How long will it be before all the susceptibles are infected and the epidemic terminates? The mean and variance of these times can be found as follows.

The epidemic rate β_y is given by (14.5). For this epidemic,

$$\beta_y = \frac{0.09 y(7 - y)}{6}. \tag{14.6}$$

The time (in days) until the first new infection is T_2, where $T_2 \sim M(\beta_2)$, and

$$\beta_2 = \frac{0.09 \times 2 \times 5}{6} = 0.15.$$

Therefore the mean and variance of the time until the first new infection are

$$E(T_2) = \frac{1}{\beta_2} = \frac{1}{0.15} \simeq 6.67 \text{ days},$$

$$V(T_2) = \frac{1}{\beta_2^2} = \frac{1}{0.15^2} \simeq 44.44 \text{ (days)}^2.$$

After the first new infection, there are 3 infectives, so the waiting time between the first new infection and the second new infection is T_3, where $T_3 \sim M(\beta_3)$. Using (14.6),

$$\beta_3 = \frac{0.09 \times 3 \times 4}{6} = 0.18,$$

so

$$E(T_3) = \frac{1}{0.18}, \quad V(T_3) = \frac{1}{0.18^2}.$$

The total time until the second new infection is $T_2 + T_3$, and

$$E(T_2 + T_3) = E(T_2) + E(T_3) = \frac{1}{0.15} + \frac{1}{0.18} \simeq 12.22 \text{ days}.$$

Since T_2 and T_3 are independent,

$$V(T_2 + T_3) = V(T_2) + V(T_3) = \frac{1}{0.15^2} + \frac{1}{0.18^2} \simeq 75.31 \text{ (days)}^2.$$

The **duration** of an epidemic, denoted W, is the waiting time until all the susceptibles are infected. In general,

$$W = T_{y_0} + T_{y_0+1} + \cdots + T_n.$$

For this epidemic, $y_0 = 2$ and $n + 1 = 7$, so

$$W = T_2 + T_3 + T_4 + T_5 + T_6.$$

Notice that there are five terms in this sum as the epidemic terminates when the fifth new infection occurs.

The mean and variance of the times between the second and third new infections, the third and fourth new infections, and the fourth and fifth new infections can be found similarly: $T_4 \sim M(\beta_4)$, $T_5 \sim M(\beta_5)$ and $T_6 \sim M(\beta_6)$, where

$$\beta_4 = \frac{0.09 \times 4 \times 3}{6} = 0.18,$$

$$\beta_5 = \frac{0.09 \times 5 \times 2}{6} = 0.15,$$

$$\beta_6 = \frac{0.09 \times 6 \times 1}{6} = 0.09.$$

Therefore the expected time (in days) until everyone is infected is

$$\begin{aligned}
E(W) &= E(T_2) + E(T_3) + \cdots + E(T_6) \\
&= \frac{1}{0.15} + \frac{1}{0.18} + \frac{1}{0.18} + \frac{1}{0.15} + \frac{1}{0.09} \\
&\simeq 35.56.
\end{aligned}$$

Since the times between infections are independent, the variance of the time until everyone is infected is

$$\begin{aligned}
V(W) &= V(T_2) + V(T_3) + \cdots + V(T_6) \\
&= \frac{1}{0.15^2} + \frac{1}{0.18^2} + \frac{1}{0.18^2} + \frac{1}{0.15^2} + \frac{1}{0.09^2} \\
&= 274.074\ldots.
\end{aligned}$$

The standard deviation of this time (in days) is

$$\sqrt{V(W)} = \sqrt{274.074\ldots} \simeq 16.56. \quad \blacklozenge$$

Activity 14.4   A simple epidemic

Suppose that initially three people in a household of total size 5 have an infectious disease, and that the spread of the infection through the household is modelled as a stochastic simple epidemic with contact rate $\beta = 2$ per day.

(a) Write down an expression for the epidemic rate β_y, and calculate the values of β_3 and β_4.

(b) Calculate the expected waiting time until the first new infection.

(c) Calculate the mean and variance of the time until everyone in the household is infected.

Activity 14.5   Waiting times

In a closed community of total size 9, five people are suffering from an infectious disease that is incurable but not serious; the other four are susceptible. The spread of the infection through the community is modelled as a stochastic simple epidemic with contact rate $\beta = 0.2$ per day.

(a) Write down an expression for the epidemic rate β_y, and calculate the values of β_5, β_6, β_7 and β_8.

(b) Calculate the expected waiting time until a sixth person catches the disease (that is, until the first new infection).

(c) Calculate the expected waiting time until all nine members of the community have caught the disease.

(d) Calculate the standard deviation of the waiting time until all nine members of the community have caught the disease.

In general, if $Y(0) = y_0$ and the size of the community is $n + 1$, then the duration of the epidemic is given by

$$W = T_{y_0} + T_{y_0+1} + \cdots + T_n. \tag{14.7}$$

Therefore the expected duration of the epidemic is finite. In Subsection 14.2, you saw that in the deterministic model, the whole community will become infected only after an infinite time. This difference illustrates that the deterministic approach is of limited use.

14.4   The stochastic model: distribution of $Y(t)$

The p.m.f. of $Y(t)$ is denoted $p_y(t)$:

$$p_y(t) = P(Y(t) = y).$$

To be precise,
$$p_y(t) = P(Y(t) = y \mid Y(0) = y_0).$$

The differential–difference equations for the simple epidemic can be written down using the Kolmogorov forward equations (5.7). In this case, $\nu_y = 0$ for all y, and β_y is given by (14.5) for $y = 0, 1, \ldots, n+1$ ($\beta_y = 0$ otherwise). Hence the differential–difference equations take the form

$$\frac{d}{dt} p_y(t) = -\beta_y\, p_y(t) + \beta_{y-1}\, p_{y-1}(t), \quad y = 0, 1, \ldots, n+1. \tag{14.8}$$

As in Part I, the set of differential–difference equations can be used to obtain a partial differential equation for $\Pi(s, t)$, the probability generating function of $Y(t)$. This leads to

$$\frac{\partial \Pi}{\partial t} = -\beta s(1 - s)\left(\frac{\partial \Pi}{\partial s} - \frac{s}{n}\frac{\partial^2 \Pi}{\partial s^2}\right).$$

This partial differential equation is not of Lagrange form since it contains the second-order partial derivative $\partial^2\Pi/\partial s^2$. This term arises because β_y is quadratic in y. Since using Lagrange's method is not an option, the p.m.f. of $Y(t)$ will be derived for any given situation through iterative solution of the differential–difference equations. The method is illustrated in Example 14.3.

Example 14.3   A simple epidemic

Suppose that, as in Activity 14.4, three people in a household of size 5 have an infectious disease, and that the spread of the infection through the household is modelled as a stochastic simple epidemic with contact rate $\beta = 2$ per day.

Since three individuals are infected initially, $p_1(t) = p_2(t) = 0$ for all t. Therefore, from (14.8), the differential–difference equations necessary to find the p.m.f. of $Y(t)$ are

$$\frac{d}{dt} p_y(t) = -\beta_y\, p_y(t) + \beta_{y-1}\, p_{y-1}(t), \quad y = 3, 4, 5.$$

Since $\beta = 2$ and $n + 1 = 5$, the epidemic rate is given by

$$\beta_y = \frac{\beta y(n + 1 - y)}{n} = \frac{2y(5 - y)}{4}.$$

Therefore $\beta_3 = 3$, $\beta_4 = 2$ and $\beta_5 = 0$, and hence the three differential equations are

$$\frac{d}{dt} p_3(t) = -3\, p_3(t), \tag{14.9}$$

$$\frac{d}{dt} p_4(t) = -2\, p_4(t) + 3\, p_3(t), \tag{14.10}$$

$$\frac{d}{dt} p_5(t) = 2\, p_4(t). \tag{14.11}$$

The differential equation (14.9) has the solution

$$p_3(t) = \text{constant} \times e^{-3t}.$$

Since there are three infectives at the start, $p_3(0) = P(Y(0) = 3) = 1$. So the constant is 1, and hence

$$p_3(t) = e^{-3t}.$$

Substituting this result in (14.10) and rearranging the equation gives

$$\frac{d}{dt} p_4(t) + 2\, p_4(t) = 3e^{-3t}.$$

This equation can be solved using the integrating factor method. Since $h(t) = 2$, the integrating factor is $\exp(\int 2\, dt) = e^{2t}$. Multiplying both sides by the integrating factor gives

$$\left(\frac{d}{dt} p_4(t)\right) e^{2t} + 2\, p_4(t)\, e^{2t} = 3e^{-t},$$

which can be written as

$$\frac{d}{dt}(p_4(t)\, e^{2t}) = 3e^{-t}.$$

The integrating factor method is described in *Book 1* and in the *Handbook*.

Integrating this gives

$$p_4(t)\, e^{2t} = \text{constant} - 3e^{-t}.$$

Since there are three infectives at the start, $p_4(0) = P(Y(0) = 4) = 0$. So the constant is 3, and hence

$$p_4(t) = 3e^{-2t} - 3e^{-3t}.$$

Finally, substituting this result in (14.11) gives

$$\frac{d}{dt} p_5(t) = 6e^{-2t} - 6e^{-3t},$$

so

$$p_5(t) = -3e^{-2t} + 2e^{-3t} + \text{constant}.$$

Since $p_5(0) = 0$, the constant is 1, and hence

$$p_5(t) = 1 - 3e^{-2t} + 2e^{-3t}.$$

Therefore the p.m.f. of $Y(t)$ is

$$p_3(t) = e^{-3t},$$
$$p_4(t) = 3e^{-2t} - 3e^{-3t},$$
$$p_5(t) = 1 - 3e^{-2t} + 2e^{-3t}.$$
$$p_y(t) = 0 \quad \text{for } y \neq 3, 4, 5.$$

As a check, note that $p_3(t) + p_4(t) + p_5(t) = 1$. ♦

Activity 14.6   Another simple epidemic

Suppose that the spread of an infection through a household of size 4 is modelled as a stochastic simple epidemic, and that initially two individuals are infected. The contact rate β is 0.3 per day.

(a) Obtain the differential–difference equations for

$$p_y(t) = P(Y(t) = y), \quad y = 2, 3, 4,$$

and write down the initial values $p_2(0)$, $p_3(0)$, $p_4(0)$.

(b) Solve the differential equations.

(c) What happens to the values of $p_2(t)$, $p_3(t)$ and $p_4(t)$ as $t \to \infty$? Interpret your answer.

If the p.m.f. of $Y(t)$ is known, then the distribution of W, the duration of the epidemic, can be found as follows.

Since everyone will have contracted the infection by time t ($Y(t) = n + 1$) if and only if the last infection occurred at or before time t ($W \leq t$),

$$P(W \leq t) = P(Y(t) = n + 1). \tag{14.12}$$

This identity can be used to write down the c.d.f. of W, and hence the probability distribution can be found.

Example 14.4   The c.d.f. of W

For the household of total size 5 described in Example 14.3,

$$P(Y(t) = 5) = p_5(t) = 1 - 3e^{-2t} + 2e^{-3t}.$$

Therefore, using (14.12) with $n + 1 = 5$, the c.d.f. of W is

$$P(W \leq t) = 1 - 3e^{-2t} + 2e^{-3t}, \quad t \geq 0.$$

The c.d.f. can be used to calculate the expected duration of the epidemic, as follows. Since W takes only non-negative values, the alternative formula for the mean can be used:

$$E(W) = \int_0^\infty (1 - F_W(t)) \, dt = \int_0^\infty P(W > t) \, dt.$$

Therefore

$$E(W) = \int_0^\infty (3e^{-2t} - 2e^{-3t})\, dt$$
$$= \left[-\tfrac{3}{2}e^{-2t} + \tfrac{2}{3}e^{-3t}\right]_0^\infty$$
$$= \tfrac{3}{2} - \tfrac{2}{3}$$
$$= \tfrac{5}{6}. \quad \blacklozenge$$

You obtained the mean and variance of W in Activity 14.4 using the fact that the waiting times between infections are independent exponential variates. In general, using the method of Activity 14.4 is much easier than using the c.d.f. of W, even when the distribution of $Y(t)$ is known. So if only the mean and variance of W are required, then that method is preferred.

Activity 14.7 The duration of a simple epidemic

(a) Write down the c.d.f. of W, the duration of the epidemic described in Activity 14.6.

(b) Use the c.d.f. of W to calculate the expected duration of the epidemic.

(c) Use the distributions of the waiting times between infections to find $E(W)$, and hence check your answer to part (b).

Summary of Section 14

In this section, the stochastic simple epidemic model for the spread of an infection through a community has been described, and the deterministic analogue has been discussed briefly. For a given stochastic simple epidemic, you have learned how to find the mean and variance of the time until any specific number of individuals are infected, and how to find the probability distribution of $Y(t)$, the number of infectives at time t.

Exercises on Section 14

Exercise 14.1 Waiting times

The spread of an infectious disease through a family of size 8 may be modelled as a stochastic simple epidemic. Initially, four members of the family are infected. The contact rate β is 4 per day.

(a) Calculate the expected times until the first, second and third new infections occur.

(b) Calculate the mean and standard deviation of the time until all eight members of the family are infected.

Exercise 14.2 The distribution of $Y(t)$

Suppose that the spread of an infection through a family of size 3 is modelled as a stochastic simple epidemic, and that initially one member of the family is infected. The contact rate β is 0.2 per day.

(a) Obtain the differential–difference equations for

$$p_y(t) = P(Y(t) = y), \quad y = 1, 2, 3,$$

and write down the values of $p_1(0)$, $p_2(0)$, $p_3(0)$.

(b) Solve the differential equations, and hence write down the c.d.f. of W, the duration of the epidemic.

15   The general epidemic

The term **general epidemic** has come to be commonly used for the model that is introduced in this section, although many more general models have since been developed. It was first developed in the 1920s by W.O. Kermack and A.G. McKendrick, although a thorough investigation of the stochastic version was begun by M.S. Bartlett only in the 1950s. The stochastic model is described in Subsection 15.1. In order to gain some insight into the possible behaviour of the stochastic model, the deterministic analogue is analysed in Subsection 15.2. A variation on the general epidemic is described very briefly in Subsection 15.3.

15.1   The stochastic model

Most of the assumptions of the general epidemic model are the same as those of the simple epidemic model. The key difference is that whereas in the simple epidemic model infected individuals stay infectious and remain in the community, in the general epidemic model an infected individual is assumed to recover after some random time and is thereafter immune to further attacks. The time to recovery is assumed to be exponentially distributed with the same parameter for all individuals, and after recovery individuals remain in the community, maintaining contact with the others.

The assumptions of the general epidemic, the first five of which are the same as for the simple epidemic, are listed in the following box.

> **General epidemic model: assumptions**
> ◇   The community through which the infection is spreading is closed.
> ◇   Any two individuals are as likely to come into contact as any other two (homogeneous mixing).
> ◇   Each individual comes into contact with other individuals according to a Poisson process with rate β.
> ◇   When a susceptible meets an infective, he catches the infection with probability 1.
> ◇   The latent period has length 0.
> ◇   An infected individual recovers after some random time. This time is exponentially distributed with parameter γ. After recovery, the individual remains in the community and is immune to the infection.

Individuals who have had the infection and recovered are referred to as **removed**, and the parameter γ is known as the **removal rate**. Any individual who is infected necessarily passes through the three stages

SUSCEPTIBLE $\longrightarrow$ INFECTIVE $\longrightarrow$ REMOVED.

As in the stochastic simple epidemic, $X(t)$ denotes the number of susceptibles at time t, and $Y(t)$ denotes the number of infectives. The number of removed at time t is denoted $Z(t)$. The initial numbers in the three categories are denoted x_0, y_0, z_0, that is, $X(0) = x_0$, $Y(0) = y_0$, $Z(0) = z_0$. As for the simple epidemic, the total size of the community is $n + 1$, so since the community is closed, for all t,

$$X(t) + Y(t) + Z(t) = x_0 + y_0 + z_0 = n + 1. \tag{15.1}$$

For an epidemic to take place, there must be at least one infective and one susceptible, so $y_0 \geq 1$ and $x_0 \geq 1$.

Only two of the three categories need to be considered when analysing the model. For instance, if the numbers of infectives and susceptibles at time t are known, then $Z(t)$, the number of removed at time t can be obtained by subtraction using (15.1): $Z(t) = n + 1 - X(t) - Y(t)$.

The bivariate random process $\{(X(t), Y(t)); t \geq 0\}$ changes state whenever one of two things happens: either an infective meets a susceptible and the infection is passed on, or an infective recovers. In the first case, $X(t)$ decreases by 1 and $Y(t)$ increases by 1 (and $Z(t)$ is unchanged). In the second case, $Y(t)$ decreases by 1 (and $Z(t)$ increases by 1).

By (13.1), when there are x susceptibles and y infectives, the rate at which infectives come into contact with susceptibles is $\beta xy/n$. When a susceptible becomes infected, he remains infectious for some random time, this time being exponentially distributed with parameter γ. Therefore when there are y infectives, the probability that a removal will occur in the next short interval of length δt is $\gamma y\, \delta t + o(\delta t)$. Thus the stochastic general epidemic model can be characterised by the following two probability statements:

$$P(X(t+\delta t) = x-1,\ Y(t+\delta t) = y+1 \mid X(t) = x,\ Y(t) = y)$$
$$= \frac{\beta xy}{n}\, \delta t + o(\delta t), \tag{15.2}$$

$$P(X(t+\delta t) = x,\ Y(t+\delta t) = y-1 \mid X(t) = x,\ Y(t) = y)$$
$$= \gamma y\, \delta t + o(\delta t). \tag{15.3}$$

15.2   The deterministic model

When analysing the stochastic model, two random variables must be considered: $X(t)$, the number of susceptibles at time t, and $Y(t)$, the number of infectives at time t. The only possible change in $X(t)$ in any small interval of length δt is a decrease of 1 when a susceptible is infected. So, from (15.2),

$$P(X(t+\delta t) = x-1 \mid X(t) = x,\ Y(t) = y) = \frac{\beta xy}{n}\, \delta t + o(\delta t). \tag{15.4}$$

The number of infectives can either increase by 1 when a susceptible is infected, or decrease by 1 when an infective recovers. Thus, from (15.2) and (15.3),

$$P(Y(t+\delta t) = y+1 \mid X(t) = x,\ Y(t) = y) = \frac{\beta xy}{n}\, \delta t + o(\delta t), \tag{15.5}$$

$$P(Y(t+\delta t) = y-1 \mid X(t) = x,\ Y(t) = y) = \gamma y\, \delta t + o(\delta t). \tag{15.6}$$

In the deterministic model, the quantities corresponding to $X(t)$ and $Y(t)$ are denoted x and y, respectively. So, using (8.3), for $x \geq 0$ and $y \geq 0$, the deterministic approximation to the stochastic general epidemic model is the solution of the following pair of differential equations:

$$\frac{dx}{dt} = -\frac{\beta xy}{n}, \tag{15.7}$$

$$\frac{dy}{dt} = \frac{\beta xy}{n} - \gamma y. \tag{15.8}$$

$h_1(x, t) = 0,\ h_{-1}(x, t) = \dfrac{\beta xy}{n}.$

$h_1(y, t) = \dfrac{\beta xy}{n},\ h_{-1}(y, t) = \gamma y.$

These two equations are simultaneous differential equations in x and y at time t, with solutions for x and y of the form

$x =$ some function of t,

$y =$ some other function of t.

In fact, it is not possible to obtain these functions explicitly. However, it is possible to determine how x and y are related to one another. This is done by eliminating the variable t from (15.7) and (15.8) to give a differential equation involving only x and y. Dividing (15.8) by (15.7) gives

$$\frac{dy/dt}{dx/dt} = \frac{\beta xy/n - \gamma y}{-\beta xy/n} \quad (x > 0,\ y > 0). \tag{15.9}$$

The left-hand side of this equation simplifies to dy/dx. The right-hand side may be simplified by cancelling the ys and multiplying the numerator and denominator by $-n/\beta$ to give

You may be assured that this is a valid simplification.

$$\frac{\beta xy/n - \gamma y}{-\beta xy/n} = \frac{\beta x/n - \gamma}{-\beta x/n} = \frac{n\gamma/\beta - x}{x}.$$

The quantity $n\gamma/\beta$ is denoted ρ:

$$\rho = \frac{n\gamma}{\beta}. \tag{15.10}$$

Therefore (15.9) may be rewritten as

$$\frac{dy}{dx} = \frac{\rho - x}{x} = \frac{\rho}{x} - 1 \quad (x > 0). \tag{15.11}$$

Integrating this equation with respect to x gives

$$y = \rho \log x - x + \text{constant}.$$

At time $t = 0$, $x = x_0$ and $y = y_0$, so

$$y_0 = \rho \log x_0 - x_0 + \text{constant},$$

and hence

$$\text{constant} = y_0 + x_0 - \rho \log x_0.$$

Therefore

$$y - y_0 = x_0 - x - \rho \log\left(\frac{x_0}{x}\right). \tag{15.12}$$

For $x > 0$, $y > 0$, this relationship between x and y describes the course or trajectory of the epidemic in the x-y plane. The starting point of the trajectory ($t = 0$) is the point (x_0, y_0), where it is assumed that $x_0 > 0$ and $y_0 > 0$. Figure 15.1 shows a typical trajectory for the case $x_0 > \rho$. The arrow indicates the direction of increasing time. The shape of the trajectory can be deduced from (15.7) and (15.8), as follows. From (15.7), for positive values of x and y, x decreases (from x_0) as t increases from 0; and from (15.8), $dy/dt > 0$ when $x > \rho$, $dy/dt = 0$ when $x = \rho$, and $dy/dt < 0$ when $x < \rho$. Hence y increases from y_0 to a maximum value $y_{\max}$ when $x = \rho$, and then decreases. The number of infectives in the community is at its maximum when $dy/dt = 0$, that is, when $x = \rho$. Setting $x = \rho$ in (15.12) gives

$$y_{\max} = y_0 + x_0 - \rho - \rho \log\left(\frac{x_0}{\rho}\right). \tag{15.13}$$

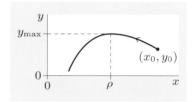

Figure 15.1   Trajectory of the general epidemic when $x_0 > \rho$

Example 15.1   *The height of an epidemic*

A deterministic general epidemic is to be used to describe the spread of an infectious disease through a closed community of 29 people. Initially, there are three infectious individuals; the others are all susceptible to the infection. The contact rate β is 1.4 per day. The recovery time of an infected individual is exponentially distributed with mean 2 days, so the removal rate γ is 0.5 per day.

There are 29 people in the community, so $n = 28$. The epidemic parameter ρ is given by (15.10):

$$\rho = \frac{n\gamma}{\beta} = \frac{28 \times 0.5}{1.4} = 10.$$

The maximum number infectious at the same time, $y_{\max}$, is given by (15.13). For this epidemic, $x_0 = 26$, $y_0 = 3$ and $\rho = 10$, so

$$y_{\max} = 3 + 26 - 10 - 10\log\left(\tfrac{26}{10}\right)$$
$$= 19 - 10\log 2.6$$
$$\simeq 9.44.$$

Remember that the natural logarithm is required here.

At the height of the epidemic, approximately 9 people are infectious.   ◆

Activity 15.1 Another epidemic

A deterministic general epidemic model is used to describe the progress of an infectious disease through a closed community of 31 people. Initially, there are two infected individuals; the others are all susceptible. The contact rate β is 3 per week, and the removal rate γ is 1.2 per week.

(a) Calculate the value of the epidemic parameter ρ.

(b) When the epidemic is at its height, how many people are infectious?

Suppose that at some point, all those who have caught the infection have recovered, so that there are no infectives ($y = 0$) – they have all been removed. Then the epidemic is over as there is no one from whom any remaining susceptibles can catch the infection. The number of susceptibles remaining uninfected at the end of a deterministic general epidemic is denoted x_∞, and is the value of x corresponding to $y = 0$. Substituting $y = 0$ in (15.12) gives an equation satisfied by x_∞:

The subscript ∞ is used because it can be shown that $y = 0$ when $t = \infty$.

$$y_0 = \rho \log\left(\frac{x_0}{x}\right) - (x_0 - x). \tag{15.14}$$

This equation has two solutions, both of which are positive. One solution is greater than ρ, and the other is less than ρ.

You have seen that when $x_0 > \rho$, the number of infectives increases to a maximum when $x = \rho$, then decreases (as in Figure 15.1). Therefore, in this case, x_∞ is less than ρ – see Figure 15.2.

If $x_0 < \rho$, then since the number of susceptibles cannot increase, $x < \rho$ throughout the epidemic. In this case y, the number of infectives, decreases from y_0, and the trajectory of the epidemic is as shown in Figure 15.3. Again, $x_\infty < \rho$.

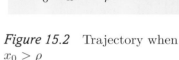

Figure 15.2 Trajectory when $x_0 > \rho$

Activity 15.2 The third case

Sketch the trajectory of the general epidemic in the case $x_0 = \rho$. Is x_∞ less than ρ in this case?

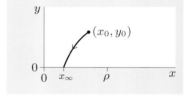

Figure 15.3 Trajectory when $x_0 < \rho$

You have seen that x_∞, the number of susceptibles remaining when the epidemic ends, is always less than ρ. Hence x_∞ is the smaller solution of (15.14), the one that is less than ρ.

Equation (15.14) can be rewritten as

$$x = x_0 \exp\left(\frac{x - (x_0 + y_0)}{\rho}\right). \tag{15.15}$$

The smaller solution of this equation can be found using the formula iteration method. Starting with the initial value $x_{\infty,0} = 0$, the value of x_∞ can be obtained to any required accuracy using the iteration formula

Other starting values can be used, but if $x_{\infty,0} = 0$, then the iteration always converges to the smaller solution.

$$x_{\infty,j+1} = x_0 \exp\left(\frac{x_{\infty,j} - (x_0 + y_0)}{\rho}\right), \quad j = 0, 1, \ldots. \tag{15.16}$$

The method is illustrated in Example 15.2.

Example 15.2   The number of survivors

For the deterministic general epidemic of Example 15.1, $x_0 = 26$, $y_0 = 3$ and $\rho = 10$. Hence using (15.15), x_∞, the number of susceptibles when the epidemic ends, is the smaller solution of

$$x = 26 \exp\left(\frac{x - 29}{10}\right).$$

The iteration formula is given by (15.16):

$$x_{\infty,j+1} = 26 \exp\left(\frac{x_{\infty,j} - 29}{10}\right), \quad j = 0, 1, \dots.$$

Taking $x_{\infty,0} = 0$ gives

$$x_{\infty,1} = 26 \exp(-2.9) \simeq 1.4306.$$

Substituting this value in the iteration formula with $j = 1$ gives

$$x_{\infty,2} = 26 \exp\left(\frac{1.4306 - 29}{10}\right) \simeq 1.6506.$$

Continuing the iteration gives $x_{\infty,3} \simeq 1.6874$, $x_{\infty,4} \simeq 1.6936$, $x_{\infty,5} \simeq 1.6946$, $x_{\infty,6} \simeq 1.6948$, $x_{\infty,7} \simeq 1.6948$. Therefore, correct to two decimal places, $x_\infty = 1.69$. That is, according to the deterministic model, approximately 2 people have not had the infection when the epidemic ends.

The number of people who have had the infection and recovered is obtained by subtraction. Since $x + y + z = n + 1$ throughout the epidemic, and $y = 0$ when the epidemic ends,

$$z_\infty = n + 1 - x_\infty.$$

In this case,

$$z_\infty \simeq 29 - 1.69 = 27.31.$$

Approximately 27 people have had the infection and recovered.   ♦

Activity 15.3   Another epidemic

For the epidemic described in Activity 15.1, find the number of individuals who survive the epidemic uninfected. How many have had the infection and recovered when the epidemic is over?

The main results obtained in this subsection are summarised in the following box.

Deterministic general epidemic: two results

Suppose that the spread of an infection through a community is modelled as a deterministic general epidemic with epidemic parameter $\rho = n\gamma/\beta$, and that initially there are x_0 susceptibles and y_0 infectives.

◇ If $x_0 > \rho$, then $y_{\max}$, the maximum number of individuals that are simultaneously infectious, is given by

$$y_{\max} = y_0 + x_0 - \rho - \rho \log\left(\frac{x_0}{\rho}\right).$$

If $x_0 \leq \rho$, then $y_{\max} = y_0$.

◇ When the epidemic is over, x_∞, the number of surviving susceptibles, is the solution less than ρ of the equation

$$x = x_0 \exp\left(\frac{x - (x_0 + y_0)}{\rho}\right).$$

This solution may be found using the iteration formula

$$x_{\infty,j+1} = x_0 \exp\left(\frac{x_{\infty,j} - (x_0 + y_0)}{\rho}\right), \quad j = 0, 1, \ldots.$$

Activity 15.4 covers the main ideas concerning the deterministic general epidemic that have been discussed.

Activity 15.4   *The spread of a disease*

Suppose that the spread of an infection through a community of size 31 is modelled as a deterministic general epidemic. Initially, one person is infectious, and the others are all susceptible. Any particular person meets others at the rate of 0.4 per day. The time that a person who catches the infection remains infectious is exponentially distributed with mean 6 days.

(a) Write down the values of x_0, y_0, z_0, n, β and γ. Hence calculate the value of the epidemic parameter ρ.

(b) When the number of infectives is at its greatest, how many susceptibles are there? How many infectives are there when the epidemic is at its height? How many people have already had the infection and recovered?

(c) How many people have had the infection and have recovered when the epidemic is over?

(d) Sketch the trajectory of the epidemic. Include on your sketch the coordinates of the starting point, the end point and the point where the epidemic is at its height.

The threshold phenomenon

The number $\rho = n\gamma/\beta$ is a threshold value for the initial number of susceptibles, in the following sense. If $x_0 < \rho$ and a trace of infection is introduced into the population ($y_0 > 0$), then the number of infectives $y(t)$ decreases monotonically and the epidemic quickly dies out. However, if $x_0 > \rho$ and a trace of infection is introduced, then the number of infectives builds up, a genuine epidemic outbreak occurs, and the number of susceptibles surviving uninfected when the epidemic terminates is less than ρ. This aspect of the model is known as the **threshold phenomenon**. It is illustrated in Figure 15.4.

The case $x_0 = \rho$ is essentially the same as the case $x_0 < \rho$.

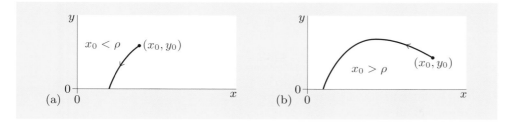

Figure 15.4   The threshold phenomenon

Associated with the threshold phenomenon is the concept of 'herd immunity'. If, in some population, the number of individuals susceptible to an infection is less than the value of ρ (so that $x_0 < \rho$), then the population as a whole is safe from epidemic outbreaks of the infection. If an immunisation campaign is carried out, then it is not necessary for the whole population to be rendered immune to the disease provided that the number of susceptibles remaining is less than ρ. Public health control may be aimed not only at reducing the number of susceptibles but also at increasing the value of ρ by increasing the removal rate γ, by reducing the contact rate β, or by reducing the probability that on contact the disease is transmitted.

15.3   A variation on the model

In the general epidemic model, it is assumed that individuals who contract an infection recover from it after some random time. Thereafter they are not capable of transmitting the infection, or of catching it a second time. But they remain in the community, and continue to play a role in the sequence of contacts between individuals.

In one variation of this model (one of many variations), it is assumed that at some random time after contracting the infection, symptoms appear, and the affected individual is isolated. In another variation, it is assumed that the infection is rather serious, and leads eventually to death. In either case, at the end of the infectious period, the affected person is literally removed from the community, so that there are fewer left in it than there were. If at time t there are x susceptibles in the community, y infectives and $z = n + 1 - (x + y)$ who have been isolated or died, then the corresponding rate at which infectives come into contact with susceptibles is

$$\beta_y = \frac{\beta xy}{x + y - 1}.$$

The analysis of the deterministic version of this model is reasonably straightforward, but it will not be pursued here.   See Exercise 24.19.

Summary of Section 15

In this section, the assumptions of the general epidemic have been discussed and probability statements characterising the stochastic model have been obtained. The deterministic model has been analysed: you have learned how to find the number of infectives when an epidemic is at its height and the number of susceptibles remaining when the epidemic is over. The threshold phenomenon for the deterministic model has been discussed briefly.

Exercise on Section 15

Exercise 15.1   A general epidemic

The spread of an infection through a community of size 85 is to be modelled as a deterministic general epidemic. Initially, four people are infected, thirteen are immune and the other 68 are susceptible to the disease. Each member of the community meets others and passes on the infection at the rate of 0.3 per day. The time that a person who catches the infection remains infectious is exponentially distributed with mean one week.

(a) Write down the numbers x_0, y_0, z_0 and n, and the values of the parameters β and γ, and hence calculate the value of the epidemic parameter ρ.

(b) When the epidemic is at its height, how many susceptibles are there? How many infectives are there at this time?

(c) At the end of the epidemic, how many susceptibles from the original 68 have caught the infection and recovered?

(d) Sketch the trajectory of the epidemic.

16   *The stochastic general epidemic model*

In the stochastic general epidemic model, the numbers of susceptibles, infectives and removed at time t are denoted $X(t)$, $Y(t)$ and $Z(t)$, respectively. The number of people who have had the infection and recovered at time t can be obtained by subtraction: $Z(t) = n + 1 - (X(t) + Y(t))$. Therefore, as for the deterministic model, only the numbers of susceptibles and infectives need to be considered when analysing the model.

Any individual who is infected necessarily passes through the three stages

SUSCEPTIBLE $\longrightarrow$ INFECTIVE $\longrightarrow$ REMOVED.

This means that the bivariate random process $\{(X(t), Y(t)); t \geq 0\}$ changes state whenever one of two types of transition occurs: SUSCEPTIBLE $\longrightarrow$ INFECTIVE or INFECTIVE $\longrightarrow$ REMOVED. In the first case, when an infective meets a susceptible and the infection is passed on, the number of susceptibles decreases by 1 and the number of infectives increases by 1. In the second case (INFECTIVE $\longrightarrow$ REMOVED), an infective recovers, so the total number of infectives decreases by 1. These transitions are illustrated in Figure 16.1. An infection corresponds to a move diagonally upwards and to the left, and a removal to a move downwards.

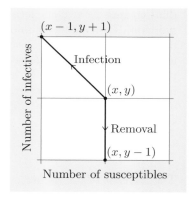

Figure 16.1   Possible transitions

As for the deterministic model, the analysis will be limited to exploring the relationship between the numbers of susceptibles and infectives as the epidemic progresses. In particular, the path that the epidemic maps out in the x-y plane and the number of susceptibles who survive the epidemic uninfected will be investigated. The times at which infections and removals take place will not be considered.

Example 16.1 Epidemic paths

Two individuals in a community of size 15 have an infection, and the others are susceptible (so $x_0 = 13$, $y_0 = 2$). The contact rate β is 0.7 per day, and the removal rate γ is 0.3 per day. How will the epidemic develop? How many susceptibles will survive the epidemic uninfected?

Three realisations of the epidemic are shown in Figure 16.2.

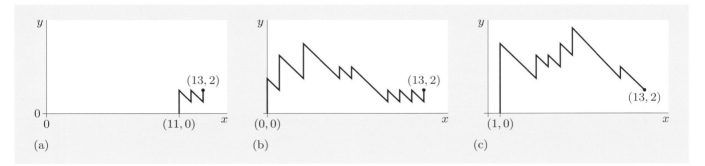

Figure 16.2 Three realisations of a general epidemic starting at $(13, 2)$

Several points are worth noting at this stage. First, the transitions are such that a path can never pass through the same point twice. Also, the coordinates of points on a path can take only integer values, whereas in the deterministic model, the epidemic path is a continuous curve. Moreover, there are many possible paths for a stochastic epidemic, whereas in the corresponding deterministic model the epidemic path is determined by the parameters of the epidemic.

An epidemic terminates when the number of infectives is zero ($y = 0$), that is, when the path hits the x-axis. It is possible for the path to hit the y-axis first. This corresponds to the situation where everyone in the community has been infected. The remaining infectives will eventually recover and become removed, and the epidemic will end at $(0, 0)$, as in Figure 16.2(b). The number of susceptibles remaining uninfected at the end of an epidemic is a random variable denoted X_∞. The distribution of X_∞ is known as the **survivor distribution**. ◆

The stochastic general epidemic model is characterised by the two conditional probability statements (15.2) and (15.3), which are reproduced below:

$$P(X(t + \delta t) = x - 1, \ Y(t + \delta t) = y + 1 \mid X(t) = x, \ Y(t) = y) = \frac{\beta x y}{n} \, \delta t + o(\delta t),$$

$$P(X(t + \delta t) = x, \ Y(t + \delta t) = y - 1 \mid X(t) = x, \ Y(t) = y) = \gamma y \, \delta t + o(\delta t).$$

Therefore when there are x susceptibles and y infectives ($y > 0$), the probability that a transition occurs in the next short interval of length δt is $(\beta x y/n + \gamma y) \, \delta t + o(\delta t)$. Given that a transition occurs, the probability that it is due to an infection, that is, $(x, y) \to (x - 1, y + 1)$, is

$$\frac{(\beta x y/n) \, \delta t + o(\delta t)}{(\beta x y/n + \gamma y) \, \delta t + o(\delta t)} = \frac{x + o(\delta t)/\delta t}{x + n\gamma/\beta + o(\delta t)/\delta t} = \frac{x + o(\delta t)/\delta t}{x + \rho + o(\delta t)/\delta t},$$

where $\rho = n\gamma/\beta$. By definition, $o(\delta t)/\delta t \to 0$ as $\delta t \to 0$. Therefore when there are x susceptibles and y infectives ($y > 0$), the probability that the next transition will be due to an infection is $x/(x + \rho)$. Similarly, the probability that the next transition will be due to a removal is $\rho/(x + \rho)$.

The probabilities of the two possible transitions are shown in Figure 16.3, and may be summarised as follows:

$$P(\text{infection}) = P((x,y) \to (x-1, y+1)) = \frac{x}{x+\rho}, \qquad (16.1)$$

$$P(\text{removal}) = P((x,y) \to (x, y-1)) = \frac{\rho}{x+\rho}. \qquad (16.2)$$

Notice that these probabilities depend on x, the number of susceptibles, but not on y, the number of infectives. The use of (16.1) and (16.2) is illustrated in Example 16.2.

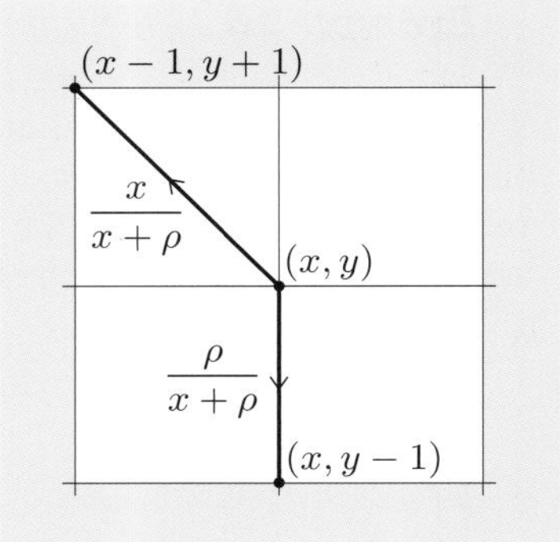

Example 16.2   Infections

The spread of an infectious disease through a community of size 6 is to be modelled as a stochastic general epidemic. Initially, two people have the infection, and the others are susceptible, so $x_0 = 4$, $y_0 = 2$. The contact rate β is 3 per day, and the removal rate γ is 1.8 per day.

The probability that there will be no new infection before the epidemic ends, and the probability that there will be one new infection, will be calculated.

The epidemic parameter ρ will be calculated first: since $n + 1 = 6$, $\beta = 3$ and $\gamma = 1.8$,

$$\rho = \frac{n\gamma}{\beta} = \frac{5 \times 1.8}{3} = 3.$$

Diagrams showing the paths that result in either no infection or one infection are shown in Figure 16.4.

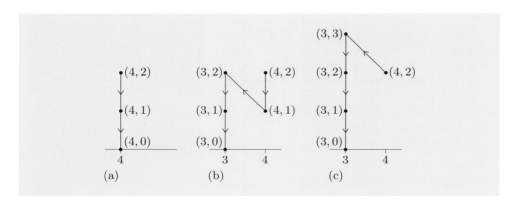

Figure 16.4   Epidemic paths

Probabilities will now be assigned to the transitions and to the paths.

If there is no new infection before the epidemic ends, then $X_\infty = 4$ and the epidemic path is as shown in Figure 16.4(a). The first transition is a removal $((4,2) \to (4,1))$, and this is followed by another removal $((4,1) \to (4,0))$. Using (16.2), each of these transitions has probability

$$\frac{\rho}{x+\rho} = \frac{3}{4+3} = \frac{3}{7}.$$

These probabilities are shown on the path in Figure 16.5. Hence the probability that there will be no new infection before the epidemic ends is

$$P(X_\infty = 4) = \tfrac{3}{7} \times \tfrac{3}{7} = \tfrac{9}{49} \simeq 0.184.$$

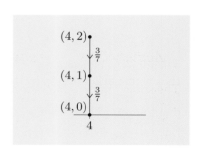

Figure 16.3   Transition probabilities for the general epidemic

Figure 16.5   No infection

If there is one new infection, then there will be three susceptibles remaining when the epidemic ends, so $X_\infty = 3$. The two possible paths that end at $(3, 0)$ are shown in Figure 16.4(b) and Figure 16.4(c). In Figure 16.4(b), the first transition is a removal, then an infection occurs and this is followed by two further removals. In Figure 16.4(c), the first transition is an infection, and this is followed by three removals.

First consider the path in Figure 16.4(b). The probability that the first transition is a removal has already been calculated: it is $\frac{3}{7}$. The probability that the next transition is an infection is obtained using (16.1):

$$P((4, 1) \to (3, 2)) = \frac{x}{x + \rho} = \frac{4}{4 + 3} = \frac{4}{7}.$$

When there are three susceptibles, the probability that a removal occurs next is given by (16.2) with $x = 3$, so

$$P((3, 2) \to (3, 1)) = \frac{\rho}{x + \rho} = \frac{3}{3 + 3} = \frac{1}{2},$$

and similarly, $P((3, 1) \to (3, 0)) = \frac{1}{2}$. These probabilities are shown on the path in Figure 16.6. Hence the probability of the path in Figure 16.4(b) is

$$\tfrac{3}{7} \times \tfrac{4}{7} \times \tfrac{1}{2} \times \tfrac{1}{2} = \tfrac{3}{49}.$$

The probabilities of the transitions for the path in Figure 16.4(c) are shown on the path in Figure 16.7. Thus the probability of this path is

$$\tfrac{4}{7} \times \tfrac{1}{2} \times \tfrac{1}{2} \times \tfrac{1}{2} = \tfrac{1}{14}.$$

Therefore the probability of one new infection is given by

$$P(X_\infty = 3) = \tfrac{3}{49} + \tfrac{1}{14} = \tfrac{13}{98} \simeq 0.133. \quad \blacklozenge$$

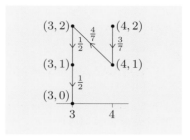

Figure 16.6   An epidemic path for one infection

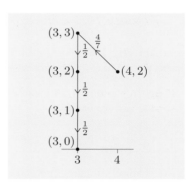

Figure 16.7   A second path for one infection

Activity 16.1   A stochastic general epidemic

The spread of an infectious disease through a community of size 8 is modelled as a stochastic general epidemic. Initially, two people have the infection, and the others are susceptible. The contact rate β is 3.5 per day, and the removal rate γ is 2 per day.

(a) Calculate the value of the epidemic parameter ρ.

(b) Calculate the probability that none of the original susceptibles catches the infection before the epidemic ends.

(c) Calculate the probability that at the end of the epidemic exactly one of the original susceptibles will have caught the infection and recovered.

Activity 16.2   One infection

The spread of an infectious disease through a community of size 21 is modelled as a stochastic general epidemic. Initially, three people have the infection, and the others are susceptible. The contact rate β is 0.5 per day, and the removal rate γ is 0.15 per day.

(a) Calculate the value of the epidemic parameter ρ.

(b) Draw diagrams showing the three paths for which exactly one of the original susceptibles is infected before the epidemic ends.

(c) Calculate the probability that exactly one of the original susceptibles catches the infection before the epidemic ends.

Activity 16.3   Survivor distribution

The spread of an infectious disease through a family of size 4 is modelled as a stochastic general epidemic. Initially, one member of the family is infected and the others are susceptible. The contact rate β is 1.8 per day, and the removal rate γ is 1.2 per day.

(a) Calculate the value of the epidemic parameter ρ.

(b) Calculate the probability that none of the three susceptibles catches the infection.

(c) Calculate the probability that exactly one of the susceptibles catches the infection.

(d) Calculate the probability that exactly two of the susceptibles catch the infection.

(e) Hence calculate the probability that all the family catch the infection.

(f) Write the values of the p.m.f. of X_∞ in a table.

Activity 16.4   The expected number of survivors

In Activity 16.3, you found the survivor distribution for an epidemic. Values of the p.m.f. of X_∞ are given in Table 16.1, rounded to three decimal places.

Table 16.1   The p.m.f. of X_∞

x	0	1	2	3
$P(X_\infty = x)$	0.294	0.156	0.150	0.400

(a) Calculate the expected number of survivors.

(b) According to the corresponding deterministic model, how many members of the family survive the epidemic without catching the infection? Is this equal to the expected number of survivors in the stochastic epidemic?

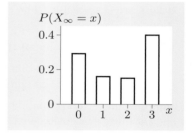

Figure 16.8   The survivor distribution

The survivor distribution for the epidemic of Activities 16.3 and 16.4 is shown in Figure 16.8. Notice that it is U-shaped: the most likely outcome of the epidemic is that no one catches the infection ($X_\infty = 3$), and the next most likely outcome is that everyone catches the infection ($X_\infty = 0$). Is this a general feature of survivor distributions? In Activity 16.3, you saw that even for a small community, quite a lot of work is involved in calculating the survivor distribution. For larger communities, the calculations can be done by computer. In Section 17, you will use the M343 software to explore the survivor distribution for larger communities, for various values of x_0 and ρ.

Summary of Section 16

In this section, you have learned how to calculate the probability of any given path for a stochastic general epidemic, and hence how to find the probability of any particular outcome. You have found the survivor distribution for a specific small community, and it has been observed that the distribution is U-shaped.

Exercise on Section 16

Exercise 16.1   A stochastic general epidemic

The spread of an infectious disease through a community of 29 people is modelled as a stochastic general epidemic. Initially, three individuals are infected, and the others are susceptible. The contact rate β is 7 per day, and the removal rate γ is 2.5 per day.

(a) Calculate the value of the epidemic parameter ρ.

(b) Draw diagrams showing the possible paths of the epidemic if exactly one of the susceptibles catches the infection before the epidemic ends. Hence calculate the probability that exactly one susceptible will catch the infection.

17   *The threshold phenomenon*

The threshold phenomenon for the deterministic version of the general epidemic model was described in Subsection 15.2. It is summarised in the following box.

Threshold phenomenon: deterministic general epidemic

The number $\rho = n\gamma/\beta$ is a threshold value for the development of the deterministic general epidemic.

◇   If $x_0 < \rho$ and a trace of infection is introduced into the population ($y_0 > 0$), then the number of infectives decreases monotonically and the epidemic quickly dies out.

◇   If $x_0 > \rho$ and a trace of infection is introduced, then the number of infectives builds up, a genuine epidemic outbreak occurs, and the number of susceptibles surviving uninfected when the epidemic terminates is less than ρ.

There is also a threshold phenomenon for the stochastic model, but it is more complicated. The number of susceptibles remaining uninfected when an epidemic ends is a random variable X_∞: when $x_0 > \rho$, it is possible for the number of survivors to be less than ρ, equal to ρ or greater than ρ. In Activity 16.3, you saw that when $x_0 = 3$, $y_0 = 1$ and $\rho = 2$, the survivor distribution is U-shaped. In Subsection 17.1, you will use the M343 software to explore the behaviour of the stochastic general epidemic model for various values of x_0 and ρ. The threshold phenomenon is discussed in Subsection 17.2.

17.1   Exploring the stochastic model

In this subsection, you are invited to explore the behaviour of the stochastic general epidemic model using the M343 software.

Refer to Chapter 5 of the computer book for the work in this subsection.

17.2 The threshold phenomenon for the stochastic general epidemic model

In Subsection 17.1, you explored the behaviour of the stochastic general epidemic model when a trace of infection is introduced for several values of x_0 and ρ. For each pair of values, the number of survivors was recorded for each of a large number of realisations, and an estimate of the survivor distribution was obtained by plotting the relative frequencies of the possible numbers of survivors. You saw that for some values of x_0 and ρ, the most likely outcome is that only a few infections will occur, and hence the epidemic dies out quickly. For other values, the survivor distribution is U-shaped: with high probability, either there will be very few infections or nearly everyone will be infected, and intermediate numbers of infections are unlikely.

As a general rule, U-shaped survivor distributions occur when $x_0 > \rho$. When $x_0 \leq \rho$, with high probability there will be only a minor epidemic outbreak. As in the deterministic version of the model, there is a **threshold phenomenon**, with ρ a threshold value for the initial number of susceptibles. However, the nature of the threshold phenomenon is more complicated in the stochastic case: when $x_0 > \rho$, there is the possibility of a minor outbreak, which is a not a possibility in the deterministic case.

The threshold phenomenon for the stochastic general epidemic model is summarised in the following box.

Threshold phenomenon: stochastic general epidemic

The number $\rho = n\gamma/\beta$ is a threshold value for the development of the stochastic general epidemic.

◇ If $x_0 \leq \rho$ and a trace of infection is introduced, then with high probability there is only a minor epidemic outbreak.

◇ If $x_0 > \rho$ and a trace of infection is introduced, then as a general rule the survivor distribution is U-shaped. With high probability there is either a minor or a major epidemic outbreak, and an outbreak of intermediate size is unlikely to occur.

When x_0 is large and a trace of infection is introduced (y_0 small), an approximate value for the probability that there will be a minor epidemic outbreak can be obtained as follows.

The stochastic general epidemic model is characterised by the conditional probability statements (15.2) and (15.3). If x_0 is large, then during the initial stages of the epidemic while x does not differ much from x_0, $\beta xy/n \simeq \beta x_0 y/n$, and hence, for the susceptibles,

$$P(Y(t+\delta t) = y + 1 \mid Y(t) = y) \simeq \frac{\beta x_0 y}{n}\, \delta t + o(\delta t),$$
$$P(Y(t+\delta t) = y - 1 \mid Y(t) = y) = \gamma y\, \delta t + o(\delta t).$$

These are the probability statements that characterise a simple birth–death process with individual birth rate $\beta x_0/n$ and individual death rate γ.

In Subsection 6.2, it was shown that extinction of a simple birth–death process is certain if the individual birth rate is less than or equal to the individual death rate. Therefore extinction is certain for the simple birth–death process used to approximate the epidemic in its initial stages if $\beta x_0/n \leq \gamma$, that is, if $x_0 \leq n\gamma/\beta = \rho$. Hence if $x_0 \leq \rho$, then the probability of a minor epidemic outbreak is approximately 1.

In Subsection 6.2, you also saw that for a simple birth–death process with individual birth rate β and individual death rate ν starting with n individuals, the probability of extinction is $(\nu/\beta)^n$ if $\beta > \nu$. Therefore for a simple birth–death process with individual birth rate $\beta x_0/n$ and individual death rate γ starting with

y_0 individuals, if $\beta x_0/n > \gamma$, then the probability of extinction is

$$\left(\frac{\gamma}{\beta x_0/n}\right)^{y_0} = \left(\frac{n\gamma/\beta}{x_0}\right)^{y_0} = \left(\frac{\rho}{x_0}\right)^{y_0}.$$

It follows that if $\beta x_0/n > \gamma$, that is, if $x_0 > \rho$, then the probability that there will be a minor epidemic outbreak is approximately $(\rho/x_0)^{y_0}$, and hence the probability that there will be a major outbreak is approximately $1 - (\rho/x_0)^{y_0}$.

These results are summarised in the following box.

Stochastic general epidemic: minor and major outbreaks

If $x_0 \le \rho$ and a trace of infection is introduced, then with high probability there will be only a minor outbreak.

If $x_0 > \rho$ and a trace of infection is introduced, then

$$P(\text{minor outbreak}) \simeq (\rho/x_0)^{y_0}, \tag{17.1}$$

$$P(\text{major outbreak}) \simeq 1 - (\rho/x_0)^{y_0}. \tag{17.2}$$

When $x_0 > \rho$, the survivor distribution is in general U-shaped and an approximate value for the probability that there will be only a minor outbreak is given by (17.1). How good is the approximation, and what constitutes a minor outbreak? The approximate probability of a minor outbreak, calculated using (17.1), is given in Table 17.1 for two values of ρ when $x_0 = 20$ and $y_0 = 1$.

Table 17.1   Probabilities of a minor outbreak

	$\rho = 5$	$\rho = 10$
Approximating probability $(\rho/x_0)^{y_0}$	0.250	0.500
3 or fewer infections	0.254	0.477
4 or fewer infections	0.257	0.495

Also given in Table 17.1 are the probabilities of 3 or fewer infections and 4 or fewer infections. As you can see, the approximating probabilities are quite good, whether a minor outbreak is taken to be 3 or fewer infections, or 4 or fewer infections.

Activity 17.1   Minor and major outbreaks

The spread of an infectious disease through a community of size 36 is modelled as a stochastic general epidemic. Initially, there are two infected individuals, and the others are all susceptible. The contact rate β is 7 per week, and the removal rate γ is 1.2 per week.

Calculate an approximate value for the probability that there will be only a minor outbreak. What is the probability that there will be a major outbreak?

Summary of Section 17

In this section, you have used computer simulations to explore the behaviour of the stochastic general epidemic model. You have seen that, as for the deterministic version of the model, the epidemic parameter ρ is a threshold value for the initial number of susceptibles, but the threshold phenomenon is more complicated for the stochastic model. You have also learned how to calculate an approximate value for the probability that there will be only a minor outbreak when the initial number of susceptibles is greater than ρ.

Exercise on Section 17

Exercise 17.1   Minor and major epidemic outbreaks

In Exercise 16.1, a stochastic general epidemic model was used to describe the spread of an infectious disease through a community of size 29. Initially, three individuals are infected, and the others are susceptible. The contact rate β is 7 per day, and the removal rate γ is 2.5 per day.

Calculate an approximate value for the probability that there will be only a minor epidemic outbreak. What is the probability that there will be a major outbreak?

18   Other models for epidemics

Two basic models for epidemics have been discussed – the simple epidemic model and the general epidemic model. These models both assume that the epidemic can be modelled by a Markov process in continuous time, and that the latent period is 0. However, for many infectious diseases, neither of these assumptions is realistic, so other models have been developed.

Models have been developed that allow for the latent and infectious periods to vary according to probability distributions that may be chosen to suit particular applications. Much work has been done on trying to make models more realistic in other ways. For example, in the simple epidemic model and the general epidemic model, it is assumed that homogeneous mixing occurs within the community. This is seldom a realistic assumption. Generally, within the community, people tend to mix preferentially with others of a similar age and with similar habits – a phenomenon known as assortative mixing. However, contacts within the family, particularly between parents and children, are also important. Models have thus been developed to allow for different levels of contacts – within families as well as within the community.

Epidemic models have been developed to model the rate at which an infection spreads spatially. This has been applied to rabies, a typical question of interest being: if there is an outbreak in one part of a country, how long will it be before the disease travels 100 miles? This model must take account of the behaviour pattern of the dogs and foxes who spread the disease.

Other diseases are spread by insect carriers. For example, malaria is spread by single-celled parasites carried by mosquitoes, and people are infected through being bitten by infected mosquitoes. Models for the spread of malaria must take account of the life cycle of mosquitoes.

Much research has been done on modelling the spread of AIDS. Models must take account of features including the very long incubation period, and the fact that people can be carriers and pass on the disease without knowing that they have it.

Only a brief introduction to the study of epidemics has been possible here. Thanks to advances in computing power, both stochastic and deterministic epidemic models are increasingly used in practical situations, for example to investigate the likely effect of control measures to reduce the spread of hospital infections such as MRSA, or to evaluate the impact of school closures on the spread of pandemic influenza. New and better models are constantly being developed in collaborations between research workers in probability and epidemiologists.

Part IV More population models

Introduction to Part IV

For the simple birth–death process discussed in Part I, it is assumed that the birth rate is independent of the ages of the individuals in the population, and that each individual is as likely to die at any one age as at any other. However, in reality, birth rates are different for females of different ages, and death rates are different for different age groups. The models discussed in Part IV take this into account. Although they are developed with human populations in mind, models of this type are also used in population ecology.

Records of births and deaths have been kept in many countries for many years, and information on the size and age-structure of human populations is readily available. Bills of Mortality for London were first published early in the 16th century. At first, these recorded only deaths from the plague, but later they were expanded to include christenings as well as plague deaths, and towards the end of that century, deaths from other diseases were also included. But it was only from the 17th century that populations were studied from a scientific point of view. The Englishman John Graunt (1620–1674) was probably the first to do so. Despite the unreliable nature of the data in the Bills of Mortality, Graunt made an exhaustive study of the information contained in them. In 1662, he published a book entitled *Natural and Political Observations on the Bills of Mortality*. Among the topics that he discussed was the sex-ratio: he noted that the proportion of births that are male is slightly greater than the proportion that are female, an observation that seems to have been new and surprising in 1662. He also discussed the general mortality from different kinds of diseases, and attempted to develop a mortality table of the type used by insurance companies today. In his book, he gave the proportions of people dying in each of a number of age groups, and deduced the following:

> that of ... 100 conceived there remains alive at six years end 64

At Sixteen years end	40
At Twenty six	25
At Tirty six	16
At Fourty six	10
At Fifty six	6
At Sixty six	3
At Seventy six	1
At Eighty	0.

This simple table is an example of a **life table**. It was the first life table to be compiled and is the forerunner of the more detailed life tables that are used today.

In Section 19, the idea of a life table is used as the basis for the development of a population model that allows for different death rates at different ages. Life tables are discussed in Section 20. In Section 21, a deterministic model for a population whose size and age-structure do not change with time is studied. The properties of a population whose size may change but whose age-structure remains constant are discussed briefly in Section 22. A diagram for representing the age-structure of a population is introduced in Section 23.

19 Modelling lifetimes

A **life table** is a table that gives, for various ages, the proportion of the individuals born into a population who are still alive at each age. For example, in the population for which John Graunt constructed the first life table, only 40 out of every 100 born into the population were still alive at age 16.

Associated with any life table, and hence with the population it describes, is a function called the life table function, defined as follows.

The life table function

Suppose that the lifetimes of the individuals in a population are independent and identically distributed, and that the length of life of an individual born into the population is a positive random variable X. Then the **life table function**, denoted $Q(x)$, is defined by

$$Q(x) = P(X > x), \quad x \geq 0.$$

A random variable is positive if the only values that it can take are positive. Thus only live births are considered.

In a stochastic model, the life table function is simply a function that gives, for each age x, the probability that any individual will be still alive at age x. That is, $Q(x)$ is the probability that the length of life of an individual will exceed x. In a deterministic model, $Q(x)$ is the proportion of members of the population who live beyond age x.

Note that x denotes the age of an individual in Part IV, whereas x denoted the size of a population in Parts I to III.

If X has p.d.f. $f(x)$ and c.d.f. $F(x)$, then

$$Q(x) = \int_x^\infty f(u)\, du = 1 - F(x).$$

Note that since the length of life of an individual is a positive random variable, $Q(0) = P(X > 0) = 1$.

The additional length of time that an individual aged x can be expected to live, which is denoted e_x, is of importance in insurance. For $x \geq 0$,

$$e_x = E(X - x \mid X > x) = E(X \mid X > x) - x.$$

The **expectation of life at birth**, $e_0 = E(X)$, is of particular interest:

$$e_0 = E(X) = \int_0^\infty x\, f(x)\, dx.$$

Since X is a positive random variable, the alternative formula for the mean can be used to calculate e_0:

$$e_0 = E(X) = \int_0^\infty (1 - F(x))\, dx.$$

Since $1 - F(x) = Q(x)$, this gives a formula for calculating the expectation of life at birth directly from the life table function:

$$e_0 = \int_0^\infty Q(x)\, dx. \tag{19.1}$$

Note that e_0 is the mean lifetime of members of the population or, equivalently, the mean age at which death occurs.

Example 19.1   Uniform lifetimes

Suppose that the lifetimes of the members of a population are uniformly distributed and may be anything between 0 and 100 years. Then

$$f(x) = \frac{1}{100}, \quad 0 \le x < 100,$$

$$F(x) = \frac{x}{100}, \quad 0 \le x < 100,$$

and

$$Q(x) = 1 - \frac{x}{100}, \quad 0 \le x < 100.$$

Since $X \sim U(0, 100)$, the mean lifetime e_0 is 50 years. Alternatively, using (19.1), the expectation of life at birth is given by

If $X \sim U(a, b)$, then $E(X) = (a + b)/2$.

$$e_0 = \int_0^\infty Q(x)\, dx = \int_0^{100} \left(1 - \frac{x}{100}\right) dx$$

$$= \left[x - \frac{x^2}{200}\right]_0^{100}$$

$$= 50. \quad \blacklozenge$$

Activity 19.1   Another life table function

Suppose that the life table function for the members of a population is given by

$$Q(x) = \frac{900}{(30 + x)^2}, \quad x \ge 0,$$

where x is measured in years.

(a) What proportion of members of the population live beyond the age of 70 years? What proportion of members of the population live for less than 20 years?

(b) Find the expectation of life at birth for members of the population.

The death rate for individuals aged x in a population is represented by a function $h(x)$ that is defined as follows. The probability that an individual aged exactly x will die in the next short time interval of length δx is $h(x)\, \delta x + o(\delta x)$, that is,

$$P(x < X \le x + \delta x \mid X > x) = h(x)\, \delta x + o(\delta x). \tag{19.2}$$

The function $h(x)$ is called the **age-specific death rate** of the population; it is also sometimes known as the **force of mortality**.

Notice that $h(x)$ is an *individual* death rate.

A formula for $h(x)$ involving the life table function $Q(x)$ can be obtained. Using the definition of conditional probability, the probability on the left-hand side of (19.2) can be written in terms of $Q(x)$ as follows:

$$P(x < X \le x + \delta x \mid X > x) = \frac{P(x < X \le x + \delta x)}{P(X > x)}$$

$$= \frac{P(X > x) - P(X > x + \delta x)}{P(X > x)}$$

$$= \frac{Q(x) - Q(x + \delta x)}{Q(x)}, \quad Q(x) \ne 0.$$

Therefore

$$\frac{Q(x) - Q(x + \delta x)}{Q(x)} = h(x)\, \delta x + o(\delta x).$$

This can be rewritten as

$$h(x) = -\frac{1}{Q(x)} \frac{Q(x + \delta x) - Q(x)}{\delta x} + \frac{o(\delta x)}{\delta x}.$$

By definition, $o(\delta x)/\delta x \to 0$ as $\delta x \to 0$, so letting δx tend to 0 gives

$$h(x) = -\frac{1}{Q(x)} \frac{dQ}{dx}, \quad Q(x) \neq 0.$$

By definition,
$$\frac{dQ}{dx} = \lim_{\delta x \to 0} \frac{Q(x + \delta x) - Q(x)}{\delta x}.$$

An expression for $Q(x)$ in terms of $h(x)$ can be obtained by integrating both sides of this formula:

$$\begin{aligned}
\int_0^x h(u)\, du &= \int_0^x -\frac{1}{Q(u)} \frac{dQ}{du}\, du \\
&= \left[-\log Q(u) \right]_0^x, \\
&= -\log Q(x) + \log Q(0) \\
&= -\log Q(x),
\end{aligned}$$

Since $Q(0) = 1$, $\log Q(0) = 0$.

so

$$\log Q(x) = -\int_0^x h(u)\, du.$$

Taking exponentials gives

$$Q(x) = \exp\left(-\int_0^x h(u)\, du \right).$$

These results are summarised in the following box.

The age-specific death rate

The **age-specific death rate** or **force of mortality** of a population, denoted $h(x)$, is defined by

$$P(x < X \leq x + \delta x \mid X > x) = h(x)\, \delta x + o(\delta x).$$

The age-specific death rate $h(x)$ and the life table function $Q(x)$ are related by the formulas

$$h(x) = -\frac{1}{Q(x)} \frac{dQ}{dx}, \quad Q(x) \neq 0, \tag{19.3}$$

$$Q(x) = \exp\left(-\int_0^x h(u)\, du \right). \tag{19.4}$$

Example 19.2   Finding the age-specific death rate

The life table function for members of the population of Example 19.1 is

$$Q(x) = 1 - \frac{x}{100}, \quad 0 \leq x < 100.$$

Using (19.3), the age-specific death rate is

$$\begin{aligned}
h(x) &= -\frac{1}{Q(x)} \frac{dQ}{dx} \\
&= -\frac{1}{1 - x/100} \times -\frac{1}{100} \\
&= \frac{1}{100 - x}, \quad 0 \leq x < 100.
\end{aligned}$$

A sketch of $h(x)$ is shown in Figure 19.1. This shows that the death rate increases with age, and moreover, the older members become, the more rapidly the death rate increases. ◆

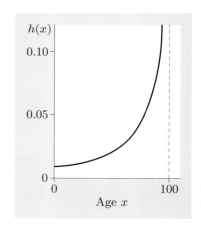

Figure 19.1   The age-specific death rate for a uniform lifetime distribution

Activity 19.2   Another age-specific death rate

The life table function for members of the population of Activity 19.1 is

$$Q(x) = \frac{900}{(30 + x)^2}, \quad x \geq 0.$$

(a) Find the age-specific death rate $h(x)$.

(b) Draw a sketch of $h(x)$, and hence describe the way in which death rates change with age.

Example 19.3   Finding the life table function

Suppose that the age-specific death rate for members of a population is given by

$$h(x) = \frac{5}{90 - x}, \quad 0 \leq x < 90.$$

The life table function $Q(x)$ is obtained using (19.4), as follows. Integrating h gives

$$\begin{aligned}
\int_0^x h(u)\, du &= \int_0^x \frac{5}{90 - u}\, du \\
&= \left[-5 \log(90 - u) \right]_0^x \\
&= -5 \log(90 - x) + 5 \log 90 \\
&= -5 \log \left(\frac{90 - x}{90} \right).
\end{aligned}$$

Therefore, for $0 \leq x < 90$,

$$\begin{aligned}
Q(x) = \exp \left(-\int_0^x h(u)\, du \right) &= \exp \left(5 \log \left(\frac{90 - x}{90} \right) \right) \\
&= \exp \left(\log \left(\frac{90 - x}{90} \right)^5 \right) \\
&= \left(\frac{90 - x}{90} \right)^5. \quad \blacklozenge
\end{aligned}$$

Activity 19.3   Finding the life table function

Suppose that the age-specific death rate for the members of a population is given by

$$h(x) = \frac{4}{2 + x}, \quad x \geq 0.$$

Find the life table function $Q(x)$.

Activity 19.4   Constant death rate

In the models for population growth discussed in Part I, such as the pure death process, the immigration–death process and the simple birth–death process, each individual alive at time t, independently of all other individuals, has probability $\nu\, \delta t + o(\delta t)$ of dying in the next short interval of length δt. No account is taken of the age of the individual: it is assumed that the age-specific death rate $h(x)$ has the constant value ν.

Find the life table function $Q(x)$ for members of a population with constant age-specific death rate ν. Hence identify the lifetime distribution for the members of a population with a constant age-specific death rate.

Activity 19.5   Another lifetime distribution

The age-specific death rate for the members of a population is given by

$$h(x) = \frac{1}{90 - x}, \quad 0 \le x < 90,$$

where x is measured in years.

(a) Find the life table function $Q(x)$, and hence write down $F(x)$, the c.d.f. of the lifetime of individuals.

(b) Identify the lifetime distribution of individuals, and hence write down the value of the expectation of life at birth.

The c.d.f.s of standard continuous distributions are given in Table 9 in the *Handbook*.

Summary of Section 19

In this section, the relationship between the distribution of the lifetimes of the members of a population and the death rates of members of different ages has been explored. The life table function and the age-specific death rate have been defined, and two formulas relating them have been derived.

Exercises on Section 19

Exercise 19.1   A population of fish

The lifetimes of fish in a certain population are uniformly distributed and may be anything between 0 and 4 years.

(a) Write down the p.d.f. of the lifetime X of a fish.

(b) Find the life table function $Q(x)$ for fish in this population.

(c) Write down the expectation of life at birth e_0. What is the median lifetime?

(d) What proportion of fish live for more than three years? What proportion of fish live for less than one year?

(e) Find the age-specific death rate $h(x)$ for fish in the population. Draw a sketch of $h(x)$, and hence describe the way in which death rates change with age.

Exercise 19.2   Another lifetime distribution

Suppose that the distribution of the lifetimes (in years) of members of a population of birds is a mixture of two exponential distributions and has p.d.f.

$$f(x) = \tfrac{1}{4}e^{-x} + \tfrac{9}{4}e^{-3x}, \quad x > 0.$$

(a) Find the corresponding life table function $Q(x)$.

(b) Find the expectation of life at birth e_0.

(c) Find the age-specific death rate $h(x)$.

(d) What proportion of the population live for longer than six months?

Suppose that the age-specific death rate for members of a population is given by

$$h(x) = \frac{x}{4 + 2x}, \quad x \geq 0,$$

where x is measured in days.

(a) Find the life table function $Q(x)$.

(b) What proportion of the population live for longer than a week?

(c) Find the p.d.f. $f(x)$ of the lifetime of members of the population, and identify the lifetime distribution.

Use Table 9 in the *Handbook*.

(d) Use Table 9 in the *Handbook* to write down the mean lifetime of members.

20   Life tables

Although examples such as those in Section 19 are useful for developing an understanding of how life table functions and age-specific death rates are related, the life table functions of human populations cannot be expressed in terms of simple mathematical functions. A life table function is a continuous function, but in practice, its value is given only at a finite sequence of ages. For example, for human populations, its value may be given at yearly intervals or at five-year intervals. These values are usually presented in tabular form, that is, in a life table.

The main part of Graunt's life table was based on ten-year intervals.

Clearly, it is not possible to tabulate a life table function for an infinite number of ages and, in any case, a model for a population is necessarily based on a finite amount of data. Therefore values are estimated and tabulated for a finite set of ages, and linear interpolation is used to estimate the life table function for values in between.

How are the tabulated values of a life table function obtained? In an ideal world, a population of newborn individuals, all born at approximately the same time, would be observed at a succession of times, and at each time point x, the number still alive would be recorded. From these values, the proportions of the population who have survived to be still alive aged x would be calculated for each x. These proportions would be the estimated values of the life table function. A life table prepared in this way is called a **cohort life table**.

However, in the real world, following the fate of a cohort is difficult for human populations (and, indeed, for any species that has a reasonably long lifespan or that cannot be reared in laboratory conditions). In practice, information is collected over a short period of time (as is the case for census data) and observations are made for a population containing individuals of all ages. A life table constructed from observing an all-age population is called a **current life table**.

In practice, cohort life tables are estimated from data collected by observation of an all-age population. The details of how this is done will not be discussed, but you should be aware that there are difficulties involved in estimating the life table function for a human population. The life tables in this book are all cohort life tables, and they will be referred to simply as life tables.

At any given time, life tables vary from region to region, and within a region they change over time as the level of health care rises. In addition, men and women have substantially different life tables. The life table described in Example 20.1 is a life table for the females in a human population.

Example 20.1   A life table

Table 20.1 provides an example of a life table for the females in a human population. In order to avoid the occurrence of fractions and decimals, when drawing up a life table, instead of tabulating values of the life table function $Q(x)$, it is usual to tabulate values of $100 \times Q(x)$, or $1000 \times Q(x)$ or $100\,000 \times Q(x)$, as appropriate. In Table 20.1, values of $100\,000 \times Q(x)$ are listed. These are denoted by l_x, so $l_x = 10^5 \times Q(x)$. So out of every $100\,000$ females born, l_x is the expected number who are still alive at age x.

When dealing with large numbers of individuals, random fluctuations can be ignored, and a deterministic interpretation of the life table can be adopted. In this case, $Q(x)$ is the proportion of females still alive at age x, and l_x is the number, out of every $100\,000$ females born, who are still alive at age x. From now on, unless otherwise stated, a deterministic interpretation will be adopted.

In Table 20.1, the values of l_x are listed at five-year intervals, plus the value for $x = 1$. The age $x = 1$ is included because of the special importance of infant mortality: death rates in the early months of life are much higher than in the following years of childhood. The last listed age is 105: no individual survives to age 105 years. ◆

Table 20.1   A life table

Age in years, x	$l_x = 10^5 \times Q(x)$
0	100 000
1	95 931
5	94 693
10	94 212
15	93 838
20	93 244
25	92 429
30	91 468
35	90 349
40	88 990
45	87 267
50	84 931
55	81 653
60	77 061
65	70 377
70	60 737
75	47 434
80	31 368
85	16 017
90	5 348
95	893
100	48
105	0

A life table can be used to calculate an approximate value of the expectation of life at birth. In Example 20.2, the life table in Table 20.1 is used to illustrate how this is done.

Example 20.2   Estimating the expectation of life at birth

In Figure 20.1(a), the values of the life table function $Q(x) = l_x \times 10^{-5}$ are plotted for the values of x listed in Table 20.1.

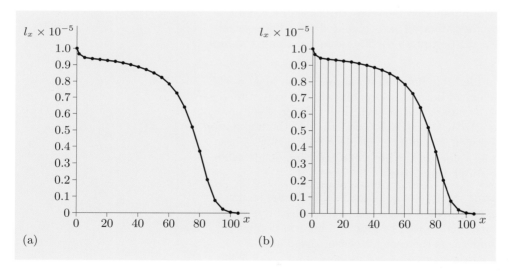

(a)

(b)

Figure 20.1   (a) The life table function   (b) Estimating the area

Since the life table function is approximated by linear interpolation for intermediate values of x, the plotted points are linked by straight-line segments in Figure 20.1.

The integral of the life table function $Q(x)$ is equal to the area under the graph of $Q(x)$, so an approximate value for the expectation of life at birth, e_0, is given by the area under the graph in Figure 20.1(a). In Figure 20.1(b), this area has been divided into trapeziums by drawing vertical lines through the plotted points. The area of the trapezium between x and $x + k$, where $x + k$ is the next age listed after x, is equal to $\frac{1}{2}k(l_x + l_{x+k}) \times 10^{-5}$. For example, the area of the trapezium from $x = 85$ to $x + k = 90$, which is illustrated in Figure 20.2, is $\frac{1}{2} \times 5 \times (l_{85} + l_{90}) \times 10^{-5}$.

The expectation of life at birth is approximately equal to the total area under the graph in Figure 20.1:

$$e_0 \simeq \sum_x \frac{k}{2}(l_x + l_{x+k}) \times 10^{-5},$$

where the summation is over all listed values of x. For $x = 0$ and $x = 1$, the values of k are 1 and 4, respectively, and for all the other values of x, k is 5. Therefore

$$10^5 \times e_0 \simeq \tfrac{1}{2}(l_0 + l_1) + \tfrac{4}{2}(l_1 + l_5) + \tfrac{5}{2}(l_5 + l_{10}) + \tfrac{5}{2}(l_{10} + l_{15})$$
$$+ \cdots + \tfrac{5}{2}(l_{100} + l_{105})$$
$$= \tfrac{1}{2}l_0 + \tfrac{5}{2}l_1 + \tfrac{9}{2}l_5 + 5 \times (l_{10} + l_{15} + \cdots + l_{100}) + \tfrac{5}{2}l_{105}$$
$$= 6\,754\,266.$$

Hence the expectation of life at birth for females in this population is approximately 67.5 years.   ◆

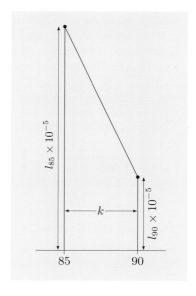

Figure 20.2   A trapezium

Activity 20.1   Graunt's life table

(a)   Plot the life table function for Graunt's life table, which is reproduced in Table 20.2.

(b)   Use the life table to calculate an approximate value of the expectation of life at birth.

Table 20.2   Graunt's life table

Age in years, x	$l_x = 100 \times Q(x)$
0	100
6	64
16	40
26	25
36	16
46	10
56	6
66	3
76	1
80	0

The age-specific death rate $h(x)$ is given by (19.3):

$$h(x) = -\frac{1}{Q(x)}\frac{dQ}{dx}.$$

To use this formula, the life table function is required in the form of a mathematical function that can be differentiated. The life table function as drawn in Figure 20.1(a), for example, is not differentiable at the plotted points, where two straight-line segments meet, and the values of $Q(x)$ for values of x between plotted points are only approximations obtained by linear interpolation. Approximate values of the age-specific death rate can be obtained in various ways when the life table function is given only for the ages listed in a life table. One method is illustrated in Example 20.3.

Example 20.3   Estimating death rates

For each listed age x, a value m_x that approximates the age-specific death rate $h(x)$ can be calculated in the following way. First, the life table function Q is approximated over the range x to $x + k$ by the average of its values at x and $x + k$. For the population of Table 20.1, this is equal to

$$\frac{Q(x) + Q(x+k)}{2} = \frac{l_x + l_{x+k}}{2 \times 10^5}.$$

In Figure 20.1(a), the plotted points are joined by straight-line segments, so this value is equal to the value of the plotted life table function midway between x and $x + k$; that is, at the centre of the age range x to $x + k$. The derivative dQ/dx is approximated by the gradient of the line segment between the ages x and $x + k$. For Table 20.1, the gradient is

$$\frac{Q(x+k) - Q(x)}{k} = \frac{l_{x+k} - l_x}{k \times 10^5}.$$

Then m_x, the approximate value for the age-specific death rate $h(x)$, is given by

$$m_x = -\frac{2 \times 10^5}{l_x + l_{x+k}} \times \frac{l_{x+k} - l_x}{k \times 10^5},$$

that is,

$$m_x = \frac{2(l_x - l_{x+k})}{k(l_x + l_{x+k})}. \tag{20.1}$$

For each listed age x, (20.1) can be used to calculate an approximate value m_x of the age-specific death rate. Values m_x for the population whose life table is given in Table 20.1 are listed in Table 20.3. For example,

$$m_0 = \frac{2(l_0 - l_1)}{1(l_0 + l_1)} \simeq 0.0415,$$

$$m_1 = \frac{2(l_1 - l_5)}{4(l_1 + l_5)} \simeq 0.0032,$$

$$m_5 = \frac{2(l_5 - l_{10})}{5(l_5 + l_{10})} \simeq 0.0010,$$

$$m_{10} = \frac{2(l_{10} - l_{15})}{5(l_{10} + l_{15})} \simeq 0.0008,$$

and so on.

The quantity m_x is called the **central mortality rate**. The word *central* reflects the fact that the approximation is based on the estimated value of $Q(x)$ at the centre of the age range x to $x + k$.

More sophisticated calculations of mortality can be carried out, but this relatively crude measure is sufficient to show how death rates vary with age. The values of the central mortality rate m_x are plotted against x (up to 70) in Figure 20.3.

As you can see, after the relatively high mortality of infancy, death rates are at their lowest in the age range of 5 to 15 years. Mortality increases slowly during early adulthood, but in later years it increases ever more rapidly, and after the age of 70 it is large enough to disappear off the top of Figure 20.3.   ◆

Activity 20.2   Graunt's life table

Calculate values of the central mortality rate for Graunt's life table (Table 20.2).

Table 20.3   Values m_x

x	m_x	x	m_x
0	0.0415	50	0.0079
1	0.0032	55	0.0116
5	0.0010	60	0.0181
10	0.0008	65	0.0294
15	0.0013	70	0.0492
20	0.0018	75	0.0816
25	0.0021	80	0.1296
30	0.0025	85	0.1997
35	0.0030	90	0.2855
40	0.0039	95	0.3592
45	0.0054	100	0.4000

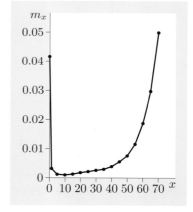

Figure 20.3   Central mortality rates

Summary of Section 20

Cohort life tables and current life tables have been discussed briefly in this section. You have learned how to use a (cohort) life table to calculate an approximate value for the expectation of life at birth and to estimate values of the age-specific death rate.

21 Stationary populations

The models discussed in this section are models for an idealised population for which the life table function does not change over time. The population is assumed to be living over a long period of time in conditions that undergo little change, and it is unaffected by any major catastrophe such as a famine, a plague or a war. Furthermore, it is assumed that the population is closed: there is no immigration or emigration. Again this is an idealisation, approximating to a situation in which migration plays a negligible part in the growth of the population.

As already mentioned, males and females have different life tables. In fact, women tend to live longer than men. As a consequence, the distributions of the ages of the males and the females in a population are different. Since the age distribution of females is more critical for the birth rate, and hence for the rate of growth of a population, attention will be restricted to the size and age distribution of the female population. Hence reference to a life table will imply a life table for females, and reference to birth rates will imply the rates at which daughters are born to women.

It is assumed that there are always enough males in the population to maintain the birth rate.

The models discussed in this section are for a population that does not change in size and in which the proportion of the population in any given age range remains fixed. Such a population is called a **stationary population**, and is defined in the following box.

Stationary population

A population for which the life table function $Q(x)$ does not change over time is **stationary** if:

$\diamond$ the population size remains constant over time;

$\diamond$ the age distribution of the population remains constant over time, that is, the proportion of the population in any given age range does not change over time.

In a stationary population, the age distribution does not change with time and the size of the population remains fixed, so births must occur at a constant rate. Suppose that the size of a stationary population is n, and that births occur at the constant rate of b births per year. Then the per capita birth rate of the population, which is called the **crude birth rate** of the population, is b/n. Since births are balanced by deaths in a stationary population, the crude death rate (that is, the per capita death rate) is equal to the crude birth rate.

By definition, the proportion of a stationary population aged between x_1 and x_2 remains constant over time for any x_1 and x_2 such that $0 \le x_1 < x_2$, so the age distribution of the population may be represented by a probability density function that is independent of time. The age distribution of a stationary population is called the **stationary age distribution** and its p.d.f. is denoted by $g(x)$. Hence, for example, the proportion of the population aged between x_1 and x_2 years is given by

$$\int_{x_1}^{x_2} g(x)\,dx,$$

and the total number of individuals in the population aged between x_1 and x_2 is

$$n \int_{x_1}^{x_2} g(x)\,dx.$$

Note that the stationary age distribution for a population is not the same as the lifetime distribution for individuals. To see this, consider a stationary population in which every individual lives for exactly the same length of time C, so that the lifetime of an individual is a degenerate random variable. At any time, there will be individuals of all ages up to C in the population, so the p.d.f. of the age distribution has range 0 to C. Therefore the lifetime distribution and the age distribution are not the same.

Clearly, the age distribution of a population depends on $Q(x)$, the life table function of the population. For example, if $Q(100) = 0$, then all individuals die by age 100, so $g(x) = 0$ for $x \geq 100$. The relationship between the p.d.f. $g(x)$ and the life table function $Q(x)$ will now be obtained.

You will not be expected to reproduce this derivation.

Let N denote the number of individuals in the population at time t who are aged between x and $x + \delta x$. Two expressions for N will be found, one involving the p.d.f. $g(x)$ and the other involving the life table function $Q(x)$.

First, by the definition of the p.d.f.,

$$N = n \int_x^{x+\delta x} g(y) \, dy.$$

Therefore $N \simeq n \, g(x) \, \delta x$ for small δx, and hence

$$N = n \, g(x) \, \delta x + o(\delta x). \tag{21.1}$$

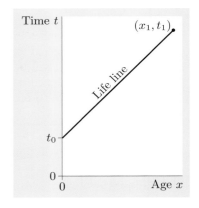

To obtain an expression for N involving the life table function $Q(x)$, it is helpful to use a type of diagram known as a **Lexis diagram**, an example of which is shown in Figure 21.1. An individual aged x at time t is represented on the diagram by a point (x, t). The collection of all such points for an individual from her birth to her death is her **life line**. An individual's life line is a diagonal line starting at $(0, t_0)$, where t_0 is the time of her birth, and ending at (x_1, t_1), where t_1 is the time of her death and $x_1 = t_1 - t_0$ is her age at death. (If the scales on the axes are the same, then the life line is at $45°$ to the time axis.)

Figure 21.1   A Lexis diagram

The Lexis diagram in Figure 21.2 will be used to obtain an expression for N involving the life table function $Q(x)$.

The life line of an individual who is aged between x and $x + \delta x$ at time t intersects the horizontal line at time t between ages x and $x + \delta x$. Figure 21.2 shows one such life line. An individual aged x at time t was born at time $t - x$, and an individual aged $x + \delta x$ at time t was born at time $t - x - \delta x$; the life lines of such individuals are shown by the broken lines on the diagram. Individuals who are aged between x and $x + \delta x$ at time t are those who were born in the time interval $[t - x - \delta x, t - x]$ and who have survived to be still alive at time t. Since the birth rate is b, the number of individuals born in any time interval of duration δx is $b \, \delta x$. Also, the proportion of those born in the interval $[t - x - \delta x, t - x]$ who are still alive at time t is approximately $Q(x)$. Hence for small δx,

$$N = b \, Q(x) \, \delta x + o(\delta x). \tag{21.2}$$

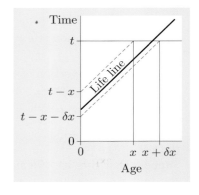

Figure 21.2   Life line for an individual aged between x and $x + \delta x$ at time t

Comparing the two expressions for N in (21.1) and (21.2) leads to

$$n \, g(x) \, \delta x = b \, Q(x) \, \delta x + o(\delta x).$$

Rearranging this and letting $\delta x \to 0$ gives

$$g(x) = \frac{b}{n} Q(x). \tag{21.3}$$

Therefore the p.d.f. of the stationary age distribution is proportional to the life table function, and the constant of proportionality is equal to the crude birth rate b/n.

Since $g(x)$ is a p.d.f.,

$$\int_0^\infty g(x) \, dx = 1.$$

Also, by (19.1),

$$\int_0^\infty Q(x)\, dx = e_0.$$

Therefore integrating both sides of (21.3) gives

$$1 = \frac{b}{n} e_0,$$

and hence

$$\frac{b}{n} = \frac{1}{e_0}.$$

That is, the crude birth rate is equal to the reciprocal of the expectation of life at birth. Substituting for b/n in (21.3) gives the result stated in the following box.

The stationary age distribution

The age distribution of a stationary population with life table function $Q(x)$ is called the **stationary age distribution**. Its p.d.f. $g(x)$ is given by

$$g(x) = \frac{Q(x)}{e_0}. \tag{21.4}$$

This result means that if it is reasonable to assume that a given population is stationary (or at least approximately stationary), then the life table function is proportional to the p.d.f. of the age distribution. In this case, the life table function can be estimated very simply from data collected on a population containing individuals of all ages, that is, from a current life table. Thus it is not necessary to observe a cohort of individuals over a long period of time in order to estimate the life table function.

Example 21.1   Uniform lifetimes

Suppose that the lifetimes of individuals in a stationary population are uniformly distributed and may be anything between 0 and 100 years. Then the life table function for the population is

$$Q(x) = 1 - \frac{x}{100}, \quad 0 \le x < 100,$$

See Example 19.1.

and e_0, the expectation of life at birth, is 50 years.

Therefore, using (21.4), the p.d.f. of the age distribution is

$$g(x) = \frac{Q(x)}{e_0} = \frac{1}{50}\left(1 - \frac{x}{100}\right), \quad 0 \le x < 100.$$

The p.d.f. can be used to calculate the proportion of the population that are in any given age range at any time. For example, the proportion of the population aged over 50 years is given by

$$\int_{50}^{100} g(x)\, dx = \frac{1}{50} \int_{50}^{100} \left(1 - \frac{x}{100}\right) dx$$

$$= \frac{1}{50}\left[x - \frac{x^2}{200}\right]_{50}^{100}$$

$$= 0.25.$$

Note that this is not the same as the proportion of individuals who live beyond the age of 50 years, which is given by $Q(50) = 0.5$. Half of all individuals who are born will live beyond the age of 50 years, but at any particular time, only a quarter of those alive will be over 50 years old.

A statistic of social and economic significance for any population is the ratio of the number of individuals aged under 15 or 65 and over to the number aged 15 and over but under 65. This is called the **dependency ratio**.

For the population of this example, the proportion of the population under 15 years old is given by

$$\int_0^{15} g(x)\, dx = \frac{1}{50} \int_0^{15} \left(1 - \frac{x}{100}\right) dx$$
$$= \frac{1}{50} \left[x - \frac{x^2}{200} \right]_0^{15}$$
$$= 0.2775.$$

That is, at any time, approximately 28% of the population are under 15 years old. Similarly, the proportion of the population aged 65 and over is given by

$$\int_{65}^{\infty} g(x)\, dx = \frac{1}{50} \int_{65}^{100} \left(1 - \frac{x}{100}\right) dx = 0.1225.$$

Thus the dependency ratio for the population is

$$\frac{0.2775 + 0.1225}{1 - (0.2775 + 0.1225)} = \frac{2}{3} \simeq 0.6667.$$

So, roughly speaking, in this case, for every 100 members of the population of working age, there are 67 'dependent' individuals. ◆

Activity 21.1   *A stationary population*

Suppose that the life table function for members of a stationary population is

$$Q(x) = \frac{900}{(30 + x)^2}, \quad x \geq 0,$$

where x is measured in years.

(a) Find the p.d.f. of the stationary age distribution.

(b) Calculate the dependency ratio for this population.

You found the expectation of life at birth in Activity 19.1.

Activity 21.2   *Another stationary population*

The life table function for members of a stationary population is

$$Q(x) = \left(1 - \frac{x}{90}\right)^5, \quad 0 \leq x < 90,$$

where x is measured in years.

(a) Find the p.d.f. of the stationary age distribution.

(b) What proportion of members of the population live for more than 30 years?

(c) At any time, what proportion of the population are more than 30 years old?

Example 21.2   The average age of a stationary population

The mean age of members of a stationary population is the mean of the age
distribution, and is given by

$$\int_0^\infty x\, g(x)\, dx.$$

Thus the mean age (in years) of the members of the stationary population of
Example 21.1 is

$$
\begin{aligned}
\int_0^\infty x\, g(x)\, dx &= \int_0^{100} \frac{1}{50} x \left(1 - \frac{x}{100}\right) dx \\
&= \frac{1}{50} \int_0^{100} \left(x - \frac{x^2}{100}\right) dx \\
&= \frac{1}{50} \left[\frac{x^2}{2} - \frac{x^3}{300}\right]_0^{100} \\
&= 33\tfrac{1}{3}.
\end{aligned}
$$

Note that this is the mean age of all members alive at a particular time. This is
not equal to e_0, which is the mean length of time that an individual lives.

The median age m of members of a stationary population satisfies

$$\int_0^m g(x)\, dx = 0.5.$$

In this case, the median m satisfies

$$\int_0^m \frac{1}{50} \left(1 - \frac{x}{100}\right) dx = 0.5,$$

that is,

$$\frac{1}{50} \left[x - \frac{x^2}{200}\right]_0^m = 0.5,$$

so

$$m - \frac{m^2}{200} = 25,$$

or

$$m^2 - 200m + 5000 = 0.$$

Therefore

$$m = \frac{200 - \sqrt{200^2 - 20\,000}}{2} \simeq 29.3 \text{ years.} \quad \blacklozenge$$

The median must be between 0
and 100.

Activity 21.3   Mean age and median age

The lifetimes of members of a stationary population are uniformly distributed
with life table function

$$Q(x) = 1 - \frac{x}{90}, \quad 0 \le x < 90,$$

where x is measured in years.

(a) Find the p.d.f. of the stationary age distribution.

(b) Find the mean age of members of the population.

(c) Find the median age of members of the population.

Activity 21.4   *A stationary insect population*

The life table function for members of a stationary insect population is

$$Q(x) = 1 - \frac{x^5}{32}, \quad 0 \le x < 2,$$

where x is measured in weeks.

(a) Find the mean lifetime of insects in the population.

(b) At any time, find the mean age of insects in the population.

(c) What proportion of insects live for less than one week?

(d) At any time, what proportion of insects in the population are less than one week old?

Activity 21.5   *Another stationary population*

The life table function for members of a stationary population is

$$Q(x) = \frac{16}{(2 + x)^4}, \quad x \ge 0,$$

where x is measured in days.

(a) Find the expectation of life at birth.

(b) Find the mean age of members of the population.

Summary of Section 21

In this section, a deterministic model for a population whose size and age distribution remain fixed over time has been described – that is, for a stationary population. You have seen that the p.d.f. of the age distribution of a stationary population is proportional to the life table function for members of the population.

Exercises on Section 21

Exercise 21.1   *A stationary fish population*

The life table function for the fish population of Exercise 19.1 is

$$Q(x) = 1 - \frac{x}{4}, \quad 0 \le x < 4,$$

where x is measured in years.

Suppose that the fish population is stationary.

(a) Write down the p.d.f. of the age distribution of the fish population.

(b) Calculate the mean age of fish in the population at any time.

(c) Calculate the median age of fish in the population.

(d) At any time, what proportion of fish in the population are more than three years old? What proportion are less than a year old?

Exercise 21.2   *A stationary bird population*

Suppose that the bird population of Exercise 19.2, for which the lifetime distribution is a mixture of exponential distributions, is stationary.

Calculate the mean age of birds in the population at any time.

Exercise 21.3   A stationary animal population

The life table function for members of a stationary animal population is

$$Q(x) = e^{-x^2/8}, \quad x \geq 0,$$

where x is measured in years.

(a) Write down the c.d.f. of the lifetime of the animals, and identify the lifetime distribution. Hence find the expectation of life at birth.

(b) Calculate the mean age of animals in the population.

Use Table 9 in the *Handbook*.

22   Stable populations

The models discussed in this section are for a population for which the proportion of the population in any given age range remains fixed. Such a population is called a **stable population**, and is defined in the following box.

Stable population

A population for which the life table function $Q(x)$ does not change over time is a **stable population** if the age distribution remains constant over time.

Note that the adjective 'stable' does not necessarily apply to the population's size: the size of the population may grow or decline.

As in Section 21, the models discussed are models for an idealised population for which the life table function does not change over time. The population is assumed to be living over a long period of time in conditions that undergo little change, and it is unaffected by any major catastrophe such as a famine, a plague or a war. Furthermore, it is assumed that the population is closed: there is no immigration or emigration. Again this is an idealisation, approximating to a situation in which migration plays a negligible part in the growth of the population.

In general, the overall birth rate and the size of a stable population change over time. The way in which they change is investigated in Subsection 22.1. The form taken by the p.d.f. of the age distribution of a stable population is studied in Subsection 22.2, and the relationship between stable distributions and stationary distributions is discussed briefly. You will not be expected to reproduce the derivations of any of the results obtained in this section.

22.1   The growth of a stable population

The size of a stable population may change over time, so it is a function of time. The number of females at time t will be denoted $n(t)$ and, as in Section 21, the males will be ignored.

Since it is assumed that there is no immigration, new members can join the population only by births. Moreover, since the age distribution of a stable population remains fixed, births must occur; otherwise, the population would age and the distribution would change. The overall birth rate at time t is, in general, a function of t, so it will be denoted $b(t)$.

In this subsection, the way in which the size of a stable population changes over time will be investigated. An equation satisfied by the overall birth rate $b(t)$ will be obtained first. This will be done by finding two expressions for the number of females in the population at time t who are aged between x and $x + \delta x$.

The age distribution of a stable population, which is called the **stable age distribution**, remains constant over time, so its p.d.f. is denoted $g(x)$. It follows that the proportion of the population aged between x and $x + \delta x$ at any time t is $g(x)\,\delta x + o(\delta x)$, and hence the number of females in the population at time t who are aged between x and $x + \delta x$ is $n(t)\,g(x)\,\delta x + o(\delta x)$, or approximately $n(t)\,g(x)\,\delta x$.

From now on, for simplicity, the term $o(\delta x)$ will often be omitted.

A second expression for the number of females aged between x and $x + \delta x$ at time t can be found using the Lexis diagram in Figure 22.1. From this diagram, it can be seen that the individuals who are aged between x and $x + \delta x$ at time t are those who were born in the time interval $[t - x - \delta x, t - x]$ and who have survived to be still alive at time t. The birth rate during the short time interval $[t - x - \delta x, t - x]$ is approximately $b(t - x)$, so the number of births in the interval is approximately $b(t - x)\,\delta x$. A proportion $Q(x)$, approximately, of the females born in this interval survive to be still alive at time t, so the number of females aged between x and $x + \delta x$ at time t is approximately $b(t - x)\,Q(x)\,\delta x$. Therefore

$$n(t)\,g(x)\,\delta x = b(t - x)\,Q(x)\,\delta x,$$

and hence

$$n(t) = \frac{b(t - x)\,Q(x)}{g(x)}. \tag{22.1}$$

But $Q(0) = 1$, so setting $x = 0$ in (22.1) gives

$$n(t) = \frac{b(t)}{g(0)}. \tag{22.2}$$

From (22.1) and (22.2),

$$\frac{b(t)}{g(0)} = \frac{b(t - x)\,Q(x)}{g(x)}.$$

Hence for $x \geq 0$,

$$b(t) = b(t - x)\,c(x), \tag{22.3}$$

where

$$c(x) = Q(x)\,g(0)/g(x), \tag{22.4}$$

which is a function of x only.

The form taken by $b(t)$ can be deduced as follows. Setting $t = y + \delta y$ and $x = \delta y$ in (22.3), and then setting $t = y$ and $x = 0$ in (22.3), gives the two equations

$$b(y + \delta y) = b(y)\,c(\delta y),$$
$$b(y) = b(y)\,c(0).$$

Subtracting the second of these equations from the first and dividing by δy leads to

$$\frac{b(y + \delta y) - b(y)}{\delta y} = b(y)\,\frac{c(\delta y) - c(0)}{\delta y}.$$

Letting δy tend to 0 gives

$$b'(y) = \theta\,b(y),$$

where θ is the real constant $c'(0)$. This differential equation has the solution $b(y) = b(0)\,e^{\theta y}$ for $y \geq 0$, so the birth rate $b(t)$ is given by

$$b(t) = b(0)\,e^{\theta t}, \quad t \geq 0. \tag{22.5}$$

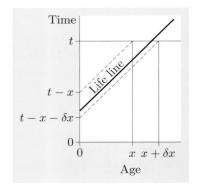

Figure 22.1 A Lexis diagram

Hence from (22.2),

$$n(t) = \frac{b(t)}{g(0)} = \frac{b(0)}{g(0)} e^{\theta t},$$

that is,

$$n(t) = n(0) e^{\theta t}, \quad t \geq 0. \tag{22.6}$$

Therefore in any stable population, both $b(t)$, the overall birth rate, and $n(t)$, the size of the population, grow or decline exponentially with time. Whether the population grows or shrinks depends on the sign of θ. If $\theta > 0$, then the population grows exponentially with time; if $\theta < 0$, then the population size declines exponentially towards 0. The parameter θ is called the **intrinsic growth rate** of the population.

22.2   Stable populations and stationary populations

From (22.6), when the intrinsic growth rate of a stable population is 0, the population size remains constant over time, and hence the population is a stationary population. In this case, the p.d.f. of the age distribution is given by (21.4):

$$g(x) = \frac{Q(x)}{e_0},$$

where e_0, the expectation of life at birth, is given by

$$e_0 = \int_0^\infty Q(x) \, dx.$$

The form taken by the p.d.f. of the age distribution of a stable population with life table function $Q(x)$ will now be found.

From (22.4), the p.d.f. $g(x)$ is given by

$$g(x) = \frac{g(0) \, Q(x)}{c(x)}.$$

From (22.3), $c(x)$ is given by

$$c(x) = \frac{b(t)}{b(t - x)},$$

so, using (22.5) to substitute for $b(t)$ and $b(t - x)$,

$$c(x) = \frac{b(0) \, e^{\theta t}}{b(0) \, e^{\theta(t-x)}} = e^{\theta x}.$$

Therefore

$$g(x) = g(0) \, e^{-\theta x} \, Q(x), \quad x \geq 0. \tag{22.7}$$

The value of $g(0)$ can be obtained by using the fact that $g(x)$ is a p.d.f. Integrating both sides of (22.7) between the limits 0 and ∞ gives

$$\int_0^\infty g(x) \, dx = g(0) \int_0^\infty e^{-\theta x} \, Q(x) \, dx.$$

Since $g(x)$ is a p.d.f., the value of the integral on the left-hand side is 1, and hence

$$g(0) = \frac{1}{\int_0^\infty e^{-\theta x} \, Q(x) \, dx}.$$

Therefore the p.d.f. of the stable age distribution is

$$g(x) = \frac{e^{-\theta x} \, Q(x)}{\int_0^\infty e^{-\theta x} \, Q(x) \, dx}. \tag{22.8}$$

Note that since $\theta = 0$ for a stationary population, in this case (22.8) reduces to $g(x) = Q(x)/e_0$. Thus the p.d.f. of the stable age distribution may be regarded as a generalisation of the p.d.f. of the age distribution of a stationary population with the same life table function. The p.d.f. in (22.8) is of the form

$$g(x) = k(\theta)\, e^{-\theta x}\, Q(x),$$

where $k(\theta)$ is a constant depending on θ. For a stationary population with the same life table function, the p.d.f. of the age distribution takes the form

$$g(x) = k(0)\, Q(x),$$

where $k(0)$ is the constant $1/e_0$. For a growing stable population, $\theta > 0$. The function $e^{-\theta x}$ decreases as x increases, so the population will include fewer older people, as a proportion of the total, than the corresponding stationary population. Thus the proportion of the population in the younger age groups will be greater than that in the corresponding stationary population. Furthermore, the greater the value of θ, the larger the proportion of the stable population in the youngest age groups. For a declining stable population, $\theta < 0$, and $e^{-\theta x}$ increases with x. Therefore the proportion of the population in the younger age groups is smaller than in the corresponding stationary population. These ideas are illustrated in Example 22.1.

Example 22.1   Uniform lifetimes

Suppose that the lifetimes of individuals in a population are uniformly distributed and may be anything between 0 and 100 years. Then the life table function is

$$Q(x) = 1 - \frac{x}{100}, \quad 0 \le x < 100,$$

and e_0, the expectation of life at birth, is 50 years.   See Example 19.1.

If the population is stationary, then the p.d.f. of the age distribution is

$$g(x) = \frac{1}{50}\left(1 - \frac{x}{100}\right), \quad 0 \le x < 100.$$ See Example 21.1.

A sketch of the p.d.f. is shown in Figure 22.2.

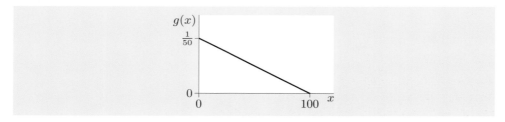

Figure 22.2   The p.d.f. of the stationary age distribution

Now suppose that the population is stable with intrinsic growth rate θ, so that the p.d.f. of the age distribution is given by (22.8) and hence takes the form

$$g(x) = ke^{-\theta x}\, Q(x).$$

In this case,

$$g(x) = ke^{-\theta x}\left(1 - \frac{x}{100}\right), \quad 0 \le x < 100.$$

If $\theta > 0$, then the population is growing, and a larger proportion of the population is in the younger age groups than for the corresponding stationary population. The shape of the p.d.f. of the age distribution might be as shown in Figure 22.3 in this case.

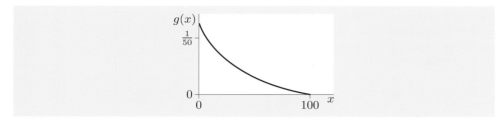

Figure 22.3   The p.d.f. of the stable age distribution when $\theta > 0$

If $\theta < 0$, then the population is declining, and a smaller proportion of the population is in the younger age groups than for the corresponding stationary population. The shape of the p.d.f. of the age distribution will depend on how rapidly the population is declining, that is, on the magnitude of θ. The gradient of the p.d.f. when $x = 0$ may be negative, zero or positive, depending on the value of θ. These possibilities are illustrated in Figure 22.4.

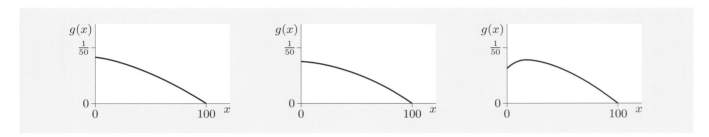

Figure 22.4   The p.d.f. of the stable age distribution: possible shapes when $\theta < 0$ ◆

Activity 22.1   A stable population

In Activity 21.1, you found the p.d.f. of the age distribution of a stationary population for which the life table function is

$$Q(x) = \frac{900}{(30 + x)^2}, \quad x \geq 0.$$

(a) Sketch the p.d.f. of the stationary age distribution.

(b) Now suppose that a population with the life table function given above is stable but not stationary. Draw sketches to show what the p.d.f. of the age distribution might look like if the population is (i) growing, (ii) declining.

You have seen that the size of a stable population may increase, decrease or remain constant depending on whether the intrinsic growth rate θ is greater than, less than or equal to 0. Whether the population grows or declines depends on the birth and death rates in the population. Specifically, it depends on the age-specific death rate $h(x)$, or equivalently on the life table function $Q(x)$, which are assumed to be fixed over time. The different propensities of women of different ages to give birth can be modelled using the **age-specific birth rate** of the population, which is denoted $\lambda(x)$ and is defined to be the rate at which females of age x give birth to females. For the birth and death processes discussed in Part I, the (individual) birth and death rates are assumed to be independent of age. However, the models for stationary and stable populations studied in Part IV include models that allow for the birth and death rates to vary with age, so they are more widely applicable.

The practical importance of stable population models is a consequence of the following result, whose proof is beyond the scope of M343: any population whose age-specific birth and death rates do not change will become approximately stable in the long run. Since, in practice, many human populations have age-specific birth and death rates that change fairly slowly with time, their development over time can be modelled reasonably accurately by treating them as stable.

Summary of Section 22

In this section, stable population models have been discussed briefly. A population is stable if the life table function and the age distribution do not vary with time. You have seen that for a stable population, the overall size of the population changes exponentially over time. The rate θ at which the size changes is called the intrinsic growth rate of the population. If $\theta = 0$, then the population is stationary. The age distribution of a stable population has been compared with the age distribution of a stationary population with the same life table function.

Exercise on Section 22

Exercise 22.1   The age distribution of an animal population

In Exercise 21.3, you found the p.d.f. of the age distribution of a stationary animal population for which the life table function is

$$Q(x) = e^{-x^2/8}, \quad x \geq 0,$$

where x is measured in years.

(a) Sketch the p.d.f. of the stationary age distribution.

(b) Now suppose that an animal population with the life table function given above is stable but not stationary. Draw sketches to show what the p.d.f. of the age distribution might look like if the population is (i) growing, (ii) declining.

23   Population pyramids

A diagram for representing the age distribution of the males and females in a population is introduced in this section. A **population pyramid** is a histogram that plots population size by age group as a percentage of the total population size, with males on the left-hand side and females on the right-hand side. This is illustrated for an imaginary population in Example 23.1.

Example 23.1   A population pyramid

Suppose that as in Example 22.1, the life table function of the females in a population is

$$Q(x) = 1 - \frac{x}{100}, \quad 0 \le x < 100.$$

If the population is stationary, then the p.d.f. of the age distribution is

$$g(x) = \frac{1}{50}\left(1 - \frac{x}{100}\right), \quad 0 \le x < 100.$$

A sketch of this p.d.f. is shown in Figure 23.1.

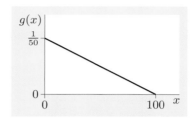

Figure 23.1   The p.d.f. of the age distribution

For simplicity, suppose that the numbers of males and females in the population are equal and that the age distribution of the males is the same as the age distribution of the females. Figure 23.2 shows a population pyramid for the population.

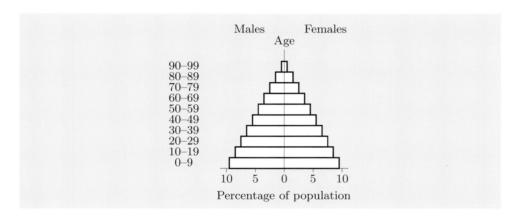

Figure 23.2   A population pyramid

In this pyramid, ages are grouped in ten-year intervals, and the length of the bar for an age group is equal to the percentage of the population in that age group. For the age group 0–9, for instance, which includes children up to just before their tenth birthday, the proportion of the population in that age group is equal to the area under the p.d.f. of the age distribution between 0 and 10. This area is shaded in Figure 23.3. Therefore the shape of a histogram for the males (or for the females) would be as shown in Figure 23.4, and this is essentially the same as the shape of the p.d.f. In a population pyramid, histograms for the males and the females are drawn on opposite sides of a common vertical age axis, as in Figure 23.2.   ♦

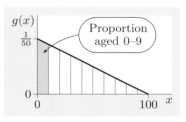

Figure 23.3   The p.d.f. of the age distribution

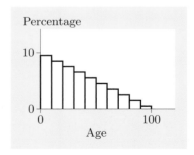

Figure 23.4   A histogram for the males (or females)

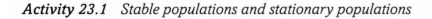

Activity 23.1   Stable populations and stationary populations

Suppose that the population of Example 23.1 is stable but not stationary.

Describe briefly how the shape of the population pyramid would differ from that for the stationary population (see Figure 23.2) if the population is (a) growing, (b) declining. Draw diagrams of population pyramids to illustrate your answer.

The shape of the p.d.f. of the age distribution was discussed in Example 22.1.

Two examples of age distributions are discussed qualitatively in Example 23.2.

Example 23.2   Population pyramids for two populations

The data used in this example are taken from the published results of the 1970 census of the former USSR. In 1970, the USSR comprised fifteen union republics. The age distributions of the Uzbek republic and the Latvian republic are illustrated in Figure 23.5.

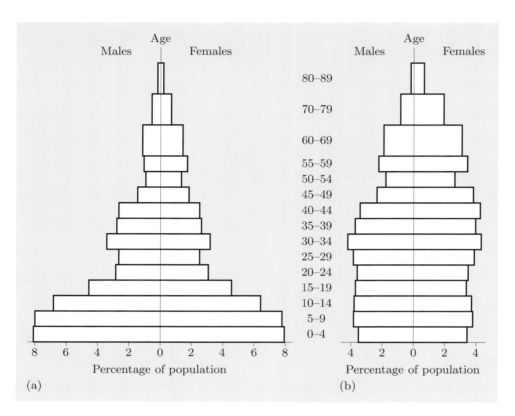

Figure 23.5   Population pyramids: (a) the Uzbek republic in 1970; (b) the Latvian republic in 1970

In the published census data, and in the population pyramids in Figure 23.5, ages are grouped in five-year intervals up to the age of 60 and in ten-year intervals thereafter. The percentage scale along the horizontal axis of each pyramid is for the five-year intervals. Since a population pyramid is a histogram, the area of each bar is proportional to the percentage of the population in that age group. Thus the length of a bar for a ten-year interval is half the percentage in that age group.

The pyramid for the Central Asian Uzbek republic in Figure 23.5(a) has a broad base, showing that the younger age groups are very strongly represented, and hence indicating that the population has been growing rapidly. On the other hand, the pyramid for the European Latvian republic in Figure 23.5(b) has a much narrower base, showing that the younger age groups are somewhat less represented than they would be in a stationary population, and hence at first sight suggesting that the population may even have been contracting slightly.

These comments have to be qualified by the observation that the history of both republics in the preceding decades was such that the conditions assumed in the development of stable population theory have not been approached even approximately. Levels of fertility have changed over time, the populations have been affected significantly by migration, and the effects of the Second World War and its aftermath are clearly visible in the population pyramids. The detailed study of the age-structure of the populations would require considerable knowledge of the history of the USSR, and lies in the domain of the historical demographer rather than the mathematical statistician. Nevertheless, some of the effects of the war are easy to see. For instance, in the population pyramid for the Uzbek republic, the relatively small numbers in the age groups from 20 to 29 years old are a consequence of the decrease in birth rates during the war and the years immediately following. In the population pyramid for the Latvian republic, this feature is masked by the effects of immigration on a large scale. During the 1940s, the Latvian republic suffered enormous population losses due to war deaths, deportations and emigration, balanced to a large extent by post-war immigration. This immigration, mainly of young adults, strongly influenced population growth. War losses reveal themselves in the population pyramids through the under-representation of the male population in the age groups over 45 and the especially small numbers of both sexes in the 50–54 age group. ♦

The population pyramids in Example 23.2 highlight the limitations of stable population theory. However, the mathematical theory does help to give a general understanding of the age-structure of populations and provides a yardstick against which to measure observed population pyramids. In some cases, populations will have a more or less stable age-structure. Where this is not the case, the difference between the observed structure and that predicted by stable population theory may provide the demographer with a focus for further investigation.

Summary of Section 23

In this section, population pyramids have been introduced. A population pyramid is a diagram for representing the age distribution of a population. You have seen how the shape of a population pyramid for a stable population differs from that for a stationary population with the same life table function. Two examples of age distributions of human populations have been discussed qualitatively using population pyramids.

Exercise on Section 23

Exercise 23.1   The age distribution of an animal population

In Exercise 22.1, you drew a sketch of the p.d.f. of the age distribution of a stationary animal population with life table function

$$Q(x) = e^{-x^2/8}, \quad x \geq 0.$$

You also drew sketches showing what the p.d.f. might look like if the population was stable but not stationary.

Draw a sketch showing what a population pyramid for an animal population with this life table function might look like in each of the following cases:

(a) stationary,

(b) stable and growing,

(c) stable and declining.

24 Exercises on Book 4

This section consists of exercises on *Book 4*; some of these exercises cover material from more than one section. The exercises in Subsection 24.1 provide practice in techniques and are of a routine nature. On the other hand, some of the exercises in Subsection 24.2 may involve further development of ideas and models from *Book 4*.

24.1 Routine exercises

Exercise 24.1   Lagrange's method

(a) Given that at time 0, $\Pi(s,t)$ is equal to s^4, solve the partial differential equation

$$t\frac{\partial \Pi}{\partial s} + s\frac{\partial \Pi}{\partial t} = s\Pi.$$

(b) Given that at time 0, $\Pi(s,t)$ is equal to s, solve the partial differential equation

$$\Pi\frac{\partial \Pi}{\partial t} = s.$$

Exercise 24.2   Waiting times in a simple birth process

Suppose that a simple birth process starts with one individual.

(a) Find the mean time to the sixth birth.

(b) Find the median time to the sixth birth.

Exercise 24.3   The simple birth–death process

In a simple birth–death process with birth rate β and death rate ν, with $\beta > \nu$, there are initially ten individuals. Find the probability that the population size drops to 4, but no lower, then increases indefinitely.

Exercise 24.4   The pure death process

The integer-valued random variable $X(t)$ denotes the number of individuals alive at time t in a pure death process $\{X(t); t \geq 0\}$. A partial differential equation for $\Pi(s,t)$, the p.g.f. of $X(t)$, is

$$\frac{\partial \Pi}{\partial t} = \nu(1-s)\frac{\partial \Pi}{\partial s},$$

where ν is the individual death rate.

(a) Use Lagrange's method to obtain the general solution of this partial differential equation.

(b) Suppose that at time 0, there are n individuals alive in the pure death process. Find the particular solution of the partial differential equation in this case, and hence identify the distribution of $X(t)$.

(c) Suppose that a different initial condition holds: $X(0) \sim G_1(0.2)$. Show that in this case the p.g.f. of the number of individuals alive at time t is given by

$$\Pi(s,t) = \frac{1 - e^{-\nu t} + se^{-\nu t}}{1 + 4e^{-\nu t} - 4se^{-\nu t}}.$$

(d) Hence show that for the case in part (c), the c.d.f. of W, the waiting time to the last death, is given by

$$P(W \leq t) = \frac{1 - e^{-\nu t}}{1 + 4e^{-\nu t}}, \quad t > 0.$$

Use this result to find the median waiting time to the last death in terms of the parameter ν.

Exercise 24.5   *The immigration–birth–death process*

The integer-valued random variable $X(t)$ denotes the number of individuals alive at time t in an immigration–birth–death process $\{X(t); t \geq 0\}$. A partial differential equation for $\Pi(s, t)$, the probability generating function of $X(t)$, is

$$(1 - s)(\nu - \beta s)\frac{\partial \Pi}{\partial s} - \frac{\partial \Pi}{\partial t} = \lambda(1 - s)\Pi.$$

(a) Use Lagrange's method to show that when $\beta \neq \nu$, the general solution may be written as

$$\Pi(s, t) = (\nu - \beta s)^{-\lambda/\beta} \, \psi \left(\frac{\nu - \beta s}{1 - s} \, e^{(\nu - \beta)t} \right).$$

(b) Find the particular solution when there is no one in the population at time 0.

(c) Identify the distribution of $X(t)$, and hence find $E[X(t)]$.

(d) Decide whether or not a limiting distribution exists

    (i) when $\beta < \nu$,   (ii) when $\beta > \nu$.

Exercise 24.6   *An immigration–death process*

In an immigration–death process, the immigration and death rates are given by $\lambda = 1$ and $\nu = 0.5$.

(a) If the population starts with 0 individuals at time $t = 0$, calculate the probability that it will contain more than three individuals at time $t = 3$.

You will need a result obtained in Activity 7.1.

(b) In the long run, for what proportion of the time will the population contain more than three individuals?

Exercise 24.7   *A simple queue*

Customers join a queue according to a Poisson process at the rate of 4 per hour, and are served in order of arrival by a single server whose service time is exponentially distributed with mean ten minutes.

(a) Calculate the traffic intensity of this queue.

Assume that the system has been in operation for a long time.

(b) Calculate the probability that at any time, one customer is being served and one is waiting to be served.

(c) Calculate the probability that more than one customer is waiting to be served.

(d) Calculate the probability that a customer has to wait more than half an hour before his or her service is completed.

(e) Calculate the expected number of customers to be served during a busy period, and the expected duration of a busy period.

Exercise 24.8   *A queue with three servers*

Three cashiers are on duty at a post office. Customers may be assumed to arrive independently and at random, at the rate of 72 per hour. If a cashier is free, then an arriving customer receives immediate attention; otherwise, a central queue is formed. The service time of each cashier may be assumed to be exponentially distributed with mean two minutes.

(a) Write down the specification of this queue, and calculate the traffic intensity ρ.

Assume that the queue is in equilibrium.

(b) Show that the probability that at any particular time all three cashiers will be free is $\frac{5}{89}$.

(c) Calculate the proportion of the time that at least two cashiers are busy.

(d) When Tom enters the post office, all the cashiers are busy, but no one is waiting to be served. Calculate the probability that he will have to wait for less than two minutes for a cashier to be free.

Exercise 24.9   *Queueing for advice*

Customers arrive independently and at random at an advice bureau where there is one adviser on duty. If the adviser is busy, then the customers form an orderly queue. Customers arrive at the rate of one every 20 minutes.

Suppose that a consultation is equally likely to take any time between five minutes and half an hour.

(a) Calculate the traffic intensity of this queue.

(b) Calculate the mean queue length once the queue has attained equilibrium.

The adviser is eventually replaced by a colleague who spends exactly fifteen minutes with each customer.

(c) Calculate the traffic intensity of this queue.

(d) Calculate the mean equilibrium queue size.

Exercise 24.10   *A simple epidemic*

In a household of total size 6, three individuals have an infectious disease. The spread of the disease through the household is modelled as a stochastic simple epidemic with contact rate $\beta = 1.2$ per day.

Find the mean and standard deviation of the time until everyone in the household has the disease.

Exercise 24.11   *The effect of using a barrier cream*

For the community of Exercise 15.1, suppose that each individual comes into contact with other individuals at the rate of 0.3 per day and that the probability of transmission of the infection from an infected person to a susceptible at each meeting is reduced from 1 to 0.2 by the use of a barrier cream.

Explain whether this intervention will be effective at preventing a major outbreak of the infection.

Exercise 24.12   A general epidemic

A general epidemic model is used to describe the spread of an infectious disease through a closed community of 36 people. Initially, there are three infected individuals, and the others are all susceptible. The contact rate β is 7 per day, and the removal rate γ is 3 per day.

(a) Calculate the value of the epidemic parameter ρ.

(b) Suppose that a deterministic model is used.

    (i)   Calculate the maximum number of people that are simultaneously infectious.

    (ii) Calculate the number of people who survive the epidemic without being infected.

(c) Suppose that a stochastic model is used.

    (i)   Calculate the probability that exactly one of the initial susceptibles will be infected before the epidemic ends.

    (ii) Calculate an approximate value for the probability that there will be a major outbreak of the disease.

Exercise 24.13   A stationary population

The age-specific death rate for the members of a stationary population is given by

$$h(x) = \frac{1}{80 - x}, \quad 0 \le x < 80,$$

where x is measured in years.

(a) Obtain the life table function $Q(x)$ for members of the population.

(b) Calculate the mean age at which members die.

(c) Calculate the mean age of members of the population.

(d) At any time, what proportion of members of the population are over 60 years old?

(e) What proportion of individuals live for more than 60 years?

24.2 Further exercises

Exercise 24.14   Arrivals

For a Poisson process of arrivals with rate λ, $X(t)$ denotes the number of arrivals up to time t.

(a) What is the distribution of $X(t)$?

(b) For $x = 0, 1, \ldots, n$, write down the probability

$$P(X(s + t) = n \,|\, X(t) = x).$$

(c) Hence determine the probability $P(X(t) = x \,|\, X(s + t) = n)$. Identify the probability distribution that this specifies.

(d) Given that exactly one arrival is known to have occurred in some specified time interval, what does your answer to part (c) tell you about the timing of the arrival?

Exercise 24.15   *The birth–catastrophe process*

The birth–catastrophe process $\{Y(t); t \geq 0\}$ is an integer-valued random process defined as follows. At time $t = 0$, the size of the population is 1: $Y(0) = 1$. The population grows as a result of births, as in a simple birth process with rate β. In addition, 'catastrophes' occur according to a Poisson process with rate γ. In a catastrophe, all members of the population are killed, and once there has been a catastrophe, the population size stays at 0 forever after.

(a) Write down a condition for the population not to be wiped out by time t. Hence write down the probability that the population size is non-zero at time t.

(b) Given that there has not been a catastrophe by time t, state the distribution of $Y(t)$. Hence write down the conditional probability
$$P(Y(t) = y \mid Y(t) > 0), \quad y = 1, 2, \ldots.$$

(c) Use your answers to parts (a) and (b) to write down the unconditional probability distribution of the population size $Y(t)$ at time t. Hence find $\Pi(s, t)$, the probability generating function of $Y(t)$.

(d) Identify the distribution of $Y(t)$ from its p.g.f., and hence calculate the expected population size at time t.

Exercise 24.16   *Arrivals at a simple queue*

Suppose that the arrival rate for a simple queue is λ, and that the service rate is ε. Let Y be a random variable representing the number of customers that arrive while a single customer is being served.

(a) Suppose that the service time of a particular customer is (the fixed time) t. Find the probability that y customers arrive while this customer is being served.

(b) Find the probability that y customers arrive while a single customer is being served. Hence identify the distribution of Y, and find its mean.

Exercise 24.17   *Parking spaces*

In a small village, the car park is just a lay-by, with spaces for four cars. Shoppers wishing to park their cars arrive at the lay-by independently and at random at the rate of one every ten minutes. If a space is available when a shopper arrives, it is taken; if there is no space, the shopper drives away. The durations of visits to the shops are independent exponential variates with mean half an hour.

(a) Write down expressions for β_x and ν_x for this process. State the ranges of values of x for which the expressions hold.

(b) Show that the equilibrium distribution of X, the number of cars parked in the lay-by, is given by
$$P(X = x) = \frac{8}{131} \times \frac{3^x}{x!}, \quad x = 0, 1, 2, 3, 4.$$

(c) What proportion of the time does an arriving driver, intending to shop, find that there is no space available in the lay-by?

(d) The council plans to extend the lay-by so that it can hold six cars. If it did so, and assuming that the arrival rate and shopping pattern remained unchanged, what proportion of the time would the lay-by be full?

(e) How many spaces would the lay-by need to have in order to reduce the probability that a shopper would be unable to park to less than 0.01?

Exercise 24.18   The duration of a simple epidemic

Suppose that the spread of an infectious disease through a community of size $n+1$ is modelled as a stochastic simple epidemic with contact rate β, and that $y_0 = 1$.

(a) Show that the expected duration of the epidemic is given by

$$E(W) = \frac{2n}{(n+1)\beta} \sum_{j=1}^{n} \frac{1}{j}.$$

You will need to use the identity
$$\frac{1}{j(n+1-j)}$$
$$= \frac{1}{n+1}\left(\frac{1}{j} + \frac{1}{n+1-j}\right).$$

Use this result to calculate the expected duration when $\beta = 1$ in each of the following cases:

(i) $n = 5$,   (ii) $n = 10$,   (iii) $n = 20$.

(b) Approximate values for the expected duration can be found using the result

$$1 + \frac{1}{2} + \frac{1}{3} + \cdots + \frac{1}{n} \simeq \log(n+1) - \frac{1}{2(n+1)} + 0.5772.$$

Use this result and the result from part (a) to obtain approximate values for $E(W)$ in each of the following cases when $\beta = 1$:

(i) $n = 5$,   (ii) $n = 10$,   (iii) $n = 20$,   (iv) $n = 200$,   (v) $n = 2000$.

Exercise 24.19   A variation on the general epidemic model

In Subsection 15.3, a variation on the general epidemic model is described in which the rate at which infectives meet susceptibles is given by

$$\beta_y = \frac{\beta xy}{x + y - 1}.$$

The deterministic analogue is the solution of the simultaneous differential equations

$$\frac{dx}{dt} = -\frac{\beta xy}{x + y - 1},$$
$$\frac{dy}{dt} = \frac{\beta xy}{x + y - 1} - \gamma y.$$

Assuming that there are x_0 susceptibles and y_0 infectives at time 0, show that the solution satisfies the equation

$$\frac{x + y - 1}{x^{\gamma/\beta}} = \frac{x_0 + y_0 - 1}{x_0^{\gamma/\beta}}.$$

Exercise 24.20   Stationary populations

Suppose that the p.d.f. of the age distribution of a stationary population is $g(x)$ for $x \geq 0$.

(a) (i)   Write down the mean lifetime for members of the population in terms of the function $g(x)$.

(ii)   Write down an equation satisfied by the median lifetime of members of the population that involves the function $g(x)$.

(b) In a particular population, the p.d.f. of the stationary age distribution is

$$g(x) = \frac{1}{1250}(x + 25)e^{-0.04x}, \quad x \geq 0.$$

(i)   Use the result of part (a)(i) to find the mean lifetime of members of this population.

(ii)   Find the median lifetime.

(iii)   What proportion of the population survive beyond their 60th birthday?

(iv)   What proportion of the population at any one time is aged over 60?

Summary of Book 4

Part I

A random process in continuous time is a Markov process if, given any information about the past behaviour of the process, the probability of any future behaviour depends only on the most recent information. A birth and death process is a Markov process in which the only possible changes in any small time interval are an increase of 1 and a decrease of 1. A Markov process is homogeneous if the transition probabilities do not change over time. Examples of birth and death processes include the Poisson process, the simple birth process, the immigration–birth process, the pure death process, the simple birth–death process, the immigration–death process and the immigration–birth–death process. These are all homogeneous random processes. For each of these processes, the partial differential equation for the p.g.f. of the population size at time t is an example of Lagrange's equation, and can be solved using Lagrange's method.

If the birth rate of a simple birth–death process is less than or equal to the death rate, then extinction is certain; otherwise, extinction is possible, but there is a non-zero probability that the size of the population will eventually increase without bound. For the immigration–death process, permanent extinction does not occur, and the process has an equilibrium distribution.

The deterministic analogue of a random process ignores random fluctuations, and demonstrates its 'average' behaviour with passing time.

Part II

A queueing model is specified by its arrival mechanism, the service time distribution and the number of servers.

In the $M/M/n$ queue, arrivals occur independently and at random, the service time has an exponential distribution, and there are n servers; on arrival, customers join a central queue. The traffic intensity of the queue is the ratio of the arrival rate to the total service rate when all the servers are busy.

In the $M/G/1$ queueing model, arrivals occur independently and at random, the service time can have any distribution, and there is one server. The traffic intensity of the queue is the product of the arrival rate and the mean service time.

For both the $M/M/n$ and the $M/G/1$ queueing models, the queue attains equilibrium if the traffic intensity is less than 1. The mean equilibrium queue size of an $M/G/1$ queue can be found using Pollaczek's formula. The $M/M/1$ queue, which is known as the simple queue, is a special case of the $M/M/n$ queue and of the $M/G/1$ queue.

Part III

The simple epidemic and the general epidemic, which are models for the spread of an infectious disease through a closed community, are Markov processes in continuous time. In both models, when a susceptible meets an infective, he immediately becomes infectious.

In the simple epidemic model, having caught the infection, an infective remains infectious and in the community, so eventually everyone catches the infection.

In the general epidemic model, an infective recovers after some random time, so the epidemic may end before all the susceptibles have caught the infection. The likely number of survivors depends on the relative values of x_0, the initial number of susceptibles, and the epidemic parameter ρ. The parameter ρ is also a threshold value for the initial number of susceptibles in the deterministic general epidemic model: a major outbreak will occur only if $x_0 > \rho$. In the stochastic model, if $x_0 > \rho$ and a trace of infection is introduced, then either a major outbreak or a minor outbreak will occur with high probability, and an outbreak of intermediate size is unlikely.

Part IV

The expectation of life at birth for the members of a population is the mean length of time that an individual born into the population will live. The life table function $Q(x)$ is a function that gives, for each age x, the probability that an individual will live beyond age x. A population for which $Q(x)$ does not change over time is stable if the age distribution remains constant over time; it is stationary if, in addition, the size of the population remains constant over time.

The size of a stable population either grows or declines exponentially with time. The rate of growth θ is called the intrinsic growth rate of the population. If $\theta = 0$, then the population is stationary. If $\theta > 0$, then the population is growing and a greater proportion of the population is in the younger age groups than there would be in a stationary population with the same life table function. If $\theta < 0$, then the population is declining and a smaller proportion of the population is in the younger age groups than there would be in a stationary population with the same life table function.

A population pyramid is a diagram for representing the age distribution of the males and females in a population.

Learning outcomes

You have been working to develop the following skills.

Part I

◇   Use the probability statement characterising any given Markov process to write down the distribution of the waiting time to the next event.

◇   Find the mean and variance of the waiting time for the population to reach a particular size for various random processes, including the Poisson process, the simple birth process, the pure death process and the immigration–birth process.

◇   Derive the distribution of the population size at time t in a pure death process.

◇   Use Lagrange's method to obtain the general solution of a partial differential equation that can be written in Lagrange form, and obtain the particular solution for any given initial condition.

◇   Apply Lagrange's method to obtain $\Pi(s, t)$, the p.g.f. of the population size at time t, for various birth and death processes, including the simple birth process, the pure death process, the immigration–birth process, the simple birth–death process and the immigration–death process.

◇   Identify the probability distribution $\{p_x(t)\}$ corresponding to a particular probability generating function $\Pi(s, t)$.

◇   Use the p.g.f. for a birth and death process to derive properties of the process such as the probability of extinction.

◇   Use the distribution of the population size at time t in a simple birth process to derive the c.d.f. of the waiting time to the nth birth.

◇   Use the random walk embedded in a simple birth–death process to calculate probabilities associated with the process.

◇   Obtain the equilibrium distribution of the immigration–death process.

◇   Use the probability statements characterising a birth and death process to write down the differential equation satisfied by the deterministic analogue of the random process, and solve this differential equation in particular cases.

Part II

◇   Use standard notation to characterise a queueing model.

◇   Calculate the traffic intensity for queues of types $M/M/1$, $M/M/n$ and $M/G/1$.

◇   Use the traffic intensity of a queue to determine whether the queue will attain equilibrium.

◇   Solve problems involving the queue size, the queueing time, idle periods and busy periods for a simple queue in equilibrium.

◇   When it exists, find the equilibrium queue size distribution for an $M/M/n$ queue, and use it to solve problems.

◇   Use Pollaczek's formula to calculate the mean equilibrium queue size of an $M/G/1$ queue.

Part III

◇   Describe the assumptions of the simple epidemic model and the general epidemic model for the spread of an infectious disease through a community.

◇   Find the mean and variance of the times between infections in a stochastic simple epidemic and of the duration of the epidemic.

◇   Write down the differential–difference equations for the probabilities $\{p_y(t)\}$ in the stochastic simple epidemic model, and solve these equations when the size of the community is very small.

◇   Use the deterministic version of the general epidemic model to calculate the maximum number of people who are simultaneously infectious and the number of survivors of an epidemic, and sketch the trajectory of the epidemic.

◇   Calculate probabilities for the number of susceptibles remaining uninfected when an epidemic ends, using the stochastic general epidemic model.

◇   Describe the similarities and differences between the threshold phenomena for the deterministic general epidemic model and the stochastic general epidemic model.

◇   When $x_0 > \rho$, calculate approximate values for the probability that there will be a major outbreak and the probability that there will be a minor outbreak in a stochastic general epidemic.

Part IV

◇   Find the life table function for the members of a population from the age-specific death rate, and vice versa.

◇   Interpret a sketch of the age-specific death rate.

◇   Calculate quantities for a population with a given life table function, including the expectation of life at birth and the median lifetime.

◇   Solve problems involving the age distribution of a stationary population.

◇   Describe the ways in which the size of a stable population may change over time.

◇   Explain how the age distribution of a stable population differs from the age distribution of a stationary population with the same life table function, and illustrate the differences by drawing sketches of the p.d.f. of the age distribution and of population pyramids.

Solutions to Activities

Solution 1.1

When there are x individuals alive, T_x, the waiting time to the next birth, has an exponential distribution with parameter βx: $T_x \sim M(\beta x)$. Since $\beta = 2$,
$$E(T_x) = \frac{1}{2x}, \quad V(T_x) = \frac{1}{4x^2}.$$
The random variable $W_8 = T_1 + T_2 + \cdots + T_8$ has mean
$$\begin{aligned} E(W_8) &= E(T_1) + E(T_2) + \cdots + E(T_8) \\ &= \tfrac{1}{2} + \tfrac{1}{4} + \cdots + \tfrac{1}{16} \\ &\simeq 1.359 \end{aligned}$$
and variance
$$\begin{aligned} V(W_8) &= V(T_1) + V(T_2) + \cdots + V(T_8) \\ &= \tfrac{1}{4} + \tfrac{1}{16} + \cdots + \tfrac{1}{256} \\ &\simeq 0.382. \end{aligned}$$

Solution 1.2

(a) If there are three individuals alive at the start, then $T_1 \sim M(3\beta)$, and hence
$$E(T_1) = \frac{1}{3\beta}, \quad V(T_1) = \frac{1}{9\beta^2}.$$

(b) If W is the time until there are seven individuals, that is, until the fourth birth, then
$$W = T_1 + T_2 + T_3 + T_4,$$
where $T_2 \sim M(4\beta)$, $T_3 \sim M(5\beta)$ and $T_4 \sim M(6\beta)$. Therefore
$$E(W) = \frac{1}{3\beta} + \frac{1}{4\beta} + \frac{1}{5\beta} + \frac{1}{6\beta} = \frac{0.95}{\beta},$$
$$V(W) = \frac{1}{9\beta^2} + \frac{1}{16\beta^2} + \frac{1}{25\beta^2} + \frac{1}{36\beta^2} \simeq \frac{0.2414}{\beta^2},$$
and hence the standard deviation of W is
$$\sqrt{V(W)} \simeq \frac{0.491}{\beta}.$$

Solution 1.3

(a) Since there are n individuals alive at time 0,
$$T_1 \sim M(n\nu).$$
After the first death, there are $n - 1$ individuals alive, so
$$T_2 \sim M((n-1)\nu).$$

(b) There is only one individual alive after the penultimate death, so if T_n is the time from the second to last death until the last death, then
$$T_n \sim M(\nu).$$

(c) Since $W = T_1 + T_2 + \cdots + T_n$ and $T_1, T_2, \ldots, T_n$ are independent,
$$\begin{aligned} E(W) &= E(T_1) + E(T_2) + \cdots + E(T_n) \\ &= \frac{1}{n\nu} + \frac{1}{(n-1)\nu} + \cdots + \frac{1}{\nu} \\ &= \frac{1}{\nu}\left(\frac{1}{n} + \frac{1}{n-1} + \cdots + \frac{1}{2} + 1 \right), \\ V(W) &= V(T_1) + V(T_2) + \cdots + V(T_n) \\ &= \frac{1}{\nu^2}\left(\frac{1}{n^2} + \frac{1}{(n-1)^2} + \cdots + \frac{1}{2^2} + 1 \right). \end{aligned}$$

Solution 1.4

(a) The waiting time required is W_3, the time until the third death. Since $X(0) = 10$, $T_1 \sim M(10\nu)$, $T_2 \sim M(9\nu)$ and $T_3 \sim M(8\nu)$. Therefore
$$E(W_3) = \frac{1}{10\nu} + \frac{1}{9\nu} + \frac{1}{8\nu} \simeq \frac{0.336}{\nu},$$
$$V(W_3) = \frac{1}{100\nu^2} + \frac{1}{81\nu^2} + \frac{1}{64\nu^2} \simeq \frac{0.037\,97}{\nu^2},$$
and hence the standard deviation of W_3 is
$$\sqrt{V(W_3)} \simeq \frac{0.195}{\nu}.$$

(b) The expected waiting time until the population dies out is
$$\begin{aligned} E(W) &= \frac{1}{10\nu} + \frac{1}{9\nu} + \cdots + \frac{1}{\nu} \\ &= \frac{1}{\nu}\left(\frac{1}{10} + \frac{1}{9} + \cdots + 1 \right) \\ &\simeq \frac{2.93}{\nu}. \end{aligned}$$

Solution 1.5

(a) If T is the lifetime of an individual, then $T \sim M(\nu)$, so
$$P(T > t) = e^{-\nu t}.$$

(b) The probability that each individual is alive at time t is $e^{-\nu t}$, and there are n individuals with independent lifetimes. Therefore $X(t)$, the number out of n that are alive at time t, has a binomial distribution with parameters n and $e^{-\nu t}$:
$$X(t) \sim B(n, e^{-\nu t}).$$

(c) The probability required is
$$\begin{aligned} P(X(t) = 2) &= \binom{n}{2} (e^{-\nu t})^2 (1 - e^{-\nu t})^{n-2} \\ &= \tfrac{1}{2}n(n-1)\, e^{-2\nu t}(1 - e^{-\nu t})^{n-2}. \end{aligned}$$

(d) The probability required is
$$P(X(t) = 0) = (1 - e^{-\nu t})^n.$$

Solution 1.6

(a) In a pure death process, if there are x individuals in the population at time t, then the probability of a death in the interval $[t, t + \delta t]$ is $\nu x \, \delta t + o(\delta t)$. This does not depend on the history of the process before time t; the most recent death might have occurred at any time before t. Hence this is a Markov process.

(b) In this process, the probability that an event occurs in $[t, t + \delta t]$ depends on t, but is independent of the number of events that have occurred up to time t and of when these events, if any, occurred. So this is a Markov process.

(c) For this point process, the probability that an event occurs in $[t, t + \delta t]$ depends on how long before t the previous event occurred. If it occurred less than one unit of time before t, then the probability is 0. On the other hand, if the previous event occurred at time $t - 2.9$, then the next event is certain to occur in the next 0.1 unit. In this case, the probability that the next event will occur in the interval $[t, t + \delta t]$ is $10 \, \delta t$. Hence the probability of occurrence depends on the history of the process before t, and consequently this is not a Markov process.

Solution 1.7

(a) When $X(t) = x$, the waiting time T until the next event (arrival or birth) has an exponential distribution with parameter $\lambda + \beta x$; that is, $T \sim M(\lambda + \beta x)$. Therefore

$$E(T) = \frac{1}{\lambda + \beta x}, \quad V(T) = \frac{1}{(\lambda + \beta x)^2}.$$

(b) $T_1 \sim M(\lambda)$, $T_2 \sim M(\lambda + \beta)$, $T_3 \sim M(\lambda + 2\beta)$, $T_n \sim M(\lambda + (n-1)\beta)$.

(c) Since $W_n = T_1 + \cdots + T_n$, and $T_1, \ldots, T_n$ are independent,

$$E(W_n) = E(T_1) + \cdots + E(T_n)$$
$$= \frac{1}{\lambda} + \frac{1}{\lambda + \beta} + \frac{1}{\lambda + 2\beta} + \cdots + \frac{1}{\lambda + (n-1)\beta},$$
$$V(W_n) = \frac{1}{\lambda^2} + \frac{1}{(\lambda + \beta)^2} + \frac{1}{(\lambda + 2\beta)^2} + \cdots$$
$$+ \frac{1}{(\lambda + (n-1)\beta)^2}.$$

Solution 2.1

The population changes size only when a death occurs; otherwise its size stays the same. For there to be x survivors alive at time $t + \delta t$, either there were $x + 1$ alive at time t, one of whom died during the interval $[t, t + \delta t]$, or there were x alive at time t, all of whom survived the interval $[t, t + \delta t]$. Therefore for $x = 0, 1, \ldots$,

$$p_x(t + \delta t) = p_{x+1}(t) \left(\nu(x+1) \, \delta t + o(\delta t) \right)$$
$$+ p_x(t) \left(1 - \nu x \, \delta t + o(\delta t) \right) + o(\delta t).$$

Rearranging this equation and letting $\delta t \to 0$ leads to

$$\frac{d}{dt} p_x(t) = -\nu x \, p_x(t) + \nu(x+1) \, p_{x+1}(t), \quad x = 0, 1, \ldots.$$

Solution 2.2

(a) Differentiating $f(x, y)$ with respect to x, regarding y as a constant, gives the first partial derivative with respect to x:

$$\frac{\partial f}{\partial x} = 2y^2 + 6xy.$$

Differentiating $f(x, y)$ with respect to y, regarding x as a constant, gives the first partial derivative with respect to y:

$$\frac{\partial f}{\partial y} = 4xy + 3x^2.$$

(b) Differentiating $g(x, y)$ partially with respect to x gives

$$\frac{\partial g}{\partial x} = e^y + 2xy,$$

and differentiating partially with respect to y gives

$$\frac{\partial g}{\partial y} = xe^y + x^2.$$

(c) Differentiating $h(x, y)$ partially with respect to x (using the composite rule) gives

$$\frac{\partial h}{\partial x} = \frac{1}{x^2 + y} \times 2x = \frac{2x}{x^2 + y}.$$

Differentiating partially with respect to y gives

$$\frac{\partial h}{\partial y} = \frac{1}{x^2 + y}.$$

Solution 2.3

The first partial derivatives are given in the solution to Activity 2.2.

(a) Differentiating $f(x, y)$ partially with respect to x for a second time gives the second partial derivative with respect to x:

$$\frac{\partial^2 f}{\partial x^2} = 6y.$$

Similarly, the second partial derivative with respect to y is

$$\frac{\partial^2 f}{\partial y^2} = 4x.$$

The mixed derivative is

$$\frac{\partial^2 f}{\partial x \, \partial y} = \frac{\partial}{\partial x} \left(\frac{\partial f}{\partial y} \right) = \frac{\partial}{\partial x} (4xy + 3x^2)$$
$$= 4y + 6x.$$

As a check, the mixed derivative can be found by differentiating first with respect to x then with respect to y:

$$\frac{\partial^2 f}{\partial y \, \partial x} = \frac{\partial}{\partial y} \left(\frac{\partial f}{\partial x} \right) = \frac{\partial}{\partial y} (2y^2 + 6xy)$$
$$= 4y + 6x.$$

(b) The second partial derivatives of g are
$$\frac{\partial^2 g}{\partial x^2} = 2y, \quad \frac{\partial^2 g}{\partial y^2} = xe^y.$$

The mixed derivative is
$$\frac{\partial^2 g}{\partial x\,\partial y} = \frac{\partial}{\partial x}\left(\frac{\partial g}{\partial y}\right) = \frac{\partial}{\partial x}(xe^y + x^2)$$
$$= e^y + 2x.$$

Equivalently,
$$\frac{\partial^2 g}{\partial y\,\partial x} = \frac{\partial}{\partial y}\left(\frac{\partial g}{\partial x}\right) = \frac{\partial}{\partial y}(e^y + 2xy)$$
$$= e^y + 2x.$$

(c) The second partial derivatives of h are
$$\frac{\partial^2 h}{\partial x^2} = \frac{\partial}{\partial x}\left(\frac{\partial h}{\partial x}\right) = \frac{\partial}{\partial x}\left(\frac{2x}{x^2+y}\right)$$
$$= \frac{2y - 2x^2}{(x^2+y)^2},$$
$$\frac{\partial^2 h}{\partial y^2} = \frac{\partial}{\partial y}\left(\frac{\partial h}{\partial y}\right) = \frac{\partial}{\partial y}\left(\frac{1}{x^2+y}\right)$$
$$= \frac{-1}{(x^2+y)^2}.$$

The mixed derivative is
$$\frac{\partial^2 h}{\partial x\,\partial y} = \frac{\partial}{\partial x}\left(\frac{\partial h}{\partial y}\right) = \frac{\partial}{\partial x}\left(\frac{1}{x^2+y}\right)$$
$$= \frac{-2x}{(x^2+y)^2}.$$

Equivalently,
$$\frac{\partial^2 h}{\partial y\,\partial x} = \frac{\partial}{\partial y}\left(\frac{\partial h}{\partial x}\right) = \frac{\partial}{\partial y}\left(\frac{2x}{x^2+y}\right)$$
$$= \frac{-2x}{(x^2+y)^2}.$$

Solution 2.4

The differential–difference equations are given in the solution to Activity 2.1. Multiplying the equations by s^x and summing over $x = 0, 1, \ldots$ gives
$$\frac{\partial \Pi}{\partial t} = -\nu \sum_{x=0}^{\infty} x\, p_x(t)\, s^x + \nu \sum_{x=0}^{\infty} (x+1)\, p_{x+1}(t)\, s^x.$$

Making the change of variable $j = x + 1$ in the second term on the right-hand side gives
$$\frac{\partial \Pi}{\partial t} = -\nu \sum_{x=0}^{\infty} x\, p_x(t)\, s^x + \nu \sum_{j=1}^{\infty} j\, p_j(t)\, s^{j-1}$$
$$= -\nu s \frac{\partial \Pi}{\partial s} + \nu \frac{\partial \Pi}{\partial s}.$$

Therefore
$$\frac{\partial \Pi}{\partial t} = \nu(1-s) \frac{\partial \Pi}{\partial s}.$$

Solution 3.1

In Lagrange form, (3.2) is written as follows:
$$s\frac{\partial \Pi}{\partial s} - \frac{\partial \Pi}{\partial t} = 2s^2\Pi.$$
Therefore
$$f = s, \quad g = -1, \quad h = 2s^2\Pi.$$

Solution 3.2

The auxiliary equations for (3.2) are
$$\frac{ds}{s} = \frac{dt}{-1} = \frac{d\Pi}{2s^2\Pi}.$$

Solution 3.3

The auxiliary equations are given in the solution to Activity 3.2. The equation containing ds and dt gives
$$\int \frac{1}{s}\, ds = \int -1\, dt,$$
so
$$\log s = -t + \text{constant},$$
or
$$\log s + t = \text{constant}.$$
This may be rewritten as
$$c_1 = se^t.$$
The equation containing ds and $d\Pi$ is
$$\frac{ds}{s} = \frac{d\Pi}{2s^2\Pi}.$$
It follows that
$$\int 2s\, ds = \int \frac{1}{\Pi}\, d\Pi,$$
or
$$s^2 = \log \Pi + \text{constant}.$$
This can be rewritten as
$$c_2 = \Pi \exp(-s^2).$$

Solution 3.4

Two solutions of the auxiliary equations are given in the solution to Activity 3.3. These are
$$c_1 = se^t, \quad c_2 = \Pi \exp(-s^2).$$
Since c_2 includes Π, the general solution is given by $c_2 = \psi(c_1)$:
$$\Pi \exp(-s^2) = \psi(se^t).$$
That is,
$$\Pi(s,t) = \exp(s^2)\, \psi(se^t).$$

Solution 3.5

Step 1: In Lagrange form, the partial differential equation is
$$t \frac{\partial \Pi}{\partial s} - s \frac{\partial \Pi}{\partial t} = 0,$$
so
$$f = t, \quad g = -s, \quad h = 0.$$
Step 2: The auxiliary equations are
$$\frac{ds}{t} = \frac{dt}{-s} = \frac{d\Pi}{0}.$$
Step 3: Since the third expression is of the form $d\Pi/0$, it can be deduced that one solution is
$$c_1 = \Pi.$$
From the first and second expressions,
$$-s\,ds = t\,dt,$$
so
$$\int s\,ds + \int t\,dt = 0.$$
Integrating gives
$$\tfrac{1}{2}s^2 + \tfrac{1}{2}t^2 = \text{constant},$$
which can be written as
$$c_2 = s^2 + t^2.$$
Step 4: Since c_1 includes Π, the general solution is given by $c_1 = \psi(c_2)$:
$$\Pi(s, t) = \psi(s^2 + t^2).$$

Solution 3.6

Step 1: The equation is in Lagrange form, so
$$f = 0, \quad g = s + t, \quad h = s + \Pi.$$
Step 2: The auxiliary equations are
$$\frac{ds}{0} = \frac{dt}{s + t} = \frac{d\Pi}{s + \Pi}.$$
Step 3: Since the first expression is of the form $ds/0$, it can be deduced that one solution is
$$c_1 = s.$$
From the second and third expressions,
$$\int \frac{1}{s + t}\,dt = \int \frac{1}{s + \Pi}\,d\Pi.$$
From the first solution, s may be regarded as a constant. Integrating both sides, treating s as a constant, gives
$$\log(s + t) = \log(s + \Pi) + \text{constant}.$$
This can be rewritten as
$$\text{constant} = \log(s + \Pi) - \log(s + t),$$
or, taking exponentials,
$$c_2 = \frac{s + \Pi}{s + t}.$$
Step 4: Since c_2 includes Π, the general solution is given by $c_2 = \psi(c_1)$:
$$\frac{s + \Pi}{s + t} = \psi(s).$$
That is,
$$\Pi(s, t) = (s + t)\,\psi(s) - s.$$

Solution 3.7

From the solution to Activity 3.4, the general solution of (3.2) is
$$\Pi(s, t) = \exp(s^2)\,\psi(se^t).$$
The initial condition is $\Pi(s, 0) = 2s \exp(s^2)$. Setting $t = 0$ in the general solution for $\Pi(s, t)$ gives
$$\Pi(s, 0) = \exp(s^2)\,\psi(s),$$
so
$$2s \exp(s^2) = \exp(s^2)\,\psi(s),$$
giving
$$\psi(s) = 2s.$$
Replacing s by se^t in this formula for $\psi(s)$ gives
$$\psi(se^t) = 2se^t,$$
so
$$\Pi(s, t) = \exp(s^2) \times 2se^t$$
$$= 2s \exp(s^2 + t).$$

Solution 3.8

From the solution to Activity 3.5, the general solution of (3.8) is
$$\Pi(s, t) = \psi(s^2 + t^2).$$
The initial condition is $\Pi(s, 0) = 1/s^2$. Setting $t = 0$ in the general solution for $\Pi(s, t)$ gives
$$\Pi(s, 0) = \psi(s^2),$$
so
$$\psi(s^2) = \frac{1}{s^2}.$$
Writing $s^2 = x$ gives
$$\psi(x) = \frac{1}{x}.$$
Replacing x by $s^2 + t^2$ gives $\psi(s^2 + t^2)$, so
$$\Pi(s, t) = \frac{1}{s^2 + t^2}.$$

Solution 3.9

From the solution to Activity 3.6, the general solution of (3.9) is
$$\Pi(s, t) = (s + t)\,\psi(s) - s.$$
(a) Given $\Pi(s, 0) = 1$, setting $t = 0$ in the general solution gives
$$\Pi(s, 0) = s\,\psi(s) - s = 1.$$
Therefore
$$\psi(s) = \frac{1 + s}{s},$$
and hence the particular solution is
$$\Pi(s, t) = \frac{(s + t)(1 + s)}{s} - s$$
$$= 1 + t + \frac{t}{s}.$$

(b) Given $\Pi(s,0) = s^2$, setting $t = 0$ in the general solution gives
$$\Pi(s,0) = s\,\psi(s) - s = s^2.$$
Therefore
$$\psi(s) = s + 1,$$
and hence the particular solution is
$$\begin{aligned}\Pi(s,t) &= (s+t)(s+1) - s \\ &= s^2 + t(s+1).\end{aligned}$$

Solution 3.10

Using the product rule for differentiation,
$$\frac{\partial}{\partial s}(st\Pi) = t\Pi + st\,\frac{\partial \Pi}{\partial s}.$$
So the partial differential equation may be written as
$$t\,\frac{\partial \Pi}{\partial s} = s\,\frac{\partial \Pi}{\partial t} + st\Pi + s^2 t\,\frac{\partial \Pi}{\partial s}$$
or, in Lagrange form,
$$t(1-s^2)\,\frac{\partial \Pi}{\partial s} - s\,\frac{\partial \Pi}{\partial t} = st\Pi.$$
Therefore
$$f = t(1-s^2), \quad g = -s, \quad h = st\Pi.$$
The auxiliary equations are
$$\frac{ds}{t(1-s^2)} = \frac{dt}{-s} = \frac{d\Pi}{st\Pi}.$$
The first and second expressions contain only s and t. Separating the variables gives
$$\int \frac{-s}{1-s^2}\,ds = \int t\,dt,$$
so
$$\tfrac{1}{2}\log(1-s^2) = \tfrac{1}{2}t^2 + \text{constant},$$
or
$$\text{constant} = \log(1-s^2) - t^2.$$
This may be rewritten as
$$c_1 = (1-s^2)\exp(-t^2).$$
Taking the second and third expressions together, and cancelling s, gives
$$\frac{dt}{-1} = \frac{d\Pi}{t\Pi},$$
or
$$\int -t\,dt = \int \frac{1}{\Pi}\,d\Pi.$$
From this, a second solution is
$$-\tfrac{1}{2}t^2 = \log \Pi + \text{constant},$$
or
$$\text{constant} = \log \Pi + \tfrac{1}{2}t^2,$$
which may be rewritten as
$$c_2 = \Pi \exp(t^2/2).$$

Since c_2 includes Π, the general solution of the partial differential equation is given by $c_2 = \psi(c_1)$:
$$\Pi \exp(t^2/2) = \psi((1-s^2)\exp(-t^2)),$$
that is,
$$\Pi = \Pi(s,t) = \exp(-t^2/2)\,\psi((1-s^2)\exp(-t^2)).$$
Setting $t = 0$ gives
$$\Pi(s,0) = \psi(1-s^2).$$
Given $\Pi(s,0) = s$, it follows that
$$\psi(1-s^2) = s.$$
To identify the function ψ, set $1 - s^2$ equal to x. Then $s = \sqrt{1-x}$, and hence
$$\psi(x) = \sqrt{1-x}.$$
The particular solution corresponding to the given initial condition $\Pi(s,0) = s$ is
$$\Pi(s,t) = \exp(-t^2/2)\sqrt{1 - (1-s^2)\exp(-t^2)}.$$

Solution 4.1

The partial differential equation (4.1) for the simple birth process may be written in Lagrange form (Step 1) as
$$\beta s(1-s)\,\frac{\partial \Pi}{\partial s} + \frac{\partial \Pi}{\partial t} = 0,$$
so
$$f = \beta s(1-s), \quad g = 1, \quad h = 0.$$
Therefore the auxiliary equations (Step 2) are
$$\frac{ds}{\beta s(1-s)} = \frac{dt}{1} = \frac{d\Pi}{0}.$$
Since $d\Pi/0$ appears, one solution is
$$c_1 = \Pi.$$
The first and second expressions taken together give
$$\int \frac{1}{s(1-s)}\,ds = \int \beta\,dt.$$
Since
$$\frac{1}{s(1-s)} = \frac{1}{s} + \frac{1}{1-s},$$
integration leads to
$$\log s - \log(1-s) = \beta t + \text{constant},$$
or
$$\text{constant} = \log s - \log(1-s) - \beta t.$$
Taking exponentials gives
$$c_2 = \left(\frac{s}{1-s}\right)e^{-\beta t}.$$
This completes Step 3. The general solution (Step 4) is given by $c_1 = \psi(c_2)$; that is,
$$\Pi(s,t) = \psi\left(\frac{s}{1-s}e^{-\beta t}\right).$$

Solution 4.2

(a) Since $X(0) = 3$, the p.g.f. of $X(0)$ is s^3. Setting $t = 0$ in the general solution (4.2) gives

$$\Pi(s, 0) = \psi\left(\frac{s}{1-s}\right),$$

so

$$\psi\left(\frac{s}{1-s}\right) = s^3.$$

Writing $s/(1-s) = x$ gives $s = x/(1+x)$, and hence

$$\psi(x) = \left(\frac{x}{1+x}\right)^3.$$

Therefore

$$\Pi(s, t) = \psi\left(\frac{s}{1-s}\, e^{-\beta t}\right)$$

$$= \left(\frac{\dfrac{s}{1-s}\, e^{-\beta t}}{1 + \dfrac{s}{1-s}\, e^{-\beta t}}\right)^3$$

$$= \left(\frac{s e^{-\beta t}}{1 - (1 - e^{-\beta t})s}\right)^3.$$

(b) A negative binomial distribution starting at r and with parameters r and p has p.g.f.

$$\Pi(s) = \left(\frac{ps}{1-qs}\right)^r.$$

Therefore $X(t)$ has a negative binomial distribution with range $\{3, 4, \ldots\}$ and parameters $r = 3$ and $p = e^{-\beta t}$. Hence

$$E[X(t)] = \frac{3}{e^{-\beta t}} = 3e^{\beta t}.$$

(c) Setting $r = 3$, $p = e^{-\beta t}$ and $x = 5$ in the formula for the p.m.f. of a negative binomial distribution given in Table 8 in the *Handbook*,

$$P(X(t) = 5) = \binom{4}{2}(1 - e^{-\beta t})^2\,(e^{-\beta t})^3$$

$$= 6e^{-3\beta t}(1 - e^{-\beta t})^2.$$

Solution 4.3

(a) Using (4.4), the c.d.f. of W_4 is

$$P(W_4 \le t) = (1 - e^{-\beta t})^4.$$

(b) The median waiting time to the fourth birth is the time w such that

$$P(W_4 \le w) = 0.5,$$

that is,

$$(1 - e^{-\beta w})^4 = 0.5.$$

Therefore

$$1 - e^{-\beta w} = 0.5^{1/4} \simeq 0.8409,$$

and hence

$$w \simeq \frac{1.84}{\beta}.$$

Solution 4.4

After two births, the population contains five individuals, so $W_2 \le t$ is equivalent to $X(t) \ge 5$. Therefore the c.d.f. of W_2 is

$$P(W_2 \le t) = P(X(t) \ge 5)$$

$$= 1 - P(X(t) = 3) - P(X(t) = 4).$$

From the solution to Activity 4.2, and using Table 8 in the *Handbook*,

$$P(X(t) = x) = \binom{x-1}{2}(1 - e^{-\beta t})^{x-3}(e^{-\beta t})^3.$$

So

$$P(W_2 \le t) = 1 - e^{-3\beta t} - 3e^{-3\beta t}(1 - e^{-\beta t})$$

$$= 1 - 4e^{-3\beta t} + 3e^{-4\beta t}.$$

Solution 4.5

The partial differential equation (4.5) is in Lagrange form, so

$$f = \beta s(1-s), \quad g = 1, \quad h = -\lambda(1-s)\Pi.$$

The auxiliary equations are

$$\frac{ds}{\beta s(1-s)} = \frac{dt}{1} = \frac{d\Pi}{-\lambda(1-s)\Pi}.$$

Taking the first two expressions gives

$$\int \frac{1}{s(1-s)}\, ds = \int \beta\, dt.$$

Since

$$\frac{1}{s(1-s)} = \frac{1}{s} + \frac{1}{1-s},$$

this can be written as

$$\int \left(\frac{1}{s} + \frac{1}{1-s}\right) ds = \int \beta\, dt.$$

Integrating this gives

$$\log s - \log(1-s) = \beta t + \text{constant},$$

or, taking exponentials,

$$\frac{s}{1-s} = e^{\beta t} \times \text{constant}.$$

Therefore one solution is

$$c_1 = \frac{s}{1-s}\, e^{-\beta t}.$$

Taking the first and third expressions, and cancelling the term $(1-s)$, gives

$$\int \frac{\lambda}{\beta s}\, ds = -\int \frac{1}{\Pi}\, d\Pi,$$

so

$$\frac{\lambda}{\beta} \log s = -\log \Pi + \text{constant},$$

or

$$\text{constant} = \frac{\lambda}{\beta} \log s + \log \Pi$$

$$= \log(s^{\lambda/\beta}\Pi).$$

Taking exponentials gives a second solution:

$$c_2 = s^{\lambda/\beta}\Pi.$$

Since c_2 includes Π, the general solution is given by $c_2 = \psi(c_1)$, that is,

$$s^{\lambda/\beta}\Pi = \psi\left(\frac{s}{1-s}e^{-\beta t}\right).$$

Therefore the general solution is

$$\Pi(s,t) = s^{-\lambda/\beta}\,\psi\left(\frac{s}{1-s}e^{-\beta t}\right).$$

Solution 4.6

(a) Since $X(0) = 0$, $\Pi(s,0)$, the p.g.f. of $X(0)$, is $s^0 = 1$. Setting $t = 0$ in the general solution (4.6) gives

$$\Pi(s,0) = s^{-\lambda/\beta}\,\psi\left(\frac{s}{1-s}\right).$$

Therefore

$$s^{-\lambda/\beta}\,\psi\left(\frac{s}{1-s}\right) = 1,$$

and hence

$$\psi\left(\frac{s}{1-s}\right) = s^{\lambda/\beta}.$$

Writing $s/(1-s) = x$ gives $s = x/(1+x)$, and hence

$$\psi(x) = \left(\frac{x}{1+x}\right)^{\lambda/\beta}.$$

Therefore

$$\begin{aligned}
\Pi(s,t) &= s^{-\lambda/\beta}\,\psi\left(\frac{s}{1-s}e^{-\beta t}\right) \\
&= s^{-\lambda/\beta}\left(\frac{\dfrac{s}{1-s}e^{-\beta t}}{1+\dfrac{s}{1-s}e^{-\beta t}}\right)^{\lambda/\beta} \\
&= \left(\frac{e^{-\beta t}}{1-(1-e^{-\beta t})s}\right)^{\lambda/\beta}.
\end{aligned}$$

(b) The p.g.f. $\Pi(s,t)$ has the form $(q/(1-ps))^{\lambda/\beta}$, where $p = 1 - e^{-\beta t}$. So $\Pi(s,t)$ is the p.g.f. of a negative binomial distribution with range $\{0,1,\ldots\}$ and parameters $r = \lambda/\beta$ and $p = 1 - e^{-\beta t}$.

Solution 4.7

(a) Since $X(0) = n$, $\Pi(s,0) = s^n$. Setting $t = 0$ in (4.6) gives

$$\Pi(s,0) = s^{-\lambda/\beta}\,\psi\left(\frac{s}{1-s}\right),$$

so

$$s^{-\lambda/\beta}\,\psi\left(\frac{s}{1-s}\right) = s^n,$$

giving

$$\psi\left(\frac{s}{1-s}\right) = s^{n+\lambda/\beta}.$$

Proceeding as in the solution to part (a) of Activity 4.6 leads to

$$\psi(x) = \left(\frac{x}{1+x}\right)^{n+\lambda/\beta},$$

and hence

$$\Pi(s,t) = s^{-\lambda/\beta}\left(\frac{se^{-\beta t}}{1-(1-e^{-\beta t})s}\right)^{n+\lambda/\beta}.$$

(b) The p.g.f. $\Pi(s,t)$ is the product of two p.g.f.s, $\Pi_1(s,t)$ and $\Pi_2(s,t)$, where

$$\Pi_1(s,t) = \left(\frac{e^{-\beta t}}{1-(1-e^{-\beta t})s}\right)^{\lambda/\beta},$$

$$\Pi_2(s,t) = \left(\frac{se^{-\beta t}}{1-(1-e^{-\beta t})s}\right)^n.$$

(c) The function $\Pi_1(s,t)$ is the p.g.f. of a negative binomial distribution with range $\{0,1,\ldots\}$ and parameters $r = \lambda/\beta$ and $p = 1 - e^{-\beta t}$.

The function $\Pi_2(s,t)$ is the p.g.f. of a negative binomial distribution with range $\{n, n+1, \ldots\}$ and parameters $r = n$ and $p = e^{-\beta t}$.

Solution 4.8

The p.g.f. of $X(0)$ is

$$\Pi(s,0) = \left(\frac{\frac{1}{3}}{1-\frac{2}{3}s}\right)^2 = \frac{1}{(3-2s)^2}.$$

Setting $\lambda = 2\beta$ and $t = 0$ in the general solution (4.6) gives

$$\Pi(s,0) = s^{-2}\,\psi\left(\frac{s}{1-s}\right).$$

Therefore

$$\psi\left(\frac{s}{1-s}\right) = \left(\frac{s}{3-2s}\right)^2.$$

Writing $x = s/(1-s)$ gives $s = x/(1+x)$, so

$$\psi(x) = \left(\frac{x/(1+x)}{3-2x/(1+x)}\right)^2 = \left(\frac{x}{3+x}\right)^2.$$

Hence the particular solution in this case is

$$\begin{aligned}
\Pi(s,t) &= s^{-2}\left(\frac{\dfrac{s}{1-s}e^{-\beta t}}{3+\dfrac{s}{1-s}e^{-\beta t}}\right)^2 \\
&= \left(\frac{e^{-\beta t}}{3-(3-e^{-\beta t})s}\right)^2 \\
&= \left(\frac{\frac{1}{3}e^{-\beta t}}{1-(1-\frac{1}{3}e^{-\beta t})s}\right)^2.
\end{aligned}$$

This is the p.g.f. of a negative binomial distribution with range $\{0,1,\ldots\}$ and parameters $r = 2$ and $p = 1 - \frac{1}{3}e^{-\beta t}$.

Solution 5.1

For the pure death process, $\beta_x = 0$ and $\nu_x = \nu x$.

Solution 5.2

(a) If $\beta_x = \lambda$, $\nu_x = 0$, then the probability that $X(t)$ increases by 1 in $[t, t+\delta t]$ is $\lambda\,\delta t + o(\delta t)$, and it is impossible for $X(t)$ to decrease. So $X(t)$ is the number of events that occur by time t in a Poisson process.

(b) If $\beta_x = \lambda(t)$, $\nu_x = 0$, then the process is a non-homogeneous Poisson process.

Solution 5.3

(a) For the Poisson process, $\beta_x = \lambda$, $\nu_x = 0$, so the differential–difference equations are, for $x = 0, 1, \ldots$,

$$\frac{d}{dt} p_x(t) = \lambda p_{x-1}(t) - \lambda p_x(t).$$

(b) For the simple birth process, $\beta_x = \beta x$, $\nu_x = 0$, so the differential–difference equations are, for $x = 1, 2, \ldots$,

$$\frac{d}{dt} p_x(t) = \beta(x - 1) p_{x-1}(t) - \beta x \, p_x(t).$$

There is no need to give the equation for $x = 0$, as the simple birth process must start with at least one individual, so $p_0(t) = 0$.

Solution 6.1

(a) The equation is in Lagrange form, so

$$f = (1 - s)(\nu - \beta s), \quad g = -1, \quad h = 0.$$

The auxiliary equations are

$$\frac{ds}{(1 - s)(\nu - \beta s)} = \frac{dt}{-1} = \frac{d\Pi}{0}.$$

Since $d\Pi/0$ appears, one solution is

$$c_1 = \Pi.$$

Taking the first and second expressions together, and using the identity given in the question, gives

$$\int \frac{1}{\beta - \nu} \left(\frac{1}{1 - s} - \frac{\beta}{\nu - \beta s} \right) ds = \int 1 \, dt.$$

Since a p.g.f. is defined for $|s| < 1$, and in this range $1 - s$ is positive, when doing the integration it is preferable to write $1 - s$ rather than $s - 1$. (The logarithm of a negative number is not a real number.) Integrating gives

$$\frac{1}{\beta - \nu} (-\log(1 - s) + \log(\nu - \beta s)) = t + \text{constant},$$

or

$$\log \left(\frac{\nu - \beta s}{1 - s} \right) = (\beta - \nu)t + \text{constant}.$$

Taking exponentials gives

$$\frac{\nu - \beta s}{1 - s} = e^{(\beta - \nu)t} \times \text{constant}.$$

Hence a second solution is

$$c_2 = \frac{\nu - \beta s}{1 - s} e^{-(\beta - \nu)t} = \frac{\nu - \beta s}{1 - s} e^{(\nu - \beta)t}.$$

The general solution is given by $c_1 = \psi(c_2)$:

$$\Pi(s, t) = \psi \left(\frac{\nu - \beta s}{1 - s} e^{(\nu - \beta)t} \right).$$

(b) Since $X(0) = n$, the p.g.f. of $X(0)$ is

$$\Pi(s, 0) = s^n.$$

Setting $t = 0$ in the general solution (6.2) gives

$$\Pi(s, 0) = \psi \left(\frac{\nu - \beta s}{1 - s} \right).$$

Therefore

$$\psi \left(\frac{\nu - \beta s}{1 - s} \right) = s^n.$$

Writing $x = (\nu - \beta s)/(1 - s)$, so that $s = (\nu - x)/(\beta - x)$, gives

$$\psi(x) = \left(\frac{\nu - x}{\beta - x} \right)^n,$$

and hence

$$\Pi(s, t) = \left(\frac{\nu(1 - s) - (\nu - \beta s) e^{(\nu - \beta)t}}{\beta(1 - s) - (\nu - \beta s) e^{(\nu - \beta)t}} \right)^n.$$

Solution 6.2

(a) Comparing the p.g.f. (6.4) with $(a - bs)/(c - ds)$, and writing $p = e^{(\nu - \beta)t}$, gives $a = \nu(1 - p)$, $b = \nu - \beta p$, $c = \beta - \nu p$ and $d = \beta(1 - p)$.

(b) From Table 8 in the *Handbook*,

$$E[X(t)] = \frac{ad - bc}{(c - d)^2}.$$

Substituting for a, b, c and d in the numerator and denominator, and simplifying the expressions, gives

$$ad - bc = p(\beta - \nu)^2,$$

$$c - d = p(\beta - \nu).$$

Therefore

$$E[X(t)] = \frac{p(\beta - \nu)^2}{p^2(\beta - \nu)^2} = \frac{1}{p} = e^{(\beta - \nu)t}.$$

Solution 6.3

Since $X(t)$ can be thought of as the sum of n independent variates, each with mean $e^{(\beta - \nu)t}$, as found in the solution to Activity 6.2,

$$E[X(t)] = n e^{(\beta - \nu)t}.$$

Solution 6.4

(a) Writing the partial differential equation (6.5) in Lagrange form gives

$$-\beta(1 - s)^2 \frac{\partial \Pi}{\partial s} + \frac{\partial \Pi}{\partial t} = 0,$$

so

$$f = -\beta(1 - s)^2, \quad g = 1, \quad h = 0.$$

The auxiliary equations are

$$\frac{ds}{-\beta(1 - s)^2} = \frac{dt}{1} = \frac{d\Pi}{0}.$$

Since $d\Pi/0$ appears, one solution is

$$c_1 = \Pi.$$

Taking the first two expressions and integrating gives

$$\int \frac{-1}{(1 - s)^2} ds = \int \beta \, dt,$$

so

$$-\frac{1}{1 - s} = \beta t + \text{constant}.$$

Therefore a second solution is

$$c_2 = \beta t + \frac{1}{1 - s}.$$

The general solution is given by $c_1 = \psi(c_2)$:

$$\Pi(s, t) = \psi \left(\beta t + \frac{1}{1 - s} \right).$$

(b) If there are n individuals at time $t = 0$, then the p.g.f. of $X(0)$ is

$$\Pi(s, 0) = s^n.$$

Setting $t = 0$ in the general solution gives

$$\Pi(s, 0) = \psi\left(\frac{1}{1-s}\right).$$

Therefore

$$\psi\left(\frac{1}{1-s}\right) = s^n.$$

Writing $x = 1/(1-s)$, so that $s = (x-1)/x$, leads to

$$\psi(x) = \left(\frac{x-1}{x}\right)^n.$$

Hence

$$\Pi(s, t) = \left(\frac{\beta t + \dfrac{1}{1-s} - 1}{\beta t + \dfrac{1}{1-s}}\right)^n$$

$$= \left(\frac{\beta t - s\beta t + s}{\beta t - s\beta t + 1}\right)^n.$$

(c) When $n = 1$, the particular solution may be written as

$$\Pi(s, t) = \frac{\beta t - s(\beta t - 1)}{\beta t + 1 - s\beta t}.$$

This is the p.g.f. of a modified geometric distribution with $a = \beta t$, $b = \beta t - 1$, $c = 1 + \beta t$, $d = \beta t$. So $ad - bc = 1$ and $c - d = 1$, and hence

$$E[X(t)] = \frac{ad - bc}{(c-d)^2} = 1.$$

(d) When $X(0) = n$, as for the case when $\beta \neq \nu$, $X(t)$ can be thought of as the sum of n independent variates, each of which represents the size at time t of a simple birth–death process starting with one individual. When $\beta = \nu$, each of these variates has mean 1, so

$$E[X(t)] = n.$$

Solution 6.5

(a) Setting $s = 0$ in (6.6) gives

$$\Pi(0, t) = \left(\frac{\beta t}{\beta t + 1}\right)^n.$$

This is the probability that extinction will have occurred by time t.

(b) Taking the limit as $t \to \infty$ of $\Pi(0, t)$ gives

$$\lim_{t \to \infty} \Pi(0, t) = 1.$$

So extinction is certain to occur eventually.

Solution 6.6

Since $\beta > \nu$ and $n = 5$, the probability of eventual extinction is given by $(\nu/\beta)^5 = \left(\frac{1}{2}\right)^5 = \frac{1}{32}$.

Solution 6.7

(a) Using the formula for $\Pi(0, t)$ given in the solution to Activity 6.5,

$$F(t) = \Pi(0, t) = \left(\frac{\beta t}{\beta t + 1}\right)^n.$$

(b) The median time to extinction is the solution of $F(t) = 0.5$, so when $n = 1$, the median time t is the solution of

$$\frac{\beta t}{\beta t + 1} = 0.5.$$

Therefore the median time to extinction is $t = 1/\beta$.

Solution 6.8

(a) The probability that the next event is a birth is

$$p_b = \frac{\beta}{\beta + \nu} = 0.4.$$

(b) The probability that the population will eventually die out is given by q_3 when gambling against a casino and $p = 0.4$, $q = 0.6$. Since $p < q$, $q_3 = 1$, so eventual extinction is certain.

(c) The probability required is $1 - q_3$, where q_3 is the probability of ruin in the gambler's ruin when $j = 3$, $a = 8$, $p = 0.4$ and $q = 0.6$:

$$1 - q_3 = 1 - \frac{1.5^3 - 1.5^8}{1 - 1.5^8} \simeq 0.096.$$

Solution 6.9

In each case, the probability that the population will eventually die out is equal to q_n, the probability of ruin when starting with £n and gambling against a casino, and

$$p = p_b = \frac{\beta}{\beta + \nu}, \quad q = p_d = \frac{\nu}{\beta + \nu}.$$

(a) When $\beta < \nu$, $p < q$, so $q_n = 1$.

(b) When $\beta = \nu$, $p = q$, so $q_n = 1$.

(c) When $\beta > \nu$, $p > q$, so

$$q_n = \left(\frac{q}{p}\right)^n = \left(\frac{\nu}{\beta}\right)^n.$$

These are the same as the results obtained in Subsection 6.2 and stated in the box preceding Activity 6.6.

Solution 7.1

(a) The partial differential equation (7.1) is in Lagrange form, so

$$f = \nu(1-s), \quad g = -1, \quad h = \lambda(1-s)\Pi.$$

The auxiliary equations are

$$\frac{ds}{\nu(1-s)} = \frac{dt}{-1} = \frac{d\Pi}{\lambda(1-s)\Pi}.$$

Taking the first two expressions gives

$$\int \frac{-1}{1-s}\, ds = \int \nu\, dt,$$

so

$$\log(1-s) = \nu t + \text{constant},$$

or, taking exponentials,

$$1 - s = e^{\nu t} \times \text{constant}.$$

Therefore one solution is given by

$$c_1 = (1-s)e^{-\nu t}.$$

A second solution may be obtained by taking the first and third expressions, and cancelling the term $(1-s)$:

$$\frac{ds}{\nu} = \frac{d\Pi}{\lambda\Pi}.$$

This gives

$$\int \frac{\lambda}{\nu}\, ds = \int \frac{1}{\Pi}\, d\Pi,$$

so

$$\frac{\lambda}{\nu} s = \log \Pi + \text{constant},$$

or

$$\text{constant} = \log \Pi - \frac{\lambda}{\nu} s.$$

Taking exponentials gives

$$c_2 = \Pi e^{-\lambda s/\nu}.$$

The general solution is obtained using $c_2 = \psi(c_1)$:

$$\Pi e^{-\lambda s/\nu} = \psi\left((1-s)\, e^{-\nu t}\right).$$

Therefore

$$\Pi(s,t) = e^{\lambda s/\nu}\, \psi\left((1-s)e^{-\nu t}\right).$$

(b) Since $X(0) = 0$, the p.g.f. of $X(0)$ is

$$\Pi(s,0) = s^0 = 1.$$

Setting $t = 0$ in the general solution gives

$$\Pi(s,0) = e^{\lambda s/\nu}\, \psi(1-s),$$

so

$$e^{\lambda s/\nu}\, \psi(1-s) = 1,$$

and hence

$$\psi(1-s) = e^{-\lambda s/\nu}.$$

Writing $x = 1 - s$, so that $s = 1 - x$, gives

$$\psi(x) = e^{-\lambda(1-x)/\nu}.$$

Therefore the particular solution is given by

$$\Pi(s,t) = e^{\lambda s/\nu}\, e^{-\lambda(1-(1-s)e^{-\nu t})/\nu}$$

$$= \exp\left(\frac{\lambda s}{\nu} - \frac{\lambda}{\nu}(1 - (1-s)e^{-\nu t})\right)$$

$$= \exp\left(-\frac{\lambda}{\nu}(1-s)(1 - e^{-\nu t})\right).$$

This is the p.g.f. of a Poisson distribution with parameter $\frac{\lambda}{\nu}(1 - e^{-\nu t})$, so

$$X(t) \sim \text{Poisson}\left(\frac{\lambda}{\nu}(1 - e^{-\nu t})\right).$$

Solution 7.2

(a) Letting $t \to \infty$ in (7.3) with $x = 2$ gives

$$\lambda p_1 + 3\nu p_3 - (\lambda + 2\nu)p_2 = 0.$$

Since $2\nu p_2 = \lambda p_1$, this simplifies to

$$3\nu p_3 = \lambda p_2,$$

so

$$p_3 = \frac{\lambda}{3\nu} p_2 = \frac{1}{3!}\left(\frac{\lambda}{\nu}\right)^3 p_0.$$

(b) For $x = 1, 2, \ldots,$

$$p_x = \frac{1}{x!}\left(\frac{\lambda}{\nu}\right)^x p_0.$$

(c) The sum of the probabilities is

$$\sum_{x=0}^{\infty} p_x = p_0 \sum_{x=0}^{\infty} \frac{1}{x!}\left(\frac{\lambda}{\nu}\right)^x = p_0\, e^{\lambda/\nu}.$$

Since the sum is equal to 1 for a proper probability distribution,

$$p_0 = e^{-\lambda/\nu},$$

and hence

$$p_x = \frac{e^{-\lambda/\nu}(\lambda/\nu)^x}{x!}, \quad x = 0, 1, \ldots.$$

This is the p.m.f. of a Poisson distribution with parameter λ/ν.

Solution 7.3

(a) The limiting distribution is Poisson with parameter $\lambda/\nu = 1.5$, so the expected number of individuals alive at any time is 1.5.

(b) (i) The long-run proportion of the time that there are no individuals in the population is

$$p_0 = e^{-1.5} \simeq 0.2231.$$

(ii) The long-run proportion of the time that there are three individuals in the population is

$$p_3 = \frac{e^{-1.5}\, 1.5^3}{3!} \simeq 0.1255.$$

Solution 8.1

(a) The first postulate for the simple birth process states that for a population of size x at time t, the probability of one birth during the interval $[t, t + \delta t]$ is equal to $\beta x\, \delta t + o(\delta t)$.

Since multiple births have probability $o(\delta t)$,

$$P(\text{no birth in } [t, t + \delta t] \mid X(t) = x)$$
$$= 1 - \beta x\, \delta t + o(\delta t).$$

Hence the expected number of births in $[t, t + \delta t]$ is

$$1 \times (\beta x\, \delta t + o(\delta t)) + 0 \times (1 - \beta x\, \delta t + o(\delta t))$$
$$= \beta x\, \delta t + o(\delta t).$$

(b) Let $z(t)$ denote the size of the population at time t in the deterministic model. Then

$$z(t + \delta t) = z(t) + \beta\, z(t)\, \delta t + o(\delta t).$$

Hence

$$\frac{z(t + \delta t) - z(t)}{\delta t} = \beta\, z(t) + \frac{o(\delta t)}{\delta t}.$$

Letting $\delta t \to 0$ gives

$$\frac{dz}{dt} = \beta\, z.$$

(c) This differential equation can be solved by the method of separation of variables:

$$\int \frac{1}{z}\, dz = \int \beta\, dt$$

gives

$$\log z = \beta t + c,$$

where c is a constant. Taking exponentials leads to the general solution

$$z = z(t) = e^{\beta t + c} = A\, e^{\beta t},$$

where A is a constant.

Since $z(0) = 1$, $A = 1$, and hence the deterministic solution for the simple birth process starting with one individual is

$$z(t) = e^{\beta t}.$$

Solution 8.2

(a) For the immigration–birth process,

$$h(x, t) = \lambda + \beta x.$$

Therefore the differential equation for $z(t)$ is

$$\frac{dz}{dt} = \lambda + \beta z.$$

(b) Separating the variables gives

$$\int \frac{dz}{\lambda + \beta z} = \int 1\, dt.$$

Integrating this leads to

$$\log(\lambda + \beta z) = \beta t + \text{constant}.$$

Since $z(0) = 0$, the constant is $\log \lambda$, and hence

$$\log(\lambda + \beta z) = \beta t + \log \lambda,$$

or, taking exponentials and rearranging,

$$z = \frac{\lambda}{\beta}(e^{\beta t} - 1).$$

(c) If $z(0) = z_0$, then the constant is $\log(\lambda + \beta z_0)$. Hence the particular solution is

$$\log(\lambda + \beta z) = \beta t + \log(\lambda + \beta z_0),$$

giving

$$\lambda + \beta z = (\lambda + \beta z_0)e^{\beta t}$$

or

$$z = z_0 e^{\beta t} + \frac{\lambda}{\beta}(e^{\beta t} - 1).$$

Solution 8.3

(a) Separating the variables in the differential equation gives

$$\int \frac{1}{z}\, dz = \int -\nu\, dt,$$

so

$$\log z = -\nu t + \text{constant}.$$

Since $z(0) = n$,

$$\log z = -\nu t + \log n,$$

and hence

$$z = ne^{-\nu t}.$$

(b) Half the population are alive when $z = \frac{1}{2}n$, that is, when

$$\tfrac{1}{2}n = ne^{-\nu t},$$

or

$$e^{-\nu t} = \tfrac{1}{2}.$$

Hence half the population are still alive when

$$t = \frac{1}{\nu}\log 2.$$

Since $ne^{-\nu t} > 0$ for all $t > 0$, the population never dies out completely in the deterministic model.

Solution 8.4

(a) For the simple birth–death process, $h_1(x, t) = \beta x$ and $h_{-1}(x, t) = \nu x$, so the deterministic analogue is the solution of the differential equation

$$\frac{dz}{dt} = \beta z - \nu z.$$

(b) The equation can be solved using separation of variables:

$$\int \frac{1}{z}\, dz = \int (\beta - \nu)\, dt,$$

so

$$\log z = (\beta - \nu)t + \text{constant}.$$

Since $z(0) = n$,

$$\log n = \text{constant},$$

and hence

$$\log \frac{z}{n} = (\beta - \nu)t,$$

so

$$z = ne^{(\beta - \nu)t}.$$

(c) When $\beta < \nu$, $e^{(\beta - \nu)t} \to 0$ as $t \to \infty$, so the population decreases in size but never dies out completely. In the stochastic model, the population fluctuates and eventually becomes extinct with probability 1. (Extinction of the simple birth–death process is discussed in Subsection 6.2.)

When $\beta > \nu$, $e^{(\beta - \nu)t} \to \infty$ as $t \to \infty$, so in the deterministic model the population grows without bound. However, in the corresponding stochastic model, the population may either grow without bound with probability $1 - (\nu/\beta)^n$, or eventually die out with probability $(\nu/\beta)^n$.

When $\beta = \nu$, $e^{(\beta-\nu)t} = 1$, so in the deterministic model the size of the population remains at n. But in the stochastic model, extinction is certain to occur eventually.

Notice that for all values of β and ν, the mean of the stochastic model is equal to the size of the population at time t in the analogous deterministic model. (See Activity 6.3 and part (d) of Activity 6.4 for the means.)

Solution 9.1

(a) Customers arrive at random at a place where there are six servers on duty. The time taken to complete a service is uniformly distributed.

(b) Customers arrive at equally-spaced intervals (for instance, punctually according to a regular appointment system) and there are two servers on duty. The time that each server spends with a customer is constant.

Solution 9.2

(a) $M/U/3$.

(b) $D/M/1$.

Solution 10.1

The arrival rate is
$$\lambda = \tfrac{3}{10} \text{ per minute} = 18 \text{ per hour.}$$
The mean service time is $1/\varepsilon$, so the service rate ε is given by
$$\varepsilon = \tfrac{1}{3} \text{ per minute} = 20 \text{ per hour.}$$
The traffic intensity is
$$\rho = \lambda/\varepsilon = \tfrac{3}{10} / \tfrac{1}{3} = 0.9.$$
(Alternatively, $\rho = \lambda/\varepsilon = 18/20 = 0.9$.)

Solution 10.2

For this queue, $\lambda = \tfrac{1}{5}$ per minute and $\varepsilon = \tfrac{1}{2}$ per minute, so
$$\rho = \lambda/\varepsilon = \tfrac{1}{5} / \tfrac{1}{2} = 0.4.$$
(Alternatively, $\lambda = 12$ per hour and $\varepsilon = 30$ per hour, so $\rho = 12/30 = 0.4$.)

Solution 10.3

From the solution to Activity 10.1, the traffic intensity of the queue is $\rho = 0.9$, so $X \sim G_0(0.9)$.

(a) The mean queue size is
$$E(X) = \frac{0.9}{1 - 0.9} = 9.$$
Note that since the mean of $G_0(\rho)$ is $\rho/(1-\rho)$, the mean queue size is large when ρ is close to 1.

(b) The proportion of the time for which there are at least two people in the queue is
$$P(X \geq 2) = 1 - p_0 - p_1$$
$$= 1 - 0.1 - 0.9 \times 0.1$$
$$= 0.81.$$

Solution 10.4

From the solution to Activity 10.2, the traffic intensity of the queue is $\rho = 0.4$, so $X \sim G_0(0.4)$.

The probability that there will be three people in the queue is
$$P(X = 3) = 0.4^3 \times 0.6 = 0.0384.$$

Solution 10.5

For the ticket office queue of Activity 10.1, $\lambda = \tfrac{3}{10}$ per minute and $\varepsilon = \tfrac{1}{3}$ per minute, so
$$\varepsilon - \lambda = \tfrac{1}{3} - \tfrac{3}{10} = \tfrac{1}{30}.$$
Therefore W, the queueing time, has the exponential distribution $M\left(\tfrac{1}{30}\right)$.

(a) The probability that a customer will queue for less than ten minutes is
$$P(W < 10) = 1 - e^{-\frac{1}{30} \times 10}$$
$$= 1 - e^{-\frac{1}{3}}$$
$$\simeq 0.283.$$

(b) The mean queueing time in minutes is
$$E(W) = \frac{1}{\varepsilon - \lambda} = 30.$$

Solution 10.6

For the queue of Activity 10.2, $\lambda = \tfrac{1}{5}$ per minute and $\varepsilon = \tfrac{1}{2}$ per minute, so
$$\varepsilon - \lambda = \tfrac{1}{2} - \tfrac{1}{5} = \tfrac{3}{10} = 0.3.$$
The probability that an arriving customer will have to queue for more than a quarter of an hour is
$$P(W > 15) = e^{-0.3 \times 15} = e^{-4.5} \simeq 0.011.$$

Solution 10.7

For the queue of Activity 10.1, $\lambda = \tfrac{3}{10}$ per minute, $\varepsilon = \tfrac{1}{3}$ per minute and $\rho = 0.9$.

The expected duration of a busy period in minutes is
$$\frac{1}{\varepsilon - \lambda} = 30.$$
The expected number of customers served during a busy period is
$$\frac{1}{1 - \rho} = 10.$$

Solution 10.8

For the queue of Activity 10.2, $\lambda = \tfrac{1}{5}$ per minute and $\varepsilon = \tfrac{1}{2}$ per minute, so the mean length of an idle period in minutes is
$$\frac{1}{\lambda} = 5.$$
The expected duration of a busy period in minutes is
$$\frac{1}{\varepsilon - \lambda} = \frac{1}{0.5 - 0.2} = \frac{1}{0.3} = 3\tfrac{1}{3}.$$

Solution 11.1

(a) All three cashiers are busy when there are at least three people in the queue, so the proportion of the time that all three cashiers are busy is given by
$$P(X \geq 3) = 1 - p_0 - p_1 - p_2$$
$$= 1 - \tfrac{1}{9} - \tfrac{2}{9} - \tfrac{2}{9}$$
$$= \tfrac{4}{9}.$$

(b) The probability required is $P(X = 5)$. Using (11.2),
$$P(X = 5) = \tfrac{1}{9} \times \tfrac{3^3}{3!} \times \left(\tfrac{2}{3}\right)^5 = \tfrac{16}{243}.$$

(c) Since the service time of each cashier is exponentially distributed with parameter ε, and $\varepsilon = \tfrac{1}{3}$ per minute, the time that Tom has to wait is the minimum of three service times each of which is exponentially distributed with parameter $\tfrac{1}{3}$.

Therefore W, Tom's waiting time, is exponentially distributed with parameter
$$\tfrac{1}{3} + \tfrac{1}{3} + \tfrac{1}{3} = 1.$$
Hence the probability that he will have to wait for more than 30 seconds, or 0.5 minutes, is
$$P(W > 0.5) = e^{-1 \times 0.5} \simeq 0.607.$$

Solution 11.2

(a) The queue specification is $M/M/2$.

The arrival rate λ is 16 per hour, and the service rate ε is 10 per hour, so the traffic intensity is
$$\rho = \frac{\lambda}{n\varepsilon} = \frac{16}{2 \times 10} = 0.8.$$

(b) The distribution of X, the equilibrium queue size, is given by (11.1), (11.2) and (11.3):
$$p_x = \begin{cases} \dfrac{1}{K} \dfrac{2^x}{x!}(0.8)^x, & x = 0, 1, \\ \dfrac{1}{K} \dfrac{2^2}{2!}(0.8)^x, & x = 2, 3, \ldots, \end{cases}$$
where
$$K = 1 + 2\rho + \frac{(2\rho)^2}{2!(1 - \rho)}$$
$$= 1 + 1.6 + 6.4$$
$$= 9.$$
Therefore the proportion of the time that both advisers are idle is
$$p_0 = \frac{1}{K} = \tfrac{1}{9}.$$

(c) The proportion of enquirers seen immediately is given by
$$p_0 + p_1 = \tfrac{1}{9} + \tfrac{1}{9} \times 2 \times 0.8$$
$$= \tfrac{1}{9} + \tfrac{8}{45}$$
$$= \tfrac{13}{45} \simeq 0.289.$$

(d) If both advisers are busy and three people are waiting, then the queue size is 5. Therefore the probability required is
$$p_5 = \tfrac{1}{9} \times \tfrac{2^2}{2!} \times 0.8^5$$
$$= \tfrac{1}{9} \times 2 \times 0.32768$$
$$\simeq 0.073.$$

(e) Since the service time of an adviser is exponentially distributed with parameter ε, and $\varepsilon = 10$ per hour or $\tfrac{1}{6}$ per minute, the time in minutes that Helen has to wait is the minimum of two service times each of which is $M\left(\tfrac{1}{6}\right)$. Therefore W, Helen's waiting time in minutes, is exponentially distributed with parameter
$$\tfrac{1}{6} + \tfrac{1}{6} = \tfrac{1}{3}.$$
Hence the probability that she will have to wait for more than 5 minutes is
$$P(W > 5) = e^{-\frac{1}{3} \times 5} \simeq 0.189.$$

Solution 11.3

The p.g.f. of the equilibrium queue size is
$$\Pi(s) = p_0 + p_1 s + p_2 s^2 + \cdots$$
$$= \tfrac{1}{9} + \tfrac{8}{45}s + \sum_{x=2}^{\infty} \tfrac{1}{9} \times \tfrac{2^2}{2!} \times 0.8^x s^x$$
$$= \tfrac{1}{9} + \tfrac{8}{45}s + \tfrac{2}{9}\sum_{x=2}^{\infty}(0.8s)^x.$$
The last term may be rewritten as
$$\tfrac{2}{9}(0.8s)^2 \sum_{j=0}^{\infty}(0.8s)^j = \tfrac{2}{9} \times 0.64s^2 \times \frac{1}{1 - 0.8s}$$
$$= \tfrac{2}{9} \times 0.64s^2 \times \frac{5}{5 - 4s}$$
$$= \tfrac{1}{9} \times \frac{6.4s^2}{5 - 4s}$$
$$= \tfrac{1}{45} \times \frac{32s^2}{5 - 4s}.$$
Hence the p.g.f. of X is
$$\Pi(s) = \tfrac{1}{9} + \tfrac{8}{45}s + \tfrac{1}{45} \times \frac{32s^2}{5 - 4s}$$
$$= \tfrac{1}{45}\left(5 + 8s + \frac{32s^2}{5 - 4s}\right).$$
Differentiating this gives
$$\Pi'(s) = \tfrac{8}{45} + \tfrac{32}{45}\left(\frac{2s(5 - 4s) + 4s^2}{(5 - 4s)^2}\right).$$
Therefore the mean equilibrium queue size is
$$\Pi'(1) = \tfrac{8}{45} + \tfrac{32}{45} \times 6 = \tfrac{200}{45} = \tfrac{40}{9} \simeq 4.44.$$

Solution 12.1

(a) The arrival rate is

$\lambda = \frac{1}{25}$ per minute.

The service time is constant, so

$E(T) = 20$ minutes.

Therefore the traffic intensity is

$\rho = \lambda\, E(T) = \frac{1}{25} \times 20 = 0.8.$

(b) Since the service time is constant,

$V(T) = 0.$

Using Pollaczek's formula (12.2), the mean equilibrium queue size is

$E(X) = \dfrac{0.8 - \frac{1}{2} \times 0.8^2}{1 - 0.8} = 2.4.$

Solution 12.2

(a) Working in minutes, the arrival rate is

$\lambda = \frac{24}{60}$ per minute $= 0.4$ per minute.

From Table 9 in the *Handbook*, the mean of $\Gamma(n, \lambda)$ is n/λ, so the mean service time in minutes is

$E(T) = 3/2 = 1.5.$

Therefore the traffic intensity is

$\rho = \lambda\, E(T) = 0.4 \times 1.5 = 0.6.$

(b) The variance of $\Gamma(n, \lambda)$ is n/λ^2, so

$V(T) = 3/2^2 = 0.75.$

Using (12.2), the mean equilibrium queue size is

$E(X) = \dfrac{0.6 - \frac{1}{2} \times 0.6^2 + \frac{1}{2} \times 0.4^2 \times 0.75}{1 - 0.6}$

$= 1.2.$

Solution 12.3

(a) Working in minutes, the arrival rate is

$\lambda = \frac{6}{60}$ per minute $= 0.1$ per minute.

Since $T \sim \chi^2(7)$, $E(T) = 7$, so the traffic intensity is

$\rho = \lambda\, E(T) = 0.1 \times 7 = 0.7.$

(b) The variance of $\chi^2(n)$ is $2n$, so $V(T) = 14$. Using (12.2), the mean equilibrium queue size is

$E(X) = \dfrac{0.7 - \frac{1}{2} \times 0.7^2 + \frac{1}{2} \times 0.1^2 \times 14}{1 - 0.7}$

$= 1.75.$

Solution 14.1

Of all the infective–susceptible contacts, only a proportion θ lead to the infection being passed on. So 'infective contacts' occur as a Poisson process with rate $\beta_y = (\theta\beta)y(n + 1 - y)/n$. This refinement would not be complicated to introduce into the model.

Solution 14.2

(a) Separating the variables in (14.3) and integrating gives

$$\int \frac{n}{y(n + 1 - y)}\, dy = \int \beta\, dt.$$

Using the identity given, this can be rewritten as

$$\frac{n}{n + 1} \int \left(\frac{1}{y} + \frac{1}{n + 1 - y} \right) dy = \int \beta\, dt.$$

Integrating both sides gives

$$\frac{n}{n + 1} (\log y - \log(n + 1 - y)) = \beta t + \text{constant},$$

or

$$\frac{n}{n + 1} \log \left(\frac{y}{n + 1 - y} \right) = \beta t + \text{constant}.$$

(b) If $y = 1$ at time $t = 0$, then

$$\frac{n}{n + 1} \log \frac{1}{n} = \text{constant}.$$

Therefore the particular solution corresponding to $y_0 = 1$ is given by

$$\frac{n}{n + 1} \log \left(\frac{y}{n + 1 - y} \right) = \beta t + \frac{n}{n + 1} \log \frac{1}{n},$$

or

$$\frac{n}{n + 1} \log \left(\frac{ny}{n + 1 - y} \right) = \beta t.$$

Taking exponentials gives

$$\frac{ny}{n + 1 - y} = \exp \left(\left(1 + \frac{1}{n} \right) \beta t \right).$$

Solving this equation for y leads to the formula given in the question.

Solution 14.3

(a) According to the deterministic model, when $y_0 = 1$, the number of infectives at time t is given by (14.4). Since $n + 1 = 112$ and $\beta = 4$ per day, after t days,

$$y \simeq \frac{112}{111 \exp(-4.036t) + 1}.$$

When $t = 1$, $y \simeq 37.8$, so approximately 38 inhabitants of the village are infected after one day. After two days, $y \simeq 108.2$: only about four of the original susceptibles are still free of the infection.

(b) The whole village will be infected when $y = 112$, which occurs, according to the deterministic model, only after infinite time. (But $y \simeq 111.9$ after only 3 days.)

Solution 14.4

(a) The epidemic rate is given by (14.5) with $\beta = 2$ and $n + 1 = 5$, so

$$\beta_y = \frac{2y(5 - y)}{4}.$$

Therefore

$$\beta_3 = \frac{2 \times 3 \times 2}{4} = 3,$$

$$\beta_4 = \frac{2 \times 4 \times 1}{4} = 2.$$

(b) The expected time until the first new infection is

$$E(T_3) = \tfrac{1}{3} \text{ day}.$$

(c) The time until everyone has been infected is $W = T_3 + T_4$, so

$$E(W) = \tfrac{1}{3} + \tfrac{1}{2} = \tfrac{5}{6} \text{ day},$$

$$V(W) = \tfrac{1}{3^2} + \tfrac{1}{2^2} = \tfrac{13}{36} \simeq 0.361 \ (\text{days})^2.$$

Solution 14.5

(a) The epidemic rate is given by (14.5) with $\beta = 0.2$ and $n + 1 = 9$, so

$$\beta_y = \frac{0.2y(9 - y)}{8}.$$

Therefore

$$\beta_5 = \frac{0.2 \times 5 \times 4}{8} = 0.5.$$

Similarly, $\beta_6 = 0.45$, $\beta_7 = 0.35$, $\beta_8 = 0.2$.

(b) The expected time in days until a sixth person is infected is

$$\frac{1}{\beta_5} = \frac{1}{0.5} = 2.$$

(c) The expected waiting time in days until all nine are infected is

$$E(W) = \frac{1}{\beta_5} + \frac{1}{\beta_6} + \frac{1}{\beta_7} + \frac{1}{\beta_8}$$

$$= \tfrac{1}{0.5} + \tfrac{1}{0.45} + \tfrac{1}{0.35} + \tfrac{1}{0.2}$$

$$\simeq 12.08.$$

(d) The variance of W is

$$V(W) = \frac{1}{\beta_5^2} + \frac{1}{\beta_6^2} + \frac{1}{\beta_7^2} + \frac{1}{\beta_8^2}$$

$$= 42.1015\ldots,$$

so the standard deviation of W is

$$\sqrt{V(W)} = \sqrt{42.1015\ldots} \simeq 6.49 \text{ days}.$$

Solution 14.6

(a) Using (14.8), the differential–difference equations are

$$\frac{d}{dt} p_y(t) = -\beta_y \, p_y(t) + \beta_{y-1} \, p_{y-1}(t), \quad y = 2, 3, 4.$$

Since $n + 1 = 4$ and $\beta = 0.3$ per day, the epidemic rate is

$$\beta_y = \frac{\beta y(n + 1 - y)}{n} = \frac{0.3y(4 - y)}{3} = 0.1y(4 - y).$$

Therefore $\beta_2 = 0.4$, $\beta_3 = 0.3$, $\beta_4 = 0$, and hence the three differential equations are

$$\frac{d}{dt} p_2(t) = -0.4 \, p_2(t), \tag{1}$$

$$\frac{d}{dt} p_3(t) = -0.3 \, p_3(t) + 0.4 \, p_2(t), \tag{2}$$

$$\frac{d}{dt} p_4(t) = 0.3 \, p_3(t). \tag{3}$$

Since two individuals are infected initially,

$$p_2(0) = 1, \quad p_3(0) = 0, \quad p_4(0) = 0.$$

(b) The solution of (1) is

$$p_2(t) = \text{constant} \times e^{-0.4t}.$$

Since $p_2(0) = 1$, the constant is 1, so

$$p_2(t) = e^{-0.4t}.$$

Substituting this result in (2) gives

$$\frac{d}{dt} p_3(t) + 0.3 \, p_3(t) = 0.4e^{-0.4t}.$$

Multiplying both sides by the integrating factor $e^{0.3t}$ gives

$$\left(\frac{d}{dt} p_3(t) \right) e^{0.3t} + 0.3 \, p_3(t) \, e^{0.3t} = 0.4e^{-0.1t}.$$

This can be rewritten as

$$\frac{d}{dt} \left(p_3(t) \, e^{0.3t} \right) = 0.4e^{-0.1t}.$$

Integrating both sides with respect to t gives

$$p_3(t) \, e^{0.3t} = -4e^{-0.1t} + \text{constant}.$$

Since $p_3(0) = 0$, the constant is 4, and hence

$$p_3(t) \, e^{0.3t} = 4 - 4e^{-0.1t}.$$

Therefore

$$p_3(t) = 4e^{-0.3t} - 4e^{-0.4t}.$$

Substituting this result in (3) gives

$$\frac{d}{dt} p_4(t) = 1.2e^{-0.3t} - 1.2e^{-0.4t},$$

and integration gives

$$p_4(t) = -4e^{-0.3t} + 3e^{-0.4t} + \text{constant}.$$

Since $p_4(0) = 0$, the constant is 1. Therefore the p.m.f. of $Y(t)$ is

$$p_2(t) = e^{-0.4t},$$

$$p_3(t) = 4e^{-0.3t} - 4e^{-0.4t},$$

$$p_4(t) = 1 - 4e^{-0.3t} + 3e^{-0.4t}.$$

As a check, note that $p_2(t) + p_3(t) + p_4(t) = 1$.

(c) As $t \to \infty$, $p_2(t)$ and $p_3(t)$ approach 0, and $p_4(t) \to 1$. Eventually everyone in the household will be infected.

Solution 14.7

(a) Using (14.12) with $n+1=4$ gives

$$P(W \le t) = P(Y(t) = 4)$$
$$= p_4(t)$$
$$= 1 - 4e^{-0.3t} + 3e^{-0.4t}.$$

(b) Using the alternative formula for the mean,

$$E(W) = \int_0^\infty P(W > t)\, dt$$
$$= \int_0^\infty (4e^{-0.3t} - 3e^{-0.4t})\, dt$$
$$= \left[-\tfrac{40}{3} e^{-0.3t} + \tfrac{30}{4} e^{-0.4t} \right]_0^\infty$$
$$= \tfrac{40}{3} - \tfrac{30}{4}$$
$$= 5\tfrac{5}{6}.$$

(c) The duration of the epidemic is $W = T_2 + T_3$, where $T_2 \sim M(\beta_2)$, $T_3 \sim M(\beta_3)$. From the solution to part (a) of Activity 14.6, $\beta_2 = 0.4$ and $\beta_3 = 0.3$, so

$$E(W) = \tfrac{1}{0.4} + \tfrac{1}{0.3} = 5\tfrac{5}{6}.$$

Solution 15.1

(a) For this epidemic, $\beta = 3$, $\gamma = 1.2$ and $n + 1 = 31$, so by (15.10),

$$\rho = \frac{n\gamma}{\beta} = \frac{30 \times 1.2}{3} = 12.$$

(b) The number of people who are simultaneously infectious at the height of the epidemic is given by (15.13). Since $x_0 = 29$ and $y_0 = 2$,

$$y_{\max} = 2 + 29 - 12 - 12\log(29/12) \simeq 8.41.$$

At the height of the epidemic, approximately 8 people are infectious.

Solution 15.2

From (15.11), $dy/dx = 0$ when $x = \rho$. Therefore when $x_0 = \rho$, $dy/dx = 0$ at the starting point (x_0, y_0). From (15.7) and (15.8), x and y decrease from x_0 and y_0, respectively. Hence the trajectory is as shown in Figure S.1, and $x_\infty < \rho$ in this case too.

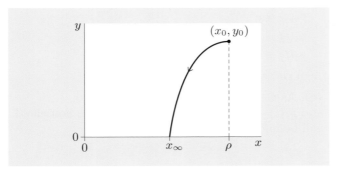

Figure S.1   Trajectory of the general epidemic when $x_0 = \rho$

Solution 15.3

From the solution to Activity 15.1, $x_0 = 29$, $y_0 = 2$ and $\rho = 12$, so using (15.15), x_∞ is the smaller solution of the equation

$$x = 29 \exp\left(\frac{x - 31}{12} \right).$$

Using (15.16), the iteration formula is

$$x_{\infty,j+1} = 29 \exp\left(\frac{x_{\infty,j} - 31}{12} \right), \quad j = 0, 1, \ldots.$$

With $x_{\infty,0} = 0$, this gives

$$x_{\infty,1} \simeq 2.1901, \quad x_{\infty,2} \simeq 2.6287,$$
$$x_{\infty,3} \simeq 2.7265, \quad x_{\infty,4} \simeq 2.7488,$$
$$x_{\infty,5} \simeq 2.7539, \quad x_{\infty,6} \simeq 2.7551,$$
$$x_{\infty,7} \simeq 2.7554, \quad x_{\infty,8} \simeq 2.7554.$$

Therefore, correct to two decimal places, $x_\infty = 2.76$. Approximately 3 susceptibles remain uninfected when the epidemic ends.

The number of people who have been infected and recovered is

$$z_\infty = 31 - x_\infty \simeq 28.24.$$

Approximately 28 people have been infected.

Solution 15.4

(a) For this epidemic, $x_0 = 30$, $y_0 = 1$ and $z_0 = 0$. The value of n is 30. The contact rate β is 0.4 per day, and the removal rate γ is $\tfrac{1}{6}$ per day. Therefore

$$\rho = \frac{n\gamma}{\beta} = \frac{30 \times \tfrac{1}{6}}{0.4} = 12.5.$$

(b) The epidemic is at its height when $x = \rho = 12.5$, at which time the number of infectives is given by (15.13):

$$y_{\max} = y_0 + x_0 - \rho - \rho \log\left(\frac{x_0}{\rho} \right)$$
$$= 1 + 30 - 12.5 - 12.5 \log\left(\frac{30}{12.5} \right)$$
$$\simeq 7.56.$$

At this stage of the epidemic, the number who have been infected and recovered is obtained by subtraction:

$$z = n + 1 - x - y$$
$$\simeq 31 - 12.5 - 7.56$$
$$= 10.94.$$

That is, approximately 11 people have so far been infected and recovered.

(c) The number of susceptibles surviving the epidemic uninfected, x_∞, is the smaller solution of the equation

$$x = 30 \exp\left(\frac{x-31}{12.5}\right).$$

Using the formula iteration method with $x_{\infty,0} = 0$, and retaining full calculator accuracy throughout, gives the following results (rounded to three decimal places): $x_{\infty,1} = 2.512$, $x_{\infty,2} = 3.072$, $x_{\infty,3} = 3.212$, $x_{\infty,4} = 3.248$, $x_{\infty,5} = 3.258$, $x_{\infty,6} = 3.260$, $x_{\infty,7} = 3.261$, $x_{\infty,8} = 3.261$.

Therefore $x_\infty \simeq 3.26$, and hence the number who have been infected and recovered is

$$z_\infty = 31 - x_\infty \simeq 27.74.$$

Approximately 28 people have been infected and recovered.

(d) A sketch of the trajectory is shown in Figure S.2.

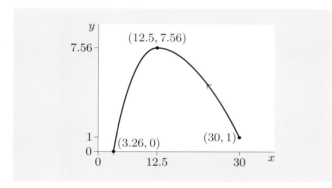

Figure S.2 Trajectory of the epidemic

Solution 16.1

(a) Since $n + 1 = 8$, $\beta = 3.5$ and $\gamma = 2$,

$$\rho = \frac{n\gamma}{\beta} = \frac{7 \times 2}{3.5} = 4.$$

(b) For this epidemic, $x_0 = 6$, $y_0 = 2$, so if no new infection occurs, $X_\infty = 6$ and the path is as shown in Figure S.3.

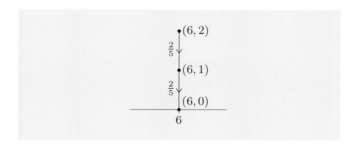

Figure S.3 No infection

Using (16.2), the probability of each removal is

$$\frac{\rho}{x+\rho} = \frac{4}{6+4} = \frac{2}{5}.$$

This probability is shown on the path in Figure S.3. Hence the probability that there is no new infection is

$$P(X_\infty = 6) = \tfrac{2}{5} \times \tfrac{2}{5} = \tfrac{4}{25} = 0.16.$$

(c) If one new infection occurs during the epidemic, then $X_\infty = 5$. The two paths for which $X_\infty = 5$ are shown in Figure S.4.

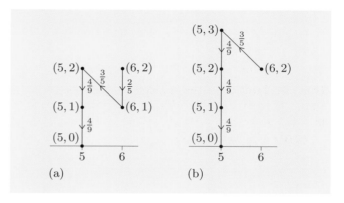

Figure S.4 One infection

When $x = 6$, the probability that the next transition is an infection is

$$\frac{x}{x+\rho} = \frac{6}{6+4} = \frac{3}{5}.$$

When $x = 5$, the probability that the next transition is a removal is

$$\frac{\rho}{x+\rho} = \frac{4}{5+4} = \frac{4}{9}.$$

These probabilities are shown on the paths in Figure S.4.

The probability of the path in Figure S.4(a) is

$$\tfrac{2}{5} \times \tfrac{3}{5} \times \tfrac{4}{9} \times \tfrac{4}{9} = \tfrac{96}{2025} \simeq 0.0474.$$

The probability of the path in Figure S.4(b) is

$$\tfrac{3}{5} \times \tfrac{4}{9} \times \tfrac{4}{9} \times \tfrac{4}{9} = \tfrac{64}{1215} \simeq 0.0527.$$

Therefore the probability of exactly one infection is

$$P(X_\infty = 5) = \tfrac{96}{2025} + \tfrac{64}{1215}$$
$$\simeq 0.0474 + 0.0527$$
$$= 0.1001.$$

Solution 16.2

(a) Since $n + 1 = 21$, $\beta = 0.5$ and $\gamma = 0.15$,
$$\rho = \frac{n\gamma}{\beta} = \frac{20 \times 0.15}{0.5} = 6.$$

(b) Since $x_0 = 18$ and $y_0 = 3$, if there is one infection, then $X_\infty = 17$. The three paths for which $X_\infty = 17$ are shown in Figure S.5.

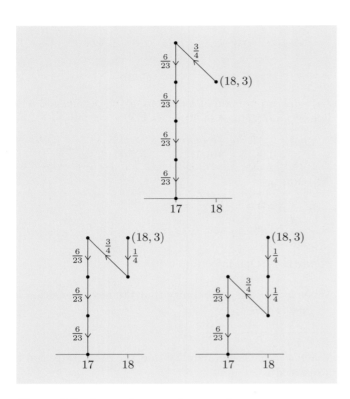

Figure S.5   One infection, three paths

(c) When $x = 18$, the probability of a removal next is
$$\frac{\rho}{x + \rho} = \frac{6}{18 + 6} = \frac{1}{4},$$
and the probability of an infection is $\frac{3}{4}$.

When $x = 17$, the probability of a removal next is
$$\frac{\rho}{x + \rho} = \frac{6}{17 + 6} = \frac{6}{23}.$$
These probabilities are shown on the paths in Figure S.5.

The probability that there will be one infection before the epidemic ends is the sum of the probabilities for the three paths, so
$$P(X_\infty = 17) = \frac{3}{4} \times \left(\frac{6}{23}\right)^4 + \frac{1}{4} \times \frac{3}{4} \times \left(\frac{6}{23}\right)^3$$
$$+ \left(\frac{1}{4}\right)^2 \times \frac{3}{4} \times \left(\frac{6}{23}\right)^2$$
$$\simeq 0.003\,47 + 0.003\,33 + 0.003\,19$$
$$\simeq 0.0100.$$

Solution 16.3

(a) Since $n + 1 = 4$, $\beta = 1.8$ and $\gamma = 1.2$,
$$\rho = \frac{n\gamma}{\beta} = \frac{3 \times 1.2}{1.8} = 2.$$

(b) Since $x_0 = 3$ and $y_0 = 1$, if no one catches the infection, then $X_\infty = 3$ and the epidemic path is as shown in Figure S.6.

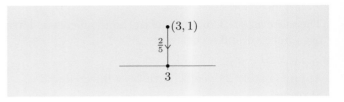

Figure S.6   No infection: $X_\infty = 3$

When $x = 3$, the probability of a removal next is
$$\frac{\rho}{x + \rho} = \frac{2}{3 + 2} = \frac{2}{5}.$$
Therefore the probability of the path in Figure S.6 is $\frac{2}{5}$.

(c) If one person catches the infection during the epidemic, then $X_\infty = 2$, and the epidemic path is as shown in Figure S.7.

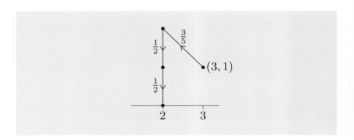

Figure S.7   One infection: $X_\infty = 2$

When $x = 3$, the probability of an infection next is
$$\frac{x}{x + \rho} = \frac{3}{3 + 2} = \frac{3}{5}.$$
When $x = 2$, the probability of a removal next is
$$\frac{\rho}{x + \rho} = \frac{2}{2 + 2} = \frac{1}{2}.$$
These probabilities are shown on the path in Figure S.7.

Hence
$$P(X_\infty = 2) = \frac{3}{5} \times \frac{1}{2} \times \frac{1}{2} = \frac{3}{20}.$$

(d) If two people catch the infection, then $X_\infty = 1$, and there are two possible epidemic paths, as shown in Figure S.8.

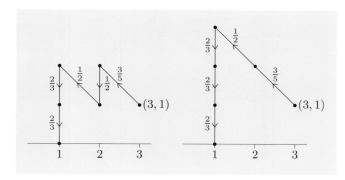

Figure S.8 Two infections: $X_\infty = 1$

The probabilities of the transitions are also shown on the paths in Figure S.8. (When $x = 2$, the probability of an infection next is $x/(x + \rho) = \frac{1}{2}$. When $x = 1$, the probability of a removal next is $\rho/(x + \rho) = \frac{2}{3}$.)

The probability that there will be two infections is

$$P(X_\infty = 1) = \frac{3}{5} \times \frac{1}{2} \times \frac{1}{2} \times \frac{2}{3} \times \frac{2}{3}$$
$$+ \frac{3}{5} \times \frac{1}{2} \times \frac{2}{3} \times \frac{2}{3} \times \frac{2}{3}$$
$$= \frac{1}{15} + \frac{4}{45}$$
$$= \frac{7}{45}.$$

(e) The probability that all the family will be infected can be found by subtraction:

$$P(3 \text{ infections}) = 1 - P(0 \text{ or } 1 \text{ or } 2 \text{ infections})$$
$$= 1 - \frac{2}{5} - \frac{3}{20} - \frac{7}{45}$$
$$= \frac{53}{180}.$$

That is,

$$P(X_\infty = 0) = \frac{53}{180}.$$

(f) The p.m.f. of X_∞ is given in the following table.

x	0	1	2	3
$P(X_\infty = x)$	$\frac{53}{180}$	$\frac{7}{45}$	$\frac{3}{20}$	$\frac{2}{5}$

This is the survivor distribution for the epidemic.

Solution 16.4

(a) The expected number of survivors is

$$E(X_\infty) = 0 \times 0.294 + 1 \times 0.156 + 2 \times 0.15 + 3 \times 0.4$$
$$\simeq 1.66.$$

(b) The number of survivors in the corresponding deterministic model is the smaller solution of

$$x = 3 \exp\left(\frac{x - 4}{2}\right).$$

Using formula iteration gives $x_\infty = 0.53$ correct to two decimal places. In this case, the community is small and the deterministic model has not provided a very 'clear' indication of what is 'likely' to happen.

Solution 17.1

Since $n + 1 = 36$, $\beta = 7$ and $\gamma = 1.2$,

$$\rho = \frac{n\gamma}{\beta} = \frac{35 \times 1.2}{7} = 6.$$

Using (17.1) with $x_0 = 34$, $y_0 = 2$ and $\rho = 6$, an approximate value for the probability of a minor outbreak is

$$P(\text{minor outbreak}) \simeq \left(\frac{6}{34}\right)^2 \simeq 0.031.$$

Using (17.2),

$$P(\text{major outbreak}) \simeq 1 - 0.031 = 0.969.$$

Solution 19.1

(a) The proportion of members of the population who live beyond the age of 70 years is

$$Q(70) = \frac{900}{100^2} = 0.09.$$

The proportion of members who live for less than 20 years is

$$1 - Q(20) = 1 - \frac{900}{50^2} = 0.64.$$

(b) Using (19.1), the expectation of life at birth (in years) is

$$e_0 = \int_0^\infty Q(x)\,dx$$
$$= \int_0^\infty \frac{900}{(30 + x)^2}\,dx$$
$$= \left[-\frac{900}{30 + x}\right]_0^\infty$$
$$= 30.$$

Solution 19.2

(a) Using (19.3), the age-specific death rate is

$$h(x) = -\frac{1}{Q(x)}\frac{dQ}{dx}$$
$$= -\frac{(30 + x)^2}{900} \times \frac{-1800}{(30 + x)^3}$$
$$= \frac{2}{30 + x}, \quad x \geq 0.$$

(b) A sketch of $h(x)$ is shown in Figure S.9.

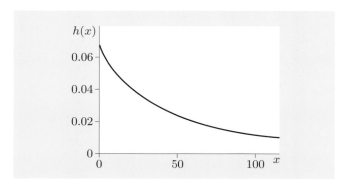

Figure S.9 The age-specific death rate

Death rates decrease with age. The longer an individual lives, the less likely it becomes that they will die in the near future.

Solution 19.3

First,

$$\int_0^x h(u)\,du = \int_0^x \frac{4}{2+u}\,du$$
$$= \left[4\log(2+u)\right]_0^x$$
$$= 4\log(2+x) - 4\log 2$$
$$= 4\log\left(\frac{2+x}{2}\right).$$

Using (19.4), it follows that for $x \geq 0$,

$$Q(x) = \exp\left(-4\log\left(\frac{2+x}{2}\right)\right)$$
$$= \exp\left(\log\left(\frac{2}{2+x}\right)^4\right)$$
$$= \left(\frac{2}{2+x}\right)^4.$$

Solution 19.4

Using (19.4) with $h(x) = \nu$ gives

$$Q(x) = \exp\left(-\int_0^x \nu\,dt\right) = e^{-\nu x}.$$

The corresponding c.d.f. $F(x)$ of the length of life X is

$$F(x) = 1 - Q(x)$$
$$= 1 - e^{-\nu x}, \quad x \geq 0.$$

This is the c.d.f. of an exponential distribution with parameter ν. Therefore the assumption of a constant death rate ν implies that the length of life of an individual member of the population has an exponential distribution with parameter ν. Thus the only lifetime distribution for which the death rate is independent of age is the exponential distribution.

Solution 19.5

(a) First,

$$\int_0^x h(u)\,du = \int_0^x \frac{1}{90-u}\,du$$
$$= \left[-\log(90-u)\right]_0^x$$
$$= -\log(90-x) + \log 90$$
$$= -\log\left(1 - \frac{x}{90}\right).$$

Using (19.4), it follows that for $0 \leq x < 90$,

$$Q(x) = \exp\left(\log\left(1 - \frac{x}{90}\right)\right)$$
$$= 1 - \frac{x}{90}.$$

Hence the c.d.f. of the lifetime of individuals is

$$F(x) = 1 - Q(x) = \frac{x}{90}, \quad 0 \leq x < 90.$$

(b) This is the c.d.f. of a continuous uniform distribution: $X \sim U(0, 90)$. This has mean 45, so $e_0 = 45$ years.

Solution 20.1

(a) The life table function for Graunt's life table is shown in Figure S.10.

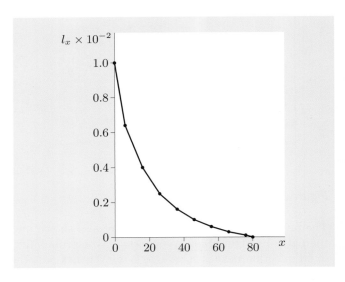

Figure S.10   The life table function

(b) An approximate value of the expectation of life at birth is given by

$$e_0 \simeq \sum_x \frac{k}{2}(l_x + l_{x+k}) \times 10^{-2},$$

so

$$10^2 \times e_0 \simeq \frac{6}{2}(l_0 + l_6) + \frac{10}{2}(l_6 + l_{16}) + \frac{10}{2}(l_{16} + l_{26}) + \cdots$$
$$+ \frac{10}{2}(l_{66} + l_{76}) + \frac{4}{2}(l_{76} + l_{80})$$
$$= 3l_0 + 8l_6 + 10(l_{16} + \cdots + l_{66}) + 7l_{76} + 2l_{80}$$
$$= 1819.$$

For the population on which Graunt based his life table, the expectation of life at birth was approximately 18.2 years.

Solution 20.2

The values of m_x are given in the table below.

x	m_x
0	0.073
6	0.046
16	0.046
26	0.044
36	0.046
46	0.050
56	0.067
66	0.100
76	0.500

For example,

$$m_0 = \frac{2(100 - 64)}{6(100 + 64)} \simeq 0.073,$$

$$m_6 = \frac{2(64 - 40)}{10(64 + 40)} \simeq 0.046$$

and

$$m_{76} = \frac{2(1 - 0)}{4(1 + 0)} = 0.500.$$

Notice that the lack of detailed information on deaths during infancy means that it is not possible to detect the high rate of infant mortality that also occurred in Graunt's time.

Solution 21.1

(a) From the solution to Activity 19.1,

$$e_0 = 30,$$

so for $x \geq 0$,

$$g(x) = \frac{1}{30} \times \frac{900}{(30 + x)^2} = \frac{30}{(30 + x)^2}.$$

(b) The proportion of individuals aged under 15 years is

$$\int_0^{15} g(x)\,dx = \int_0^{15} \frac{30}{(30 + x)^2}\,dx$$

$$= \left[-\frac{30}{30 + x} \right]_0^{15}$$

$$= \tfrac{1}{3}.$$

The proportion of individuals aged 65 years and over is

$$\int_{65}^{\infty} g(x)\,dx = \int_{65}^{\infty} \frac{30}{(30 + x)^2}\,dx$$

$$= \left[-\frac{30}{30 + x} \right]_{65}^{\infty}$$

$$= \tfrac{30}{95}.$$

Therefore the dependency ratio for the population is

$$\left(\tfrac{1}{3} + \tfrac{30}{95} \right) / \left(1 - \tfrac{1}{3} - \tfrac{30}{95} \right) = 1.85.$$

Roughly speaking, for every 100 members of the population of working age, there are 185 'dependent' individuals.

Solution 21.2

(a) Using (19.1), the expectation of life at birth (in years) is

$$e_0 = \int_0^{\infty} Q(x)\,dx$$

$$= \int_0^{90} \left(1 - \frac{x}{90} \right)^5 dx$$

$$= \left[-90 \times \frac{1}{6} \left(1 - \frac{x}{90} \right)^6 \right]_0^{90}$$

$$= 15.$$

Therefore for $0 \leq x < 90$,

$$g(x) = \frac{Q(x)}{e_0} = \frac{1}{15} \left(1 - \frac{x}{90} \right)^5.$$

(b) The proportion of members who live for more than 30 years is given by

$$Q(30) = \left(1 - \tfrac{30}{90} \right)^5 = \left(\tfrac{2}{3} \right)^5 \simeq 0.1317.$$

(c) At any time, the proportion of the population aged over 30 years is

$$\int_{30}^{\infty} g(x)\,dx = \frac{1}{15} \int_{30}^{90} \left(1 - \frac{x}{90} \right)^5 dx$$

$$= \frac{1}{15} \left[-15 \left(1 - \frac{x}{90} \right)^6 \right]_{30}^{90}$$

$$= \left(\tfrac{2}{3} \right)^6$$

$$\simeq 0.0878.$$

Solution 21.3

(a) The mean of the uniform distribution $U(0, 90)$ is 45, so

$$e_0 = 45.$$

Therefore the p.d.f. of the stationary age distribution is

$$g(x) = \frac{Q(x)}{e_0} = \frac{1}{45} \left(1 - \frac{x}{90} \right), \quad 0 \leq x < 90.$$

(b) The mean age of members of the population (in years) is

$$\int_0^{\infty} x\,g(x)\,dx = \frac{1}{45} \int_0^{90} \left(x - \frac{x^2}{90} \right) dx$$

$$= \frac{1}{45} \left[\frac{x^2}{2} - \frac{x^3}{270} \right]_0^{90}$$

$$= 30.$$

(c) The median age m satisfies

$$\int_0^m g(x)\,dx = 0.5,$$

that is,

$$\frac{1}{45} \int_0^m \left(1 - \frac{x}{90} \right) dx = 0.5,$$

so

$$\left[x - \frac{x^2}{180} \right]_0^m = 22.5,$$

thus

$$m - \frac{m^2}{180} = 22.5,$$

or

$$m^2 - 180m + 4050 = 0.$$

Hence

$$m = \frac{180 - \sqrt{180^2 - 16\,200}}{2} \simeq 26.4 \text{ years.}$$

Solution 21.4

(a) The mean lifetime (in weeks) is

$$e_0 = \int_0^{\infty} Q(x)\,dx$$

$$= \int_0^2 \left(1 - \frac{x^5}{32} \right) dx$$

$$= \left[x - \frac{x^6}{192} \right]_0^2$$

$$= 1\tfrac{2}{3}.$$

(b) The p.d.f. of the stationary age distribution is

$$g(x) = \frac{Q(x)}{e_0} = \frac{3}{5}\left(1 - \frac{x^5}{32}\right), \quad 0 \le x < 2.$$

Therefore the mean age of the insects (in weeks) is

$$\int_0^\infty x\,g(x)\,dx = \int_0^2 \frac{3}{5}x\left(1 - \frac{x^5}{32}\right)dx$$
$$= \frac{3}{5}\left[\frac{x^2}{2} - \frac{x^7}{224}\right]_0^2$$
$$= \tfrac{6}{7}.$$

(c) The proportion of insects that live for less than one week is

$$1 - Q(1) = 1 - \left(1 - \tfrac{1}{32}\right) = \tfrac{1}{32}.$$

(d) At any time, the proportion of insects that are less than one week old is

$$\int_0^1 g(x)\,dx = \int_0^1 \frac{3}{5}\left(1 - \frac{x^5}{32}\right)dx$$
$$= \frac{3}{5}\left[x - \frac{x^6}{192}\right]_0^1$$
$$\simeq 0.597.$$

Solution 21.5

(a) The expectation of life at birth (in days) is given by

$$e_0 = \int_0^\infty Q(x)\,dx$$
$$= \int_0^\infty \frac{16}{(2+x)^4}\,dx$$
$$= \left[-\frac{16}{3(2+x)^3}\right]_0^\infty$$
$$= \tfrac{2}{3}.$$

(b) The p.d.f. of the stationary age distribution is

$$g(x) = \frac{Q(x)}{e_0} = \frac{24}{(2+x)^4}, \quad x \ge 0.$$

Therefore the mean age (in days) of members of the population is given by

$$\int_0^\infty x\,g(x)\,dx = \int_0^\infty \frac{24x}{(2+x)^4}\,dx.$$

Using the substitution $u = 2 + x$, this is equal to

$$\int_2^\infty \frac{24(u-2)}{u^4}\,du = \int_2^\infty\left(\frac{24}{u^3} - \frac{48}{u^4}\right)du$$
$$= \left[-\frac{12}{u^2} + \frac{16}{u^3}\right]_2^\infty$$
$$= 1.$$

Solution 22.1

(a) From the solution to Activity 21.1, the p.d.f. of the stationary age distribution is

$$g(x) = \frac{30}{(30+x)^2}, \quad x \ge 0.$$

A sketch of the p.d.f. is shown in Figure S.11.

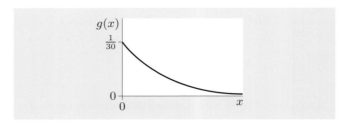

Figure S.11   The p.d.f. of the stationary age distribution

(b) The p.d.f. of the stable age distribution has the form

$$g(x) = \frac{ke^{-\theta x}}{(30+x)^2}, \quad x \ge 0.$$

(i) If the population is growing, then $\theta > 0$ and a greater proportion of the population is in the younger age groups than for the corresponding stationary population. The shape of the p.d.f. of the age distribution might be as shown in Figure S.12.

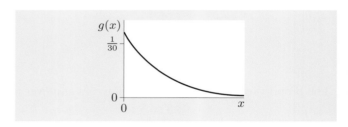

Figure S.12   The p.d.f. of the stable age distribution when $\theta > 0$

(ii) If the population is declining, then $\theta < 0$ and a smaller proportion of the population is in the younger age groups than in the corresponding stationary population. The shape of the p.d.f. depends on the value of θ. Three possibilities are shown in Figure S.13.

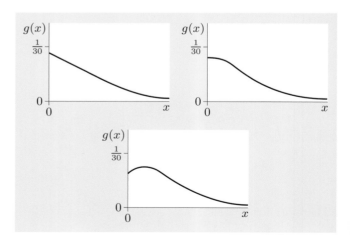

Figure S.13   The p.d.f. of the stable age distribution: possible shapes when $\theta < 0$

Solution 23.1

(a) For a growing stable population, a larger proportion of the population is in the younger age groups than for the corresponding stationary population. The p.d.f. might look that in Figure 22.3, so a population pyramid might look like the one in Figure S.14.

(b) For a stable population that is declining, a smaller proportion of the population is in the younger age groups than for the corresponding stationary population. Three possibilities for the shape of the p.d.f. of the stable distribution were shown in Figure 22.4. It follows that the shape of the population pyramid might resemble any of those in Figure S.15.

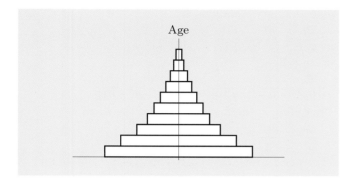

Figure S.14   Stable and growing

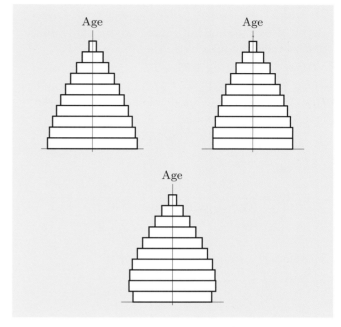

Figure S.15   Stable and declining

171

Solutions to Exercises

Solution 1.1

(a) If there are five individuals alive at the start, then $T_1 \sim M(5\beta)$, and hence
$$E(T_1) = \frac{1}{5\beta}, \quad V(T_1) = \frac{1}{25\beta^2}.$$

(b) If W is the time until there are ten individuals, that is, until the fifth birth, then
$$W = T_1 + T_2 + T_3 + T_4 + T_5,$$
where $T_2 \sim M(6\beta)$, $T_3 \sim M(7\beta)$, $T_4 \sim M(8\beta)$ and $T_5 \sim M(9\beta)$. Hence
$$E(W) = \frac{1}{5\beta} + \frac{1}{6\beta} + \frac{1}{7\beta} + \frac{1}{8\beta} + \frac{1}{9\beta}$$
$$\simeq \frac{0.746}{\beta},$$
$$V(W) = \frac{1}{25\beta^2} + \frac{1}{36\beta^2} + \frac{1}{49\beta^2} + \frac{1}{64\beta^2} + \frac{1}{81\beta^2}$$
$$\simeq \frac{0.1162}{\beta^2}.$$
Therefore the standard deviation of W is
$$\sqrt{V(W)} \simeq \frac{0.341}{\beta}.$$

Solution 1.2

(a) Since there are five individuals alive initially, the distribution of the time until the first death is $M(5\nu)$, and
$$E(W) = \frac{1}{5\nu} + \frac{1}{4\nu} + \frac{1}{3\nu} + \frac{1}{2\nu} + \frac{1}{\nu}$$
$$\simeq \frac{2.28}{\nu},$$
$$V(W) = \frac{1}{25\nu^2} + \frac{1}{16\nu^2} + \frac{1}{9\nu^2} + \frac{1}{4\nu^2} + \frac{1}{\nu^2}$$
$$\simeq \frac{1.46}{\nu^2}.$$

(b) Using (1.1), $X(t) \sim B(5, e^{-\nu t})$, so
$$P(X(t) = 3) = \binom{5}{3} e^{-3\nu t}(1 - e^{-\nu t})^2$$
$$= 10e^{-3\nu t}(1 - e^{-\nu t})^2.$$

(c) The probability required is
$$P(W > t) = 1 - P(W \le t)$$
$$= 1 - (1 - e^{-\nu t})^5,$$
using (1.2).

Solution 3.1

The partial differential equation is already in Lagrange form, with
$$f = 2st, \quad g = -s, \quad h = 2t\Pi.$$
The auxiliary equations are
$$\frac{ds}{2st} = \frac{dt}{-s} = \frac{d\Pi}{2t\Pi}$$
or, in full,
$$\frac{ds}{2st} = \frac{dt}{-s}, \quad \frac{ds}{2st} = \frac{d\Pi}{2t\Pi}, \quad \frac{dt}{-s} = \frac{d\Pi}{2t\Pi}.$$
Cancelling s, the first equation of the three is
$$\frac{ds}{2t} = \frac{dt}{-1}$$
or
$$\int -1 \, ds = \int 2t \, dt,$$
which gives
$$c_1 = s + t^2.$$
Cancelling $2t$, the second equation of the three gives
$$\int \frac{ds}{s} = \int \frac{d\Pi}{\Pi}.$$
So
$$\log s = \log \Pi + \text{constant},$$
which gives
$$c_2 = \frac{\Pi}{s}.$$
Writing $c_2 = \psi(c_1)$, the general solution to the partial differential equation is
$$\frac{\Pi}{s} = \psi(s + t^2)$$
or
$$\Pi(s, t) = s\,\psi(s + t^2).$$
Setting $t = 0$ in the general solution gives
$$\Pi(s, 0) = s\,\psi(s).$$
The initial condition is $\Pi(s, 0) = s^3$, so
$$s\,\psi(s) = s^3$$
or
$$\psi(s) = s^2.$$
Therefore the particular solution is
$$\Pi(s, t) = s\,\psi(s + t^2)$$
$$= s(s + t^2)^2.$$
(Remember that $\psi(s + t^2)$ is obtained by replacing s with $s + t^2$ in the formula for $\psi(s)$.)

Solution 3.2

The partial differential equation is already in Lagrange form, with

$$f = 0, \quad g = 1, \quad h = 1 + s\Pi.$$

The auxiliary equations are

$$\frac{ds}{0} = \frac{dt}{1} = \frac{d\Pi}{1 + s\Pi}.$$

Since $ds/0$ appears, one solution is

$$c_1 = s.$$

Taking the second and third expressions gives

$$\int 1 \, dt = \int \frac{1}{1 + s\Pi} \, d\Pi.$$

From the first solution, s may be treated as a constant, so a second solution is

$$t = \frac{1}{s} \log(1 + s\Pi) + \text{constant},$$

or (since s is treated as a constant)

$$\text{constant} = \log(1 + s\Pi) - st.$$

Taking exponentials gives

$$c_2 = (1 + s\Pi)e^{-st}.$$

Since c_2 includes Π, the general solution is given by $c_2 = \psi(c_1)$:

$$(1 + s\Pi)e^{-st} = \psi(s).$$

That is,

$$\Pi(s, t) = \frac{1}{s}(e^{st}\,\psi(s) - 1).$$

Setting $t = 0$ gives

$$\Pi(s, 0) = \frac{1}{s}(\psi(s) - 1).$$

The initial condition is $\Pi(s, 0) = s$, so

$$\frac{1}{s}(\psi(s) - 1) = s,$$

or

$$\psi(s) = 1 + s^2.$$

Therefore the particular solution is

$$\Pi(s, t) = \frac{1}{s}(e^{st}(1 + s^2) - 1).$$

Solution 4.1

(a) Since $X(0) = 2$,

$$\Pi(s, 0) = s^2.$$

Setting $t = 0$ in the general solution (4.2) gives

$$\Pi(s, 0) = \psi\left(\frac{s}{1 - s}\right).$$

Therefore

$$\psi\left(\frac{s}{1 - s}\right) = s^2.$$

Writing $x = s/(1 - s)$, so that $s = x/(1 + x)$, gives

$$\psi(x) = \left(\frac{x}{1 + x}\right)^2.$$

Hence

$$\Pi(s, t) = \psi\left(\frac{s}{1 - s}\, e^{-\beta t}\right)$$

$$= \left(\frac{\dfrac{s}{1 - s}\, e^{-\beta t}}{1 + \dfrac{s}{1 - s}\, e^{-\beta t}}\right)^2$$

$$= \left(\frac{e^{-\beta t} s}{1 - (1 - e^{-\beta t})s}\right)^2.$$

Therefore $X(t)$ has a negative binomial distribution with range $\{2, 3, \ldots\}$ and parameters $r = 2$ and $p = e^{-\beta t}$.

(b) The formula for the p.m.f. of a negative binomial distribution is given in Table 8 in the *Handbook*. Using this formula,

$$P(X(t) = 2) = e^{-2\beta t},$$

$$P(X(t) = 3) = 2e^{-2\beta t}(1 - e^{-\beta t}).$$

(c) The event $W_2 \leq t$ is equivalent to the event $X(t) \geq 4$, because after two births the population contains four individuals. Therefore the c.d.f. of W_2 is

$$P(W_2 \leq t) = P(X(t) \geq 4)$$

$$= 1 - P(X(t) = 2) - P(X(t) = 3)$$

$$= 1 - e^{-2\beta t} - 2e^{-2\beta t}(1 - e^{-\beta t})$$

$$= 1 - 3e^{-2\beta t} + 2e^{-3\beta t}.$$

Solution 4.2

(a) The p.g.f. of $X(0)$ is $\Pi(s, 0)$, so $\Pi(s, 0)$ is the p.g.f. of the negative binomial distribution with range $\{0, 1, \ldots\}$ and parameters $r = 3$ and $p = \frac{3}{4}$:

$$\Pi(s, 0) = \left(\frac{\frac{1}{4}}{1 - \frac{3}{4}s}\right)^3 = \left(\frac{1}{4 - 3s}\right)^3.$$

Setting $\lambda = 3\beta$ and $t = 0$ in the general solution (4.6) for $\Pi(s, t)$ gives

$$\Pi(s, 0) = s^{-3}\,\psi\left(\frac{s}{1 - s}\right).$$

Therefore

$$s^{-3}\,\psi\left(\frac{s}{1 - s}\right) = \left(\frac{1}{4 - 3s}\right)^3,$$

or

$$\psi\left(\frac{s}{1 - s}\right) = \left(\frac{s}{4 - 3s}\right)^3.$$

Writing $x = s/(1 - s)$, so that $s = x/(1 + x)$, gives

$$\psi(x) = \left(\frac{x/(1 + x)}{4 - 3x/(1 + x)}\right)^3$$

$$= \left(\frac{x}{4 + x}\right)^3.$$

Therefore

$$\Pi(s,t) = s^{-3}\psi\left(\frac{s}{1-s}e^{-\beta t}\right)$$

$$= s^{-3}\left(\frac{\frac{s}{1-s}e^{-\beta t}}{4+\frac{s}{1-s}e^{-\beta t}}\right)^3$$

$$= \left(\frac{e^{-\beta t}}{4(1-s)+se^{-\beta t}}\right)^3$$

$$= \left(\frac{\frac{1}{4}e^{-\beta t}}{1-(1-\frac{1}{4}e^{-\beta t})s}\right)^3.$$

(b) This is the p.g.f. of a negative binomial distribution with range $\{0,1,\dots\}$ and parameters $r = 3$ and $p = 1 - \frac{1}{4}e^{-\beta t}$. Hence

$$E[X(t)] = \frac{rp}{q} = \frac{3(1-\frac{1}{4}e^{-\beta t})}{\frac{1}{4}e^{-\beta t}}$$

$$= 3(4e^{\beta t}-1).$$

Solution 6.1

(a) Using (6.6) with $n = 1$, $\beta = 1$ gives

$$\Pi(s,t) = \frac{t-(t-1)s}{t+1-ts}.$$

Therefore $X(t)$ has a modified geometric distribution with

$$a = t, \quad b = t-1, \quad c = t+1, \quad d = t.$$

(b) When $t = 1$,

$$a = 1, \quad b = 0, \quad c = 2, \quad d = 1,$$

so the p.g.f. reduces to

$$\Pi(s,1) = \frac{1}{2-s} = \frac{\frac{1}{2}}{1-\frac{1}{2}s}.$$

Therefore $X(1) \sim G_0\left(\frac{1}{2}\right)$.

(i) $P(X(1) = 0) = \frac{1}{2}$.

(ii) $P(X(1) = 1) = \left(\frac{1}{2}\right)^2 = \frac{1}{4}$.

(iii) $P(X(1) = 2) = \left(\frac{1}{2}\right)^3 = \frac{1}{8}$.

(c) When $t = 3$,

$$a = 3, \quad b = 2, \quad c = 4, \quad d = 3.$$

Using the p.m.f. given in Table 8 in the *Handbook*,

$$P(X(3) = 0) = \frac{a}{c} = \frac{3}{4},$$

$$P(X(3) = 1) = \frac{ad-bc}{c^2} = \frac{1}{16}.$$

Therefore

$$P(X(3) > 1) = 1 - \frac{3}{4} - \frac{1}{16} = \frac{3}{16} = 0.1875.$$

Solution 6.2

(a) For each change,

$$P(\text{birth}) = \frac{\beta}{\beta+\nu} = \frac{5}{8},$$

$$P(\text{death}) = \frac{\nu}{\beta+\nu} = \frac{3}{8}.$$

So the probability of two births followed by a death is

$$\left(\frac{5}{8}\right)^2 \times \frac{3}{8} = \frac{75}{512} \simeq 0.1465.$$

(b) For the embedded random walk, $p = \frac{5}{8}$ and $q = \frac{3}{8}$. The probability required is the probability of ruin when gambling against a casino and starting with £4:

$$q_4 = \left(\frac{q}{p}\right)^4 = 0.6^4 = 0.1296.$$

(c) The probability required is the probability of ruin in the gambler's ruin when $j = 4$, $a = 10$, $p = \frac{5}{8}$ and $q = \frac{3}{8}$:

$$q_4 = \frac{(q/p)^4 - (q/p)^{10}}{1-(q/p)^{10}}$$

$$= \frac{0.6^4 - 0.6^{10}}{1-0.6^{10}}$$

$$\simeq 0.1243.$$

(d) The probability required is

$$1 - q_4 \simeq 1 - 0.1243 = 0.8757.$$

Solution 7.1

(a) Since $\lambda = 0.4$ and $\nu = 0.5$,

$$X(t) \sim \text{Poisson}(0.8(1-e^{-0.5t})).$$

(i) The expected population size at time t is

$$E[X(t)] = 0.8(1-e^{-0.5t}).$$

(ii) From above, $X(1)$ has a Poisson distribution with parameter

$$0.8(1-e^{-0.5}) \simeq 0.3148.$$

So the probability that the population contains two individuals at time $t = 1$ is

$$P(X(1) = 2) = \frac{e^{-0.3148}0.3148^2}{2!} \simeq 0.0362.$$

(b) The equilibrium distribution is Poisson with parameter $\lambda/\nu = 0.8$, so the proportion of the time in the long run that the population contains two individuals is given by

$$p_2 = \frac{e^{-0.8}0.8^2}{2!} \simeq 0.1438.$$

Solution 8.1

(a) For the immigration–death process,

$$h_1(x,t) = \lambda, \quad h_{-1}(x,t) = \nu x.$$

Using (8.3), the deterministic approximation is the solution of the differential equation

$$\frac{dz}{dt} = \lambda - \nu z.$$

(b) Using separation of variables gives

$$\int \frac{-\nu}{\lambda - \nu z} \, dz = \int -\nu \, dt,$$

so

$$\log(\lambda - \nu z) = -\nu t + \text{constant}.$$

Since $z = 0$ when $t = 0$,

$$\log \lambda = \text{constant},$$

and hence

$$\log\left(1 - \frac{\nu}{\lambda} z\right) = -\nu t.$$

Taking exponentials gives

$$1 - \frac{\nu}{\lambda} z = e^{-\nu t},$$

so

$$z = \frac{\lambda}{\nu}(1 - e^{-\nu t}).$$

Solution 9.1

(a) Customers arrive at random at a place where there are three servers on duty. The time taken to complete a service has a gamma distribution.

(b) Customers arrive at equally-spaced intervals, and there is one server on duty. The distribution of the service time is not known.

Solution 9.2

(a) $M/D/2$

(b) $D/M/1$

Solution 10.1

(a) The arrival rate is

$$\lambda = \tfrac{2}{5} \text{ per minute} = 24 \text{ per hour}.$$

The mean service time is $1/\varepsilon = 2$ minutes, so the service rate is

$$\varepsilon = \tfrac{1}{2} \text{ per minute} = 30 \text{ per hour}.$$

The traffic intensity is

$$\rho = \lambda/\varepsilon = \tfrac{2}{5} / \tfrac{1}{2} = \tfrac{4}{5} = 0.8.$$

(Alternatively, $\rho = 24/30 = 0.8$.)

(b) The average number of customers in the shop is the mean equilibrium queue size, that is, the mean of $G_0(\rho)$:

$$E(X) = \frac{\rho}{1 - \rho} = \frac{0.8}{1 - 0.8} = 4.$$

(c) The proportion of customers that receive immediate service is

$$p_0 = 1 - \rho = 0.2.$$

(d) The queueing time in minutes has an exponential distribution with parameter

$$\varepsilon - \lambda = \tfrac{1}{2} - \tfrac{2}{5} = \tfrac{1}{10} = 0.1.$$

Therefore the mean time in minutes that a customer spends in the shop is

$$\frac{1}{\varepsilon - \lambda} = 10.$$

(e) If W is the queueing time, then the probability that a customer will be in the shop for more than a quarter of an hour (15 minutes) is

$$P(W > 15) = 1 - (1 - e^{-0.1 \times 15})$$
$$= e^{-1.5}$$
$$\simeq 0.2231.$$

(f) The expected duration of a busy period in minutes is

$$\frac{1}{\varepsilon - \lambda} = 10.$$

Solution 11.1

(a) The queue specification is $M/M/5$.

Since $\lambda = 18$ per hour and $\varepsilon = 6$ per hour, the traffic intensity is

$$\rho = \frac{\lambda}{n\varepsilon} = \frac{18}{5 \times 6} = \frac{3}{5}.$$

(b) The distribution of X, the equilibrium queue size, is given by (11.1), (11.2) and (11.3):

$$p_x = \begin{cases} \dfrac{1}{K} \dfrac{5^x}{x!} \left(\dfrac{3}{5}\right)^x, & x = 0, 1, 2, 3, 4, \\[2mm] \dfrac{1}{K} \dfrac{5^5}{5!} \left(\dfrac{3}{5}\right)^x, & x = 5, 6, \dots, \end{cases}$$

where

$$K = 1 + 5\rho + \frac{(5\rho)^2}{2!} + \frac{(5\rho)^3}{3!} + \frac{(5\rho)^4}{4!} + \frac{(5\rho)^5}{5!(1 - \rho)}$$
$$= 1 + 3 + \tfrac{9}{2} + \tfrac{9}{2} + \tfrac{27}{8} + \tfrac{81}{16}$$
$$= \tfrac{343}{16} (= 21.4375).$$

Therefore the proportion of time that all five advisers are free is

$$p_0 = \frac{1}{K} = \frac{16}{343} \simeq 0.0466.$$

(c) The proportion of time that exactly three advisers are busy is

$$p_3 = \frac{1}{K} \frac{5^3}{3!} \left(\frac{3}{5}\right)^3 = \frac{16}{343} \times \frac{9}{2} = \frac{72}{343} \simeq 0.2099.$$

(d) If all five advisers are busy and one person is waiting, then the queue size is 6. Therefore the probability required is

$$p_6 = \frac{1}{K} \frac{5^5}{5!} \left(\frac{3}{5}\right)^6 = \frac{16}{343} \times \frac{729}{600} \simeq 0.0567.$$

(e) Since the service time of an adviser is exponentially distributed with parameter ε, and $\varepsilon = 6$ per hour $= 0.1$ per minute, the time in minutes that Sam has to wait is the minimum of five service times each of which is $M(0.1)$. Therefore W, Sam's waiting time, is exponentially distributed with parameter

$$0.1 + 0.1 + 0.1 + 0.1 + 0.1 = 0.5.$$

Hence the probability that he will have to wait for at least five minutes is

$$P(W > 5) = e^{-0.5 \times 5} \simeq 0.0821.$$

Alternatively, the probability that any particular adviser is busy for at least five minutes is

$$P(T \geq 5) = e^{-0.1 \times 5} = e^{-0.5}.$$

Therefore the probability that all five advisers are busy for at least five minutes is

$$(e^{-0.5})^5 = e^{-2.5} \simeq 0.0821.$$

Solution 12.1

(a) For this $M/D/1$ queue,

$\lambda = \frac{1}{20}$ per minute,

$E(T) = 12$ minutes,

so

$\rho = \frac{1}{20} \times 12 = 0.6.$

Since the service time is constant,

$V(T) = 0.$

Using Pollaczek's formula (12.2), the mean equilibrium queue size is

$$\mu_X = \frac{0.6 - \frac{1}{2} \times 0.6^2}{1 - 0.6} = 1.05.$$

(b) For this $M/U/1$ queue,

$\lambda = \frac{1}{20}$ per minute $= 0.05$ per minute,

$E(T) = 12$ minutes,

so

$\rho = \frac{1}{20} \times 12 = 0.6.$

The variance of T is

$$V(T) = \frac{1}{12}(20 - 4)^2 = \frac{256}{12} = \frac{64}{3}.$$

Using (12.2), the mean equilibrium queue size is

$$\mu_X = \frac{0.6 - \frac{1}{2} \times 0.6^2 + \frac{1}{2} \times 0.05^2 \times \frac{64}{3}}{1 - 0.6} \simeq 1.117.$$

Solution 14.1

(a) The epidemic rate β_y is given by (14.5) with $\beta = 4$ and $n + 1 = 8$, so

$$\beta_y = \frac{4y(8 - y)}{7}.$$

Therefore $\beta_4 = 64/7$, $\beta_5 = 60/7$, $\beta_6 = 48/7$ and $\beta_7 = 4$.

Since $y_0 = 4$, the time to the first new infection is T_4, where $T_4 \sim M(\beta_4)$, so the expected time (in days) to the first new infection is

$$E(T_4) = \frac{1}{\beta_4} = \frac{7}{64} \simeq 0.1094.$$

The expected time (in days) to the second new infection is

$$E(T_4) + E(T_5) = \frac{1}{\beta_4} + \frac{1}{\beta_5}$$
$$= \frac{7}{64} + \frac{7}{60}$$
$$\simeq 0.2260.$$

The expected time (in days) to the third new infection is

$$E(T_4) + E(T_5) + E(T_6) = \frac{1}{\beta_4} + \frac{1}{\beta_5} + \frac{1}{\beta_6}$$
$$= \frac{7}{64} + \frac{7}{60} + \frac{7}{48}$$
$$\simeq 0.3719.$$

(b) The expected time (in days) until all eight members are infected (four new infections) is

$$E(W) = \frac{1}{\beta_4} + \frac{1}{\beta_5} + \frac{1}{\beta_6} + \frac{1}{\beta_7}$$
$$= \frac{7}{64} + \frac{7}{60} + \frac{7}{48} + \frac{1}{4}$$
$$\simeq 0.6219.$$

The variance of W is

$$V(W) = \frac{1}{\beta_4^2} + \frac{1}{\beta_5^2} + \frac{1}{\beta_6^2} + \frac{1}{\beta_7^2}$$
$$= \left(\frac{7}{64}\right)^2 + \left(\frac{7}{60}\right)^2 + \left(\frac{7}{48}\right)^2 + \left(\frac{1}{4}\right)^2$$
$$= 0.1093\ldots,$$

so the standard deviation of W (in days) is

$$\sqrt{V(W)} = \sqrt{0.1093\ldots} \simeq 0.3307.$$

Solution 14.2

(a) Using (14.8), the differential–difference equations are

$$\frac{d}{dt}p_y(t) = -\beta_y\, p_y(t) + \beta_{y-1}\, p_{y-1}(t), \quad y = 1, 2, 3.$$

Since $n + 1 = 3$ and $\beta = 0.2$ per day, the epidemic rate is

$$\beta_y = \frac{\beta y(n + 1 - y)}{n} = 0.1y(3 - y).$$

Therefore $\beta_1 = 0.2$, $\beta_2 = 0.2$, $\beta_3 = 0$, and hence the three differential equations are

$$\frac{d}{dt}p_1(t) = -0.2\, p_1(t), \tag{1}$$

$$\frac{d}{dt}p_2(t) = -0.2\, p_2(t) + 0.2\, p_1(t), \tag{2}$$

$$\frac{d}{dt}p_3(t) = 0.2\, p_2(t). \tag{3}$$

Since one member of the family is infected at the start,

$$p_1(0) = 1, \quad p_2(0) = 0, \quad p_3(0) = 0.$$

(b) The solution of (1) is

$$p_2(t) = \text{constant} \times e^{-0.2t}.$$

Since $p_1(0) = 1$, the constant is 1, and hence

$$p_1(t) = e^{-0.2t}.$$

Substituting this result in (2), and rearranging the equation, gives

$$\frac{d}{dt}p_2(t) + 0.2\, p_2(t) = 0.2e^{-0.2t}.$$

Multiplying by the integrating factor $e^{0.2t}$ leads to

$$\frac{d}{dt}\left(p_2(t)e^{0.2t}\right) = 0.2.$$

Integrating both sides with respect to t gives

$$p_2(t)\,e^{0.2t} = 0.2t + \text{constant}.$$

Since $p_2(0) = 0$, the constant is 0, and hence

$$p_2(t) = 0.2te^{-0.2t}.$$

Since $p_1(t) + p_2(t) + p_3(t) = 1$, it follows that

$$p_3(t) = 1 - e^{-0.2t} - 0.2te^{-0.2t}.$$

(Alternatively, $p_3(t)$ can be found by solving (3).)

Therefore the c.d.f. of W is

$$\begin{aligned}P(W \leq t) &= P(Y(t) = 3)\\ &= 1 - (1 + 0.2t)e^{-0.2t}, \quad t \geq 0.\end{aligned}$$

Solution 15.1

(a) Initially, there are 68 susceptibles, so $x_0 = 68$. Four people have the infection, so $y_0 = 4$. Thirteen people are immune, so there are thirteen removed: $z_0 = 13$.

The total community size is $n + 1 = 85$, so $n = 84$. The contact rate β is 0.3 per day.

The time that a person is infectious has an exponential distribution with mean one week or 7 days, so $\gamma = 1/7$ per day. Hence

$$\rho = \frac{n\gamma}{\beta} = \frac{84 \times \frac{1}{7}}{0.3} = 40.$$

(b) The epidemic reaches its height when $x = \rho$, so there will be 40 susceptibles at this time. The number of infectives at this point is given by (15.13):

$$\begin{aligned}y_{\max} &= y_0 + x_0 - \rho - \rho\log(x_0/\rho)\\ &= 32 - 40\log(68/40)\\ &\simeq 10.77.\end{aligned}$$

The maximum number of infectives at any one time is about 11.

(c) The number of uninfected susceptibles at the end of the epidemic is the smaller solution of the equation

$$x = 68\exp\left(\frac{x - 72}{40}\right)$$

(see (15.15)). This solution can be found using the iteration formula (15.16):

$$x_{\infty,j+1} = 68\exp\left(\frac{x_{\infty,j} - 72}{40}\right).$$

Taking $x_{\infty,0} = 0$ and retaining full calculator accuracy throughout gives the following results (rounded to three decimal places): $x_{\infty,1} = 11.240$, $x_{\infty,2} = 14.887$, $x_{\infty,3} = 16.309$, $x_{\infty,4} = 16.898$, $x_{\infty,5} = 17.150$, $x_{\infty,6} = 17.257$, $x_{\infty,7} = 17.304$, $x_{\infty,8} = 17.324$, $x_{\infty,9} = 17.333$, $x_{\infty,10} = 17.337$, $x_{\infty,11} = 17.338$, $x_{\infty,12} = 17.339$, $x_{\infty,13} = 17.340$, $x_{\infty,14} = 17.340$.

Therefore $x_\infty \simeq 17.34$, and hence out of the 68 original susceptibles, the number who have caught the infection and recovered is $68 - 17.34 = 50.66$, or about 51.

(d) A sketch of the trajectory of the epidemic is shown in Figure S.16.

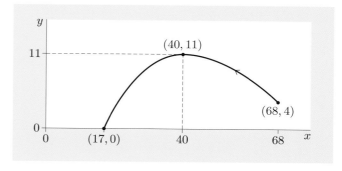

Figure S.16 Trajectory of the epidemic

Solution 16.1

(a) Since $n + 1 = 29$, $\beta = 7$ and $\gamma = 2.5$,

$$\rho = \frac{n\gamma}{\beta} = \frac{28 \times 2.5}{7} = 10.$$

(b) The three possible paths are shown in Figure S.17.

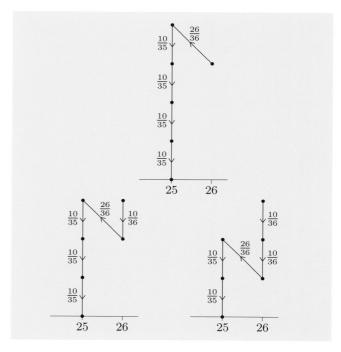

Figure S.17 Possible paths

When $x = 26$, the probability of a removal next is

$$\frac{\rho}{x + \rho} = \frac{10}{26 + 10} = \frac{10}{36},$$

and the probability of an infection next is $\frac{26}{36}$. Similarly, when $x = 25$, the probability of a removal is $\frac{10}{35}$.

The probability that exactly one susceptible will catch the infection before the epidemic ends is the sum of the probabilities of the three paths:

$$\begin{aligned}P(X_\infty = 25) &= \tfrac{26}{36} \times \left(\tfrac{10}{35}\right)^4 + \tfrac{10}{36} \times \tfrac{26}{36} \times \left(\tfrac{10}{35}\right)^3\\ &\quad + \left(\tfrac{10}{36}\right)^2 \times \tfrac{26}{36} \times \left(\tfrac{10}{35}\right)^2\\ &\simeq 0.004\,81 + 0.004\,68 + 0.004\,55\\ &\simeq 0.0140.\end{aligned}$$

Solution 17.1

From the solution to Exercise 16.1, $\rho = 10$. Using (17.1) with $x_0 = 26$, $y_0 = 3$ and $\rho = 10$,

$$P(\text{minor outbreak}) \simeq \left(\tfrac{10}{26}\right)^3 \simeq 0.057.$$

Therefore from (17.2),

$$P(\text{major outbreak}) \simeq 1 - 0.057 = 0.943.$$

Solution 19.1

(a) The p.d.f. of X is

$$f(x) = \tfrac{1}{4}, \quad 0 \le x \le 4.$$

(b) The life table function is given by

$$Q(x) = P(X > x) = \int_x^4 \tfrac{1}{4}\, du$$
$$= 1 - \frac{x}{4}, \quad 0 \le x \le 4.$$

(c) Since $X \sim U(0,4)$, the mean lifetime e_0 is 2 years, and the median lifetime is also 2 years.

(d) The proportion of fish that live for more than three years is given by

$$Q(3) = 1 - \tfrac{3}{4} = \tfrac{1}{4}.$$

The proportion of fish that live for less than one year is given by

$$1 - Q(1) = \tfrac{1}{4}.$$

(e) Using (19.3), for $0 \le x < 4$,

$$h(x) = -\frac{1}{Q(x)}\frac{dQ}{dx}$$
$$= -\frac{1}{1 - x/4} \times \left(-\tfrac{1}{4}\right)$$
$$= \frac{1}{4 - x}.$$

A sketch of $h(x)$ is shown in Figure S.18.

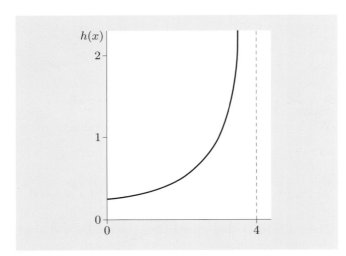

Figure S.18   Age-specific death rate

The death rate increases with age, and the older members become, the more rapidly the death rate increases.

Solution 19.2

(a) The life table function $Q(x)$ is given by

$$Q(x) = P(X > x) = \int_x^\infty f(u)\, du.$$

Therefore for $x \ge 0$,

$$Q(x) = \int_x^\infty \left(\tfrac{1}{4}e^{-u} + \tfrac{9}{4}e^{-3u}\right) du$$
$$= \left[-\tfrac{1}{4}e^{-u} - \tfrac{3}{4}e^{-3u}\right]_x^\infty$$
$$= \tfrac{1}{4}e^{-x} + \tfrac{3}{4}e^{-3x}.$$

(b) The expectation of life at birth is found using (19.1):

$$e_0 = \int_0^\infty Q(x)\, dx$$
$$= \int_0^\infty \left(\tfrac{1}{4}e^{-x} + \tfrac{3}{4}e^{-3x}\right) dx$$
$$= \left[-\tfrac{1}{4}e^{-x} - \tfrac{1}{4}e^{-3x}\right]_0^\infty$$
$$= \tfrac{1}{2}.$$

(c) The age-specific death rate is found using (19.3):

$$h(x) = -\frac{1}{Q(x)}\frac{dQ}{dx}.$$

This gives

$$h(x) = \frac{e^{-x} + 9e^{-3x}}{e^{-x} + 3e^{-3x}}, \quad x \ge 0.$$

(d) The proportion that live for longer than six months is

$$Q\left(\tfrac{1}{2}\right) = \tfrac{1}{4}e^{-0.5} + \tfrac{3}{4}e^{-1.5} \simeq 0.319.$$

Solution 19.3

(a) The life table function is found using (19.4):

$$\int_0^x h(u)\, du = \int_0^x \frac{u}{4 + 2u}\, du$$
$$= \tfrac{1}{2}\int_0^x \left(1 - \frac{4}{4 + 2u}\right) du$$
$$= \tfrac{1}{2}\int_0^x \left(1 - \frac{2}{2 + u}\right) du$$
$$= \tfrac{1}{2}\left[u - 2\log(2 + u)\right]_0^x$$
$$= \tfrac{1}{2}\left(x - 2\log(2 + x) + 2\log 2\right)$$
$$= \tfrac{1}{2}x - \log\left(1 + \tfrac{1}{2}x\right).$$

Therefore

$$Q(x) = \exp\left(-\tfrac{1}{2}x + \log(1 + \tfrac{1}{2}x)\right)$$
$$= e^{-x/2}\exp\left(\log(1 + \tfrac{1}{2}x)\right)$$
$$= \left(1 + \tfrac{1}{2}x\right)e^{-x/2}.$$

(b) The proportion of the population who live for longer than one week is

$$Q(7) = 4.5e^{-3.5} \simeq 0.136.$$

(c) The p.d.f. of the lifetime distribution is

$$f(x) = -Q'(x)$$
$$= -\tfrac{1}{2}e^{-x/2} + \tfrac{1}{2}\left(1 + \tfrac{1}{2}x\right)e^{-x/2}$$
$$= \tfrac{1}{4}xe^{-x/2}, \quad x \ge 0.$$

From Table 9 in the *Handbook*, this is the p.d.f. of a gamma distribution with parameters 2 and $\frac{1}{2}$, so $X \sim \Gamma\left(2, \frac{1}{2}\right)$.

(d) The mean lifetime is the mean of the gamma distribution $\Gamma\left(2, \frac{1}{2}\right)$. Using Table 9 in the *Handbook*,
$$e_0 = 2 \big/ \tfrac{1}{2} = 4 \text{ (days)}.$$

Solution 21.1

(a) From the solution to Exercise 19.1, $e_0 = 2$, so the p.d.f. of the age distribution of the stationary population is
$$g(x) = Q(x)/e_0 = \tfrac{1}{2}\left(1 - \tfrac{1}{4}x\right), \quad 0 \le x < 4.$$

(b) The mean age is given by
$$\int_0^\infty x\,g(x)\,dx = \int_0^4 \tfrac{1}{2}x\left(1 - \tfrac{1}{4}x\right)dx$$
$$= \int_0^4 \left(\tfrac{1}{2}x - \tfrac{1}{8}x^2\right)dx$$
$$= \left[\tfrac{1}{4}x^2 - \tfrac{1}{24}x^3\right]_0^4$$
$$= \tfrac{4}{3}.$$

The mean age is $1\tfrac{1}{3}$ years, or 1 year 4 months.

(c) The median age m is the solution of
$$\int_0^m g(x)\,dx = \tfrac{1}{2}.$$
So
$$\int_0^m \tfrac{1}{2}\left(1 - \tfrac{1}{4}x\right)dx = \tfrac{1}{2},$$
giving
$$\left[x - \tfrac{1}{8}x^2\right]_0^m = 1,$$
thus
$$m - \tfrac{1}{8}m^2 = 1,$$
or
$$m^2 - 8m + 8 = 0.$$
Since m lies between 0 and 4,
$$m = \frac{8 - \sqrt{32}}{2} = 4 - \sqrt{8} \simeq 1.17 \text{ years}.$$

(d) The proportion of fish that are more than three years old is given by
$$\int_3^4 g(x)\,dx = \int_3^4 \tfrac{1}{2}\left(1 - \tfrac{1}{4}x\right)dx = \tfrac{1}{16}.$$
The proportion that are less than one year old is given by
$$\int_0^1 g(x)\,dx = \int_0^1 \tfrac{1}{2}\left(1 - \tfrac{1}{4}x\right)dx = \tfrac{7}{16}.$$

Solution 21.2

From the solution to Exercise 19.2,
$$Q(x) = \tfrac{1}{4}e^{-x} + \tfrac{3}{4}e^{-3x}, \quad x \ge 0,$$
and
$$e_0 = \tfrac{1}{2}.$$

Therefore the p.d.f. of the stationary age distribution is
$$g(x) = \frac{Q(x)}{e_0} = \tfrac{1}{2}e^{-x} + \tfrac{3}{2}e^{-3x}, \quad x \ge 0.$$

The mean age of birds in the population (in years) is
$$\int_0^\infty x\,g(x)\,dx = \tfrac{1}{2}\int_0^\infty xe^{-x}\,dx + \tfrac{1}{2}\int_0^\infty 3xe^{-3x}\,dx$$
$$= \tfrac{1}{2} + \tfrac{1}{2} \times \tfrac{1}{3}$$
$$= \tfrac{2}{3}.$$

Solution 21.3

(a) The c.d.f. of the lifetime distribution is
$$F(x) = 1 - Q(x) = 1 - e^{-x^2/8}, \quad x \ge 0.$$
This is the c.d.f. of a Rayleigh distribution with parameter β, where
$$\tfrac{1}{2}\beta^2 = \tfrac{1}{8},$$
and hence $\beta = \tfrac{1}{2}$.
Using Table 9 in the *Handbook*,
$$e_0 = \frac{1}{\beta}\sqrt{\frac{\pi}{2}} = \sqrt{2\pi} \simeq 2.51 \text{ years}.$$

(b) The p.d.f. of the stationary age distribution is
$$g(x) = \frac{Q(x)}{e_0} = \frac{1}{\sqrt{2\pi}}e^{-x^2/8}, \quad x \ge 0.$$
Therefore the mean age of animals in the population (in years) is
$$\int_0^\infty x\,g(x)\,dx = \int_0^\infty \frac{1}{\sqrt{2\pi}}xe^{-x^2/8}\,dx$$
$$= \frac{1}{\sqrt{2\pi}}\left[-4e^{-x^2/8}\right]_0^\infty$$
$$= \frac{4}{\sqrt{2\pi}}$$
$$\simeq 1.60.$$

Solution 22.1

(a) From part (b) of the solution to Exercise 21.3, the p.d.f. of the stationary age distribution is
$$g(x) = \frac{1}{\sqrt{2\pi}}e^{-x^2/8}, \quad x \ge 0.$$
A sketch of the p.d.f. is shown in Figure S.19.

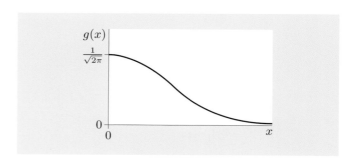

Figure S.19 The p.d.f. of the stationary age distribution

(b) The p.d.f. of the stable age distribution has the form

$$g(x) = ke^{-\theta x}e^{-x^2/8}, \quad x \geq 0.$$

(i) If the population is growing, then $\theta > 0$ and a greater proportion of the population is in the younger age groups than for the corresponding stationary population. The shape of the p.d.f. of the stable age distribution might be as shown in Figure S.20.

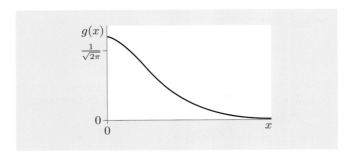

Figure S.20   The p.d.f. of the stable age distribution when $\theta > 0$

(ii) If the population is declining, then $\theta < 0$ and a smaller proportion of the population is in the younger age groups than in the corresponding stationary population. The shape of the p.d.f. of the stable age distribution might be as shown in Figure S.21.

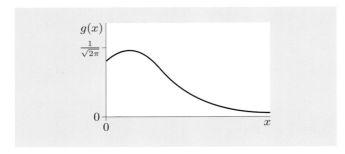

Figure S.21   The p.d.f. of the stable age distribution when $\theta < 0$

Solution 23.1

The shapes of the population pyramids will be similar to the shapes of the p.d.f.s sketched in the solution to Exercise 22.1.

(a) The p.d.f. of the stationary age distribution is shown in Figure S.19. A population pyramid might look like that in Figure S.22.

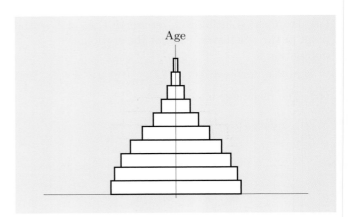

Figure S.22   Population pyramid for a stationary population

(b) For a stable population that is growing, a greater proportion of the population is in the younger age groups than for the corresponding stationary population. The p.d.f. of the age distribution might look like that in Figure S.20, and a population pyramid might look like that in Figure S.23.

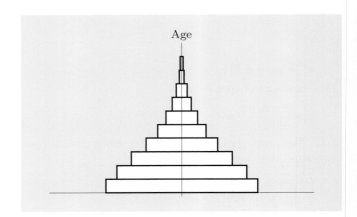

Figure S.23   Stable and growing

(c) For a stable population that is declining, a smaller proportion of the population is in the younger age groups than for the corresponding stationary population. The p.d.f. of the age distribution might look like that in Figure S.21, and a population pyramid might look like that in Figure S.24.

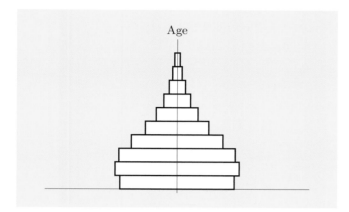

Figure S.24   Stable and declining

Solution 24.1

This exercise covers some of the ideas and techniques discussed in Section 3.

(a) The partial differential equation is in Lagrange form, with
$$f = t, \quad g = s, \quad h = s\Pi.$$
The auxiliary equations are
$$\frac{ds}{t} = \frac{dt}{s} = \frac{d\Pi}{s\Pi}.$$
Taking the first and second expressions, and separating the variables, gives
$$\int s\,ds = \int t\,dt.$$
So one solution is
$$\tfrac{1}{2}s^2 = \tfrac{1}{2}t^2 + \text{constant},$$
or
$$c_1 = s^2 - t^2.$$
Taking the second and third expressions, and cancelling s, gives
$$\int 1\,dt = \int \frac{1}{\Pi}\,d\Pi.$$
Therefore a second solution is
$$t = \log \Pi + \text{constant},$$
or
$$\text{constant} = \log \Pi - t.$$
Taking exponentials gives
$$c_2 = \Pi e^{-t}.$$

Since c_2 includes Π, the general solution is given by $c_2 = \psi(c_1)$:
$$\Pi e^{-t} = \psi(s^2 - t^2),$$
so
$$\Pi(s,t) = e^t\,\psi(s^2 - t^2).$$
Setting $t = 0$ gives
$$\Pi(s,0) = \psi(s^2).$$
Given that $\Pi(s,0) = s^4$, it follows that
$$\psi(s^2) = s^4.$$
Writing $x = s^2$ gives
$$\psi(x) = x^2.$$
Therefore the particular solution is
$$\Pi(s,t) = e^t(s^2 - t^2)^2.$$

(b) The partial differential equation is in Lagrange form, with
$$f = 0, \quad g = \Pi, \quad h = s.$$
The auxiliary equations are
$$\frac{ds}{0} = \frac{dt}{\Pi} = \frac{d\Pi}{s}.$$
Since $ds/0$ appears, one solution is
$$c_1 = s.$$
Taking the second and third expressions gives
$$\int s\,dt = \int \Pi\,d\Pi.$$
From the first solution, s may be treated as a constant, so a second solution is
$$st = \tfrac{1}{2}\Pi^2 + \text{constant},$$
or
$$c_2 = \Pi^2 - 2st.$$
Since c_2 includes Π, the general solution is given by $c_2 = \psi(c_1)$:
$$\Pi^2 - 2st = \psi(s).$$
That is,
$$\Pi(s,t) = \sqrt{\psi(s) + 2st}.$$
Setting $t = 0$ gives
$$\Pi(s,0) = \sqrt{\psi(s)}.$$
Given that $\Pi(s,0) = s$, it follows that
$$\psi(s) = s^2,$$
and hence
$$\Pi(s,t) = \sqrt{s^2 + 2st}.$$

Solution 24.2

This exercise covers some of the ideas and techniques discussed in Sections 1 and 4.

(a) Since $T_x \sim M(\beta x)$ in a simple birth process starting with one individual, the mean of $W_6 = T_1 + T_2 + \cdots + T_6$, the time to the sixth birth, is
$$E(W_6) = \frac{1}{\beta}(1 + \tfrac{1}{2} + \cdots + \tfrac{1}{6}) = \frac{2.45}{\beta}.$$

(b) From (4.4),

$$P(W_n \le t) = (1 - e^{-\beta t})^n.$$

The median of W_6 is the time w such that

$$(1 - e^{-\beta w})^6 = \tfrac{1}{2},$$

so

$$w = -\frac{1}{\beta} \log\left(1 - \left(\tfrac{1}{2}\right)^{1/6}\right) \simeq \frac{2.215}{\beta}.$$

Notice that the mean of W_6 is greater than the median. In fact, the mean of W_n is greater than the median for $n = 1, 2, \ldots$.

Solution 24.3

This exercise covers some of the ideas and techniques discussed in Section 6.

For the embedded random walk, $p = \beta/(\beta + \nu)$ and $q = \nu/(\beta + \nu)$, so $q/p = \nu/\beta$.

The first thing that has to happen is that the size decreases (possibly with fluctuations) from 10 to 4. This is the same as the ruin of a gambler who starts with $\pounds(10 - 4) = \pounds 6$ and is gambling against an opponent with unlimited resources. The probability that this happens is

$$q_6 = \left(\frac{q}{p}\right)^6 = \left(\frac{\nu}{\beta}\right)^6.$$

Since this is a Markov process, once the size has reached 4, previous events are irrelevant. The probability that the size never falls to 3, but increases indefinitely, is required next. This is equivalent to the probability that a gambler starting with $\pounds 1$ is not ruined. This probability is

$$1 - q_1 = 1 - \frac{q}{p} = 1 - \frac{\nu}{\beta}.$$

The required probability is the product of these two probabilities:

$$\left(\frac{\nu}{\beta}\right)^6 \left(1 - \frac{\nu}{\beta}\right).$$

Solution 24.4

This exercise covers some of the ideas and techniques discussed in Subsection 1.3 and Sections 3 and 4.

(a) See Section 3. In Lagrange form, the equation is

$$-\nu(1 - s)\frac{\partial \Pi}{\partial s} + \frac{\partial \Pi}{\partial t} = 0,$$

so

$$f = -\nu(1 - s), \quad g = 1, \quad h = 0.$$

The auxiliary equations are

$$\frac{ds}{-\nu(1 - s)} = \frac{dt}{1} = \frac{d\Pi}{0}.$$

Since $d\Pi/0$ features in the auxiliary equations, one solution is $c_1 = \Pi$.

From the first two expressions,

$$-\int \frac{ds}{1 - s} = \nu \, dt,$$

so

$$\log(1 - s) = \nu t + \text{constant},$$

or

$$1 - s = e^{\nu t} \times \text{constant}.$$

Hence a second solution is

$$c_2 = (1 - s)e^{-\nu t}.$$

The general solution is given by $c_1 = \psi(c_2)$:

$$\Pi(s, t) = \psi((1 - s)e^{-\nu t}).$$

(b) See Section 3. If $X(0) = n$, then the p.g.f. of $X(0)$ is

$$\Pi(s, 0) = s^n.$$

However, setting $t = 0$ in $\Pi(s, t)$ gives

$$\Pi(s, 0) = \psi(1 - s),$$

so

$$\psi(1 - s) = s^n.$$

Writing $x = 1 - s$, so that $s = 1 - x$, gives

$$\psi(x) = (1 - x)^n.$$

Therefore the particular solution is

$$\begin{aligned}\Pi(s, t) &= (1 - (1 - s)e^{-\nu t})^n \\ &= ((1 - e^{-\nu t}) + se^{-\nu t})^n.\end{aligned}$$

Hence $X(t) \sim B(n, e^{-\nu t})$.

(c) See Example 4.2, for instance.

If $X(0) \sim G_1(0.2)$, then the p.g.f. of $X(0)$ is

$$\Pi(s, 0) = \frac{0.2s}{1 - 0.8s} = \frac{s}{5 - 4s}.$$

However, setting $t = 0$ in $\Pi(s, t)$ gives

$$\Pi(s, 0) = \psi(1 - s).$$

Therefore

$$\psi(1 - s) = \frac{s}{5 - 4s}.$$

Writing $x = 1 - s$, so that $s = 1 - x$, gives

$$\psi(x) = \frac{1 - x}{5 - 4(1 - x)} = \frac{1 - x}{1 + 4x}.$$

The corresponding particular solution is

$$\begin{aligned}\Pi(s, t) &= \frac{1 - (1 - s)e^{-\nu t}}{1 + 4(1 - s)e^{-\nu t}} \\ &= \frac{1 - e^{-\nu t} + se^{-\nu t}}{1 + 4e^{-\nu t} - 4se^{-\nu t}}.\end{aligned}$$

(d) The relationship between the c.d.f. of W and the distribution of $X(t)$ in a pure death process is discussed in Subsection 1.3.

Since $W \le t$ if and only if there is no one alive at time t,

$$\begin{aligned}P(W \le t) &= P(X(t) = 0) \\ &= \Pi(0, t) \\ &= \frac{1 - e^{-\nu t}}{1 + 4e^{-\nu t}}.\end{aligned}$$

The median waiting time is the solution of

$$P(W \le t) = 0.5,$$

that is, of

$$\frac{1 - e^{-\nu t}}{1 + 4e^{-\nu t}} = 0.5.$$

Therefore the median waiting time is

$$t = \frac{1}{\nu} \log 6.$$

Solution 24.5

This exercise covers some of the ideas and techniques discussed in Sections 3 to 7.

(a) The equation is in Lagrange form, so
$$f = (1-s)(\nu - \beta s), \quad g = -1, \quad h = \lambda(1-s)\Pi.$$
The auxiliary equations are
$$\frac{ds}{(1-s)(\nu - \beta s)} = \frac{dt}{-1} = \frac{d\Pi}{\lambda(1-s)\Pi}.$$
Taking the first two expressions leads to the following solution (as for the simple birth–death process in Activity 6.1):
$$c_1 = \frac{\nu - \beta s}{1-s} e^{(\nu-\beta)t}.$$
Taking the first and third expressions together, and cancelling the term $1 - s$, gives
$$\frac{ds}{\nu - \beta s} = \frac{d\Pi}{\lambda \Pi}.$$
Integrating this leads to
$$-\frac{1}{\beta} \log(\nu - \beta s) = \frac{1}{\lambda} \log \Pi + \text{constant},$$
or
$$\text{constant} = \log \Pi + \frac{\lambda}{\beta} \log(\nu - \beta s).$$
Taking exponentials, a second solution is
$$c_2 = \Pi(\nu - \beta s)^{\lambda/\beta}.$$
The general solution is given by $c_2 = \psi(c_1)$:
$$\Pi(\nu - \beta s)^{\lambda/\beta} = \psi\left(\frac{\nu - \beta s}{1-s} e^{(\nu-\beta)t}\right).$$
Therefore
$$\Pi(s,t) = (\nu - \beta s)^{-\lambda/\beta} \psi\left(\frac{\nu - \beta s}{1-s} e^{(\nu-\beta)t}\right).$$

(b) Since $X(0) = 0$, the p.g.f. of $X(0)$ is
$$\Pi(s,0) = s^0 = 1.$$
Setting $t = 0$ in the general solution gives
$$\Pi(s,0) = (\nu - \beta s)^{-\lambda/\beta} \psi\left(\frac{\nu - \beta s}{1-s}\right).$$
Therefore
$$(\nu - \beta s)^{-\lambda/\beta} \psi\left(\frac{\nu - \beta s}{1-s}\right) = 1,$$
and hence
$$\psi\left(\frac{\nu - \beta s}{1-s}\right) = (\nu - \beta s)^{\lambda/\beta}.$$
Writing $x = (\nu - \beta s)/(1-s)$, so that $s = (x - \nu)/(x - \beta)$, gives
$$\psi(x) = \left(\nu - \frac{\beta(x - \nu)}{x - \beta}\right)^{\lambda/\beta} = \left(\frac{x(\nu - \beta)}{x - \beta}\right)^{\lambda/\beta}.$$
Therefore
$$\Pi(s,t) = (\nu - \beta s)^{-\lambda/\beta} \left(\frac{\dfrac{\nu - \beta s}{1-s} e^{(\nu-\beta)t}(\nu - \beta)}{\dfrac{\nu - \beta s}{1-s} e^{(\nu-\beta)t} - \beta}\right)^{\lambda/\beta}$$
$$= \left(\frac{(\nu - \beta)e^{(\nu-\beta)t}}{(\nu - \beta s)e^{(\nu-\beta)t} - \beta(1-s)}\right)^{\lambda/\beta}.$$

(c) The p.g.f. is of the form
$$\Pi(s,t) = \left(\frac{q}{1 - ps}\right)^r,$$
where $r = \lambda/\beta$, $p = 1 - (\nu - \beta)e^{(\nu-\beta)t}/(\nu e^{(\nu-\beta)t} - \beta)$, $q = 1 - p$. So $X(t)$ has a negative binomial distribution with range $\{0, 1, \ldots\}$ and parameters r and p (just given). Therefore
$$E[X(t)] = \frac{rp}{q} = \frac{\lambda(1 - e^{-(\nu-\beta)t})}{\nu - \beta}.$$

(d) (i) When $\beta < \nu$, $e^{(\nu-\beta)t} \to \infty$ as $t \to \infty$, so
$$\lim_{t\to\infty} \Pi(s,t) = \left(\frac{\nu - \beta}{\nu - \beta s}\right)^{\lambda/\beta}$$
$$= \left(\frac{1 - \beta/\nu}{1 - \beta s/\nu}\right)^{\lambda/\beta}.$$
In this case, a limiting distribution exists and has negative binomial form.

(ii) When $\beta > \nu$, $e^{(\nu-\beta)t} \to 0$ as $t \to \infty$, so
$$\lim_{t\to 0} \Pi(s,t) = 0.$$
A limiting distribution does not exist, and the size of the population increases without limit.

Note that the case $\beta = \nu$ must be considered separately. In this case, the solution of the partial differential equation is
$$\Pi(s,t) = \left(\frac{1}{1 + \beta t(1-s)}\right)^{\lambda/\beta}.$$
Hence, as for $\beta > \nu$, there is no limiting distribution. You may like to check this – it will give you further practice at applying Lagrange's method.

Solution 24.6

This exercise covers some of the ideas and techniques discussed in Section 7.

(a) From the solution to part (b) of Activity 7.1,
$$X(t) \sim \text{Poisson}\left(\frac{\lambda}{\nu}\left(1 - e^{-\nu t}\right)\right).$$
Since $\lambda = 1$ and $\nu = 0.5$,
$$X(t) \sim \text{Poisson}(2(1 - e^{-0.5t})),$$
and hence
$$X(3) \sim \text{Poisson}(2(1 - e^{-1.5}))$$
$$\approx \text{Poisson}(1.554).$$
Therefore
$$P(X(3) > 3)$$
$$= 1 - P(X(3) \le 3)$$
$$\simeq 1 - e^{-1.554}\left(1 + 1.554 + \frac{1.554^2}{2!} + \frac{1.554^3}{3!}\right)$$
$$\simeq 1 - 0.9274$$
$$= 0.0726.$$

(b) The equilibrium distribution is Poisson with parameter $\lambda/\nu = 2$, so the proportion of the time in the long run that there are more than three individuals in the population is

$$1 - (p_0 + p_1 + p_2 + p_3)$$
$$= 1 - e^{-2}\left(1 + 2 + \frac{2^2}{2!} + \frac{2^3}{3!}\right)$$
$$\simeq 1 - 0.8571$$
$$= 0.1429.$$

Solution 24.7

This exercise covers some of the ideas and techniques discussed in Section 10.

(a) The arrival rate is 4 per hour and the service rate is 6 per hour, so the traffic intensity is $\rho = \frac{2}{3}$.

(b) For an $M/M/1$ queue in steady state, the number of people in the queue (including the person being served) has a geometric distribution $G_0(\rho)$, so

$$p_2 = \left(\frac{2}{3}\right)^2 \times \frac{1}{3} = \frac{4}{27} \simeq 0.148.$$

(c) If one person is being served and more than one is waiting, then the queue length X is greater than 2. Therefore the probability that more than one customer is waiting to be served is given by

$$P(X > 2) = 1 - p_0 - p_1 - p_2$$
$$= 1 - \frac{1}{3} - \frac{2}{3} \times \frac{1}{3} - \left(\frac{2}{3}\right)^2 \times \frac{1}{3}$$
$$= \frac{8}{27} \simeq 0.296.$$

(d) Measuring time in hours, the queueing time W has an exponential distribution with parameter

$$\varepsilon - \lambda = 2.$$

Therefore

$$P\left(W > \tfrac{1}{2}\right) = e^{-2 \times 0.5} \simeq 0.368.$$

(e) The expected number of customers served during a busy period is

$$\frac{1}{1 - \rho} = 3.$$

The expected duration in hours of a busy period is

$$\frac{1}{\varepsilon - \lambda} = 0.5.$$

Solution 24.8

This exercise covers some of the ideas and techniques discussed in Section 11.

(a) The queue specification is $M/M/3$.

Since $\lambda = 72$ per hour and $\varepsilon = 30$ per hour, the traffic intensity is

$$\rho = \frac{\lambda}{n\varepsilon} = \frac{72}{3 \times 30} = 0.8.$$

(b) The equilibrium queue size distribution is found using (11.1), (11.2) and (11.3). Using (11.3),

$$K = 1 + 3\rho + \frac{(3\rho)^2}{2!} + \frac{(3\rho)^3}{3!(1 - \rho)}$$
$$= 1 + 2.4 + 2.88 + 11.52$$
$$= 17.8$$
$$= \frac{89}{5}.$$

The probability that all three cashiers are idle is

$$p_0 = \frac{1}{K} = \frac{5}{89}.$$

(c) The proportion of the time that at least two cashiers are busy is $1 - p_0 - p_1$. Using (11.1),

$$p_1 = \frac{1}{K} \times 3\rho = \frac{5}{89} \times 2.4 = \frac{12}{89},$$

so

$$1 - p_0 - p_1 = 1 - \frac{5}{89} - \frac{12}{89} = \frac{72}{89} \simeq 0.809.$$

(d) The exponential distribution has the memoryless property, so the distribution of the time (in minutes) until any particular cashier is free is $M(0.5)$.

The time W until one of the cashiers is free is the minimum of three exponential service times, each with parameter 0.5, so $W \sim M(0.5 + 0.5 + 0.5)$. That is, $W \sim M(1.5)$.

Therefore the probability that Tom will have to wait for less than two minutes for a cashier to be free is

$$P(W < 2) = 1 - e^{-1.5 \times 2}$$
$$= 1 - e^{-3}$$
$$\simeq 0.950.$$

Solution 24.9

This exercise covers some of the ideas and techniques discussed in Section 12.

(a) For this $M/U/1$ queue,

$$\lambda = \tfrac{1}{20} \text{ per minute.}$$

Since $T \sim U(5, 30)$,

$$E(T) = \tfrac{1}{2}(5 + 30) = 17.5 \text{ minutes,}$$

so

$$\rho = \lambda \, E(T) = \tfrac{1}{20} \times 17.5 = 0.875.$$

(b) Since $T \sim U(5, 30)$,

$$V(T) = \tfrac{1}{12}(30 - 5)^2 = \tfrac{625}{12}.$$

Using Pollaczek's formula (12.2), the mean equilibrium queue size is

$$E(X) = \frac{0.875 - \tfrac{1}{2} \times 0.875^2 + \tfrac{1}{2} \times \tfrac{1}{400} \times \tfrac{625}{12}}{1 - 0.875} \simeq 4.458.$$

(c) For this $M/D/1$ queue,

$$\lambda = \tfrac{1}{20} \text{ per minute,}$$
$$E(T) = 15 \text{ minutes,}$$

so

$$\rho = \lambda \, E(T) = 0.75.$$

(d) Since the service time is constant,

$$V(T) = 0.$$

Using (12.2), the mean equilibrium queue size is

$$E(X) = \frac{0.75 - \tfrac{1}{2} \times 0.75^2}{1 - 0.75} = 1.875.$$

Solution 24.10

This exercise covers some of the ideas and techniques discussed in Section 14.

The epidemic rate β_y is given by (14.5) with $n + 1 = 6$ and $\beta = 1.2$, so

$$\beta_y = \frac{1.2 y(6 - y)}{5} = 0.24 y(6 - y).$$

Therefore $\beta_3 = 2.16$, $\beta_4 = 1.92$ and $\beta_5 = 1.2$.

The duration of the epidemic is W, where $W = T_3 + T_4 + T_5$ and $T_y \sim M(\beta_y)$. Therefore

$$E(W) = \frac{1}{\beta_3} + \frac{1}{\beta_4} + \frac{1}{\beta_5} \simeq 1.82 \text{ days,}$$

$$V(W) = \frac{1}{\beta_3^2} + \frac{1}{\beta_4^2} + \frac{1}{\beta_5^2} = 1.1800 \ldots,$$

and hence the standard deviation of W is

$$\sqrt{V(W)} = \sqrt{1.1800 \ldots} \simeq 1.09 \text{ days.}$$

Solution 24.11

This exercise covers some of the ideas and techniques discussed in Section 15.

Of all the infective–susceptible contacts, only a proportion 0.2 lead to the disease being passed on. Therefore, in practice, the contact rate β is 0.2×0.3 per day, that is, 0.06 per day.

In this case, since $n + 1 = 85$ and $\gamma = \tfrac{1}{7}$ per day, the epidemic parameter is

$$\rho = \frac{n\gamma}{\beta} = \frac{84 \times 1/7}{0.06} = 200.$$

Since $x_0 = 68 < 200 = \rho$, only a minor outbreak will occur (the threshold phenomenon), so the barrier cream will be effective at preventing a major outbreak of the infection.

In fact, using formula iteration, it can be shown that about 66 of the original 68 susceptibles will remain uninfected when the epidemic is over: only two new infections will occur.

Solution 24.12

This exercise covers some of the ideas and techniques discussed in Sections 15, 16 and 17.

(a) Since $n + 1 = 36$, $\beta = 7$ and $\gamma = 3$,

$$\rho = \frac{n\gamma}{\beta} = \frac{35 \times 3}{7} = 15.$$

(b) The deterministic general epidemic model is discussed in Subsection 15.2.

(i) The maximum number who are simultaneously infectious, $y_{\max}$, is given by (15.13) with $x_0 = 33$, $y_0 = 3$ and $\rho = 15$:

$$\begin{aligned}
y_{\max} &= y_0 + x_0 - \rho - \rho \log(x_0/\rho) \\
&= 3 + 33 - 15 - 15 \log(33/15) \\
&= 21 - 15 \log 2.2 \\
&\simeq 9.17.
\end{aligned}$$

At the height of the epidemic, approximately 9 people are infectious.

(ii) The number of people who survive the epidemic uninfected, x_∞, is the solution smaller than ρ of (15.15):

$$x = x_0 \exp\left(\frac{x - (x_0 + y_0)}{\rho}\right),$$

that is,

$$x = 33 \exp\left(\frac{x - 36}{15}\right).$$

Using the iteration formula (15.16) with $x_{\infty,0} = 0$ gives the following results (rounded to three decimal places): $x_{\infty,1} = 2.994$, $x_{\infty,2} = 3.655$, $x_{\infty,3} = 3.820$, $x_{\infty,4} = 3.862$, $x_{\infty,5} = 3.873$, $x_{\infty,6} = 3.876$, $x_{\infty,7} = 3.876$.

Therefore $x_\infty \simeq 3.88$. Approximately 4 people will survive the epidemic without catching the infection.

(c) The stochastic general epidemic model is discussed in Sections 16 and 17.

(i) Since $x_0 = 33$ and $y_0 = 3$, if one new infection occurs, then $X_\infty = 32$ and there are three possible paths, as shown in Figure S.25.

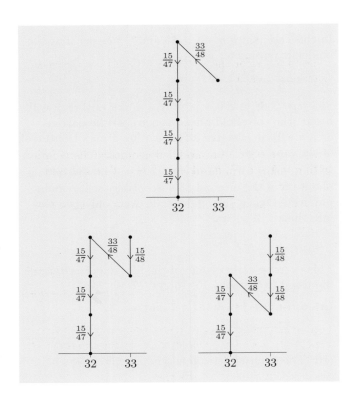

Figure S.25   Possible paths

When $x = 33$, the probability of a removal next is
$$\frac{\rho}{x + \rho} = \frac{15}{33 + 15} = \frac{15}{48},$$
and the probability of an infection next is $\frac{33}{48}$.

Similarly, when $x = 32$, the probability of a removal next is $\frac{15}{47}$.

The probability that exactly one susceptible will be infected before the epidemic ends is the sum of the probabilities of the three paths:
$$P(X_\infty = 32) = \frac{33}{48} \times \left(\frac{15}{47}\right)^4 + \frac{15}{48} \times \frac{33}{48} \times \left(\frac{15}{47}\right)^3$$
$$+ \left(\frac{15}{48}\right)^2 \times \frac{33}{48} \times \left(\frac{15}{47}\right)^2$$
$$\simeq 0.007\,13 + 0.006\,98 + 0.006\,84$$
$$\simeq 0.0210.$$

(ii) Since $x_0 > \rho$, the probability that there will be a major outbreak can be estimated using (17.2):
$$P(\text{major outbreak}) \simeq 1 - \left(\frac{\rho}{x_0}\right)^{y_0}$$
$$= 1 - \left(\frac{15}{33}\right)^3$$
$$\simeq 0.906.$$

Solution 24.13

This exercise covers some of the ideas and techniques discussed in Sections 19 and 21.

(a) The life table function is found using (19.4):
$$\int_0^x h(u)\,du = \int_0^x \frac{1}{80 - u}\,du$$
$$= \left[-\log(80 - u)\right]_0^x$$
$$= -\log(80 - x) + \log 80$$
$$= -\log\left(1 - \frac{x}{80}\right).$$
Therefore
$$Q(x) = 1 - \frac{x}{80}, \quad 0 \le x < 80.$$

(b) The lifetime of an individual has a uniform distribution, $X \sim U(0, 80)$, so $e_0 = 40$ years. Alternatively, e_0 can be found using (19.1).

(c) The p.d.f. of the age distribution is given by (21.4), $g(x) = Q(x)/e_0$, so the mean age of members is
$$\int_0^\infty x\,g(x)\,dx = \frac{1}{40} \int_0^{80} x\left(1 - \frac{x}{80}\right)dx$$
$$= 26\tfrac{2}{3} \text{ years.}$$

(d) The proportion of the population over 60 years old is given by
$$\int_{60}^\infty g(x)\,dx = \frac{1}{40} \int_{60}^{80} \left(1 - \frac{x}{80}\right)dx$$
$$= 0.0625.$$

(e) The proportion of individuals who live for more than 60 years is
$$Q(60) = 1 - \tfrac{60}{80} = 0.25.$$

Solution 24.14

This exercise covers some of the ideas and techniques discussed in Section 1.

(a) The probability distribution of $X(t)$ is Poisson(λt).

(b) The probability $P(X(s + t) = n \mid X(t) = x)$ is the probability that there are $(n - x)$ arrivals in the time interval $[t, s + t]$, which is of duration s. This probability is
$$\frac{e^{-\lambda s}(\lambda s)^{n-x}}{(n - x)!}, \quad x = 0, 1, \ldots, n.$$

(c) Using Bayes' formula,

$$P(X(t) = x \mid X(s+t) = n)$$
$$= \frac{P(X(s+t) = n \mid X(t) = x)\, P(X(t) = x)}{P(X(s+t) = n)}.$$

Since $X(s+t) \sim \text{Poisson}(\lambda(s+t))$, using the results in parts (a) and (b), this probability is equal to

$$\frac{\dfrac{e^{-\lambda s}(\lambda s)^{n-x}}{(n-x)!} \times \dfrac{e^{-\lambda t}(\lambda t)^{x}}{x!}}{\dfrac{e^{-\lambda(s+t)}(\lambda(s+t))^{n}}{n!}}.$$

Therefore for $x = 0, 1, \ldots, n$,

$$P(X(t) = x \mid X(s+t) = n)$$
$$= \binom{n}{x}\left(\frac{t}{s+t}\right)^{x}\left(\frac{s}{s+t}\right)^{n-x}.$$

That is, the conditional distribution of $X(t)$ is binomial with parameters n and $p = t/(s+t)$.

(d) Let T be the time of the arrival that is known to have occurred in the interval $[0, s+t]$. Then, using the result from part (c),

$$P(T < t) = P(X(t) = 1 \mid X(s+t) = 1)$$
$$= \frac{t}{s+t}.$$

This is the c.d.f. of the continuous uniform distribution $U(0, s+t)$. Therefore, conditional on an arrival by time $(s+t)$, the arrival is equally likely to have occurred at any time between 0 and $s+t$. In fact, however many arrivals have occurred by time $s+t$, each arrival is equally likely to have occurred at any time in the interval.

Solution 24.15

This exercise covers some of the ideas and techniques discussed in Section 4.

(a) The population has not been wiped out by time t if no catastrophe has occurred by that time. Since the catastrophe rate is γ, the distribution of the time interval between catastrophes is $M(\gamma)$. Therefore

$$P(\text{no catastrophe by time } t) = e^{-\gamma t},$$

and hence

$$P(Y(t) > 0) = e^{-\gamma t}.$$

(b) Assuming that no catastrophe has occurred by time t, the population behaves according to a simple birth process with birth rate β that started with one individual at time 0. From Example 4.1, its size at time t has a geometric distribution $G_1(e^{-\beta t})$. So for $y = 1, 2, \ldots$,

$$P(Y(t) = y \mid Y(t) > 0) = e^{-\beta t}(1 - e^{-\beta t})^{y-1}.$$

(c) The unconditional probability distribution of $Y(t)$ is given by

$$P(Y(t) = 0) = 1 - P(Y(t) > 0) = 1 - e^{-\gamma t},$$

and when $y > 0$,

$$P(Y(t) = y) = P(Y(t) = y \mid Y(t) > 0)\, P(Y(t) > 0)$$
$$= e^{-\beta t}(1 - e^{-\beta t})^{y-1}\, e^{-\gamma t}$$
$$= e^{-(\beta+\gamma)t}(1 - e^{-\beta t})^{y-1}.$$

The p.g.f. of $Y(t)$ is given by

$$\Pi(s, t) = \sum_{y=0}^{\infty} P(Y(t) = y)\, s^{y}$$
$$= 1 - e^{-\gamma t} + \sum_{y=1}^{\infty} e^{-(\beta+\gamma)t}(1 - e^{-\beta t})^{y-1}\, s^{y}$$
$$= 1 - e^{-\gamma t} + \frac{s e^{-(\beta+\gamma)t}}{1 - s(1 - e^{-\beta t})}.$$

(The formula for the sum of a geometric series has been used here.)

(d) The p.g.f. can be written in the form

$$\Pi(s, t) = \frac{1 - e^{-\gamma t} - s(1 - e^{-\beta t} - e^{-\gamma t})}{1 - s(1 - e^{-\beta t})}.$$

This is the p.g.f. of a modified geometric distribution with $a = 1 - e^{-\gamma t}$, $b = 1 - e^{-\beta t} - e^{-\gamma t}$, $c = 1$ and $d = 1 - e^{-\beta t}$.

Therefore the expected population size at time t is

$$E[Y(t)] = \frac{ad - bc}{(c-d)^2} = \frac{e^{-(\beta+\gamma)t}}{e^{-2\beta t}} = e^{(\beta-\gamma)t}.$$

Solution 24.16

This exercise covers some of the ideas and techniques discussed in Section 10.

(a) The number of customers that arrive in a fixed time t has a Poisson distribution with parameter λt. Therefore for $y = 0, 1, \ldots$,

$$P(Y = y \mid T = t) = \frac{e^{-\lambda t}(\lambda t)^{y}}{y!}.$$

(b) The service time T is a random variable: $T \sim M(\varepsilon)$. Therefore, using the Theorem of Total Probability, for $y = 0, 1, \ldots$,

$$P(Y = y) = \int_{0}^{\infty} P(Y = y \mid T = t)\, f(t)\, dt$$
$$= \int_{0}^{\infty} \frac{e^{-\lambda t}(\lambda t)^{y}}{y!}\, \varepsilon\, e^{-\varepsilon t}\, dt$$
$$= \frac{\varepsilon \lambda^{y}}{y!} \int_{0}^{\infty} t^{y}\, e^{-(\lambda+\varepsilon)t}\, dt.$$

But

$$\int_{0}^{\infty} x^{n-1}\, e^{-kx}\, dx = \frac{(n-1)!}{k^{n}}.$$

(This result is in Subsection 3.7 of the *Handbook*.) Therefore for $y = 0, 1, \ldots$,

$$P(Y = y) = \frac{\varepsilon \lambda^{y}}{y!} \times \frac{y!}{(\lambda+\varepsilon)^{y+1}} = \frac{\varepsilon}{\lambda+\varepsilon}\left(\frac{\lambda}{\lambda+\varepsilon}\right)^{y}.$$

This is the p.m.f. of a geometric distribution with range $\{0, 1, \ldots\}$ and parameter

$$p = \frac{\lambda}{\lambda+\varepsilon}.$$

That is,

$$Y \sim G_0(\lambda/(\lambda+\varepsilon)).$$

The mean of $G_0(p)$ is $p/(1-p)$, so the mean number of arrivals is

$$\frac{\lambda/(\lambda+\varepsilon)}{\varepsilon/(\lambda+\varepsilon)} = \frac{\lambda}{\varepsilon} = \rho.$$

Solution 24.17

This exercise covers some of the ideas and techniques discussed in Section 11.

(a) When there is at least one empty space in the lay-by, the arrival rate of cars is 6 per hour; otherwise, it is 0. So

$$\beta_x = \begin{cases} 6, & x = 0, 1, 2, 3, \\ 0, & x = 4, 5, \ldots. \end{cases}$$

When there are x cars in the lay-by, the departure rate is

$$\nu_x = 2x.$$

(Note that since there cannot be more than four cars in the lay-by, the value of ν_x is not required for x greater than 4.)

(b) The equilibrium distribution can be found using the general method described in Subsection 11.2. Using (11.4), (11.5) and (11.6), this is given by

$$p_x = \frac{1}{K}\rho_x,$$

where

$$K = 1 + \rho_1 + \rho_2 + \rho_3 + \rho_4,$$

$\rho_0 = 0$ and, for $x = 1, 2, 3, 4$,

$$\rho_x = \frac{\beta_0\,\beta_1\cdots\beta_{x-1}}{\nu_1\,\nu_2\cdots\nu_x} = \frac{6^x}{2^x\,x!} = \frac{3^x}{x!}.$$

Therefore

$$K = 1 + 3 + \tfrac{9}{2} + \tfrac{9}{2} + \tfrac{27}{8} = \tfrac{131}{8},$$

and hence, as required,

$$p_x = \frac{8}{131} \times \frac{3^x}{x!}, \quad x = 0, 1, 2, 3, 4.$$

(c) The proportion of time that the lay-by is full is

$$p_4 = \tfrac{8}{131} \times \tfrac{27}{8} = \tfrac{27}{131} \simeq 0.206.$$

(d) If the lay-by were extended to hold six cars, then $\beta_4 = \beta_5 = 6$, $\nu_5 = 10$ and $\nu_6 = 12$. The equilibrium distribution would be

$$p_x = \frac{1}{K} \times \frac{3^x}{x!}, \quad x = 0, 1, \ldots, 6,$$

where

$$K = 1 + \rho_1 + \rho_2 + \rho_3 + \rho_4 + \rho_5 + \rho_6$$
$$= \tfrac{131}{8} + \tfrac{81}{40} + \tfrac{81}{80} = 19.4125.$$

The proportion of time that the lay-by is full would be

$$p_6 = \frac{1}{19.4125} \times \frac{81}{80} \simeq 0.0522.$$

(e) The smallest number of spaces k such that $p_k < 0.01$ is required.

If the lay-by holds seven cars, then

$$K = 19.4125 + \frac{3^7}{7!} \simeq 19.846\,43$$

and

$$p_7 = \frac{1}{K} \times \frac{3^7}{7!} \simeq 0.0219.$$

If the lay-by holds eight cars, then

$$K = 19.846\,43 + \frac{3^8}{8!} \simeq 20.009\,15$$

and

$$p_8 = \frac{1}{K} \times \frac{3^8}{8!} \simeq 0.0081.$$

Therefore the lay-by would need to have spaces for eight cars.

Solution 24.18

This exercise covers some of the ideas and techniques discussed in Section 14.

(a) Since $y_0 = 1$, by (14.7),

$$W = T_1 + T_2 + \cdots + T_n.$$

Therefore

$$E(W) = E(T_1) + E(T_2) + \cdots + E(T_n)$$
$$= \frac{1}{\beta_1} + \frac{1}{\beta_2} + \cdots + \frac{1}{\beta_n}$$
$$= \sum_{j=1}^{n} \frac{n}{\beta j(n+1-j)}, \quad \text{using (14.5).}$$

But

$$\frac{1}{j(n+1-j)} = \frac{1}{n+1}\left(\frac{1}{j} + \frac{1}{n+1-j}\right),$$

so

$$E(W) = \frac{n}{(n+1)\beta}\left[\left(1 + \frac{1}{2} + \cdots + \frac{1}{n}\right) + \left(\frac{1}{n} + \frac{1}{n-1} + \cdots + 1\right)\right]$$
$$= \frac{2n}{(n+1)\beta}\sum_{j=1}^{n}\frac{1}{j}.$$

(i) For $\beta = 1$ and $n = 5$,
$$E(W) = \tfrac{10}{6}\left(1 + \tfrac{1}{2} + \cdots + \tfrac{1}{5}\right) \simeq 3.806.$$

(ii) For $\beta = 1$ and $n = 10$,
$$E(W) = \tfrac{20}{11}\left(1 + \tfrac{1}{2} + \cdots + \tfrac{1}{10}\right) \simeq 5.325.$$

(iii) For $\beta = 1$ and $n = 20$,
$$E(W) = \tfrac{40}{21}\left(1 + \tfrac{1}{2} + \cdots + \tfrac{1}{20}\right) \simeq 6.853.$$

(b) (i) For $\beta = 1$ and $n = 5$,
$$E(W) \simeq \tfrac{10}{6}\left(\log 6 - \tfrac{1}{12} + 0.5772\right) \simeq 3.809.$$

(ii) For $\beta = 1$ and $n = 10$,
$$E(W) \simeq \tfrac{20}{11}\left(\log 11 - \tfrac{1}{22} + 0.5772\right) \simeq 5.327.$$

(iii) For $\beta = 1$ and $n = 20$,
$$E(W) \simeq \tfrac{40}{21}\left(\log 21 - \tfrac{1}{42} + 0.5772\right) \simeq 6.853.$$

(iv) For $\beta = 1$ and $n = 200$,
$$E(W) \simeq \tfrac{400}{201}\left(\log 201 - \tfrac{1}{402} + 0.5772\right) \simeq 11.70.$$

(v) For $\beta = 1$ and $n = 2000$,
$$E(W) \simeq \tfrac{4000}{2001}\left(\log 2001 - \tfrac{1}{4002} + 0.5772\right) \simeq 16.35.$$

Notice that the first two approximations are very good and the third is better, being correct to the third decimal place.

Solution 24.19

This exercise covers some of the ideas and techniques discussed in Section 15.

Dividing the second equation by the first gives
$$\frac{dy/dt}{dx/dt} = \frac{\beta xy/(x+y-1) - \gamma y}{-\beta xy/(x+y-1)}.$$
This simplifies to give
$$\frac{dy}{dx} = -1 + \frac{\gamma(x+y-1)}{\beta x}.$$
Then, writing $\gamma/\beta = \alpha$,
$$\frac{dy}{dx} = -1 + \alpha + \frac{\alpha y}{x} - \frac{\alpha}{x},$$
or
$$\frac{dy}{dx} - \frac{\alpha}{x}y = \alpha - 1 - \frac{\alpha}{x}.$$
This can be solved using the integrating factor method. Multiplying both sides by the integrating factor $\exp(\int -\alpha/x \, dx) = x^{-\alpha}$ gives
$$x^{-\alpha}\frac{dy}{dx} - \alpha x^{-\alpha-1}y = (\alpha-1)x^{-\alpha} - \alpha x^{-\alpha-1},$$
or
$$\frac{d}{dx}(yx^{-\alpha}) = (\alpha-1)x^{-\alpha} - \alpha x^{-\alpha-1}.$$
Therefore
$$yx^{-\alpha} = \frac{(\alpha-1)x^{-\alpha+1}}{-\alpha+1} - \frac{\alpha x^{-\alpha}}{-\alpha} + \text{constant}$$
$$= -x^{\alpha+1} + x^{-\alpha} + \text{constant}.$$
Hence
$$y = -x + 1 + (\text{constant})x^{\alpha},$$
or
$$\frac{x+y-1}{x^{\alpha}} = \text{constant}.$$
Using the initial condition $x = x_0$ and $y = y_0$ leads to
$$\frac{x+y-1}{x^{\alpha}} = \frac{x_0 + y_0 - 1}{x_0^{\alpha}},$$
where $\alpha = \gamma/\beta$.

Solution 24.20

This exercise covers some of the ideas and techniques discussed in Sections 19 and 21.

(a) (i) For a stationary population,
$$g(x) = \frac{Q(x)}{e_0}.$$
In particular,
$$g(0) = \frac{Q(0)}{e_0} = \frac{1}{e_0},$$
so the mean lifetime is given by $e_0 = 1/g(0)$.

(ii) The median lifetime is the value of x satisfying the equation $Q(x) = \frac{1}{2}$. From part (a)(i), $Q(x) = e_0 \, g(x) = g(x)/g(0)$. Therefore the median is the solution of the equation $g(x) = \frac{1}{2}g(0)$.

(b) (i) For the given p.d.f.,
$$g(0) = \tfrac{1}{50},$$
so
$$e_0 = \frac{1}{g(0)} = 50.$$

(ii) The median lifetime is the solution of the equation $g(x) = \frac{1}{2}g(0)$, that is,
$$\frac{1}{1250}(x+25)e^{-0.04x} = 0.01$$
or, equivalently,
$$(x+25)e^{-0.04x} = 12.5.$$
An iterative procedure such as Newton–Raphson can be used to solve this equation. The median lifetime is approximately 41.96.

(iii) The proportion of the population surviving beyond their 60th birthday is
$$Q(60) = e_0 \, g(60)$$
$$= \tfrac{50}{1250}(60+25)e^{-0.04\times60}$$
$$= 3.4e^{-2.4}$$
$$\simeq 0.308.$$

(iv) The proportion of the population that at any one time is aged over 60 is given by
$$\int_{60}^{\infty} g(x)\,dx = \tfrac{1}{1250}\int_{60}^{\infty}(x+25)e^{-0.04x}\,dx.$$
Using integration by parts leads to
$$\tfrac{1}{1250}\left[-(25x+1250)e^{-0.04x}\right]_{60}^{\infty} = 2.2e^{-2.4}$$
$$\simeq 0.200.$$

Index

age-specific birth rate   135
age-specific death rate   117, 118
arrival process   10
auxiliary equations   28

birth and death process   44, 45
birth rate   11, 38
busy period   74, 75

central mortality rate   124
Chapman–Kolmogorov equations   44
closed community   89
cohort life table   121
crude birth rate   125
current life table   121

death rate   14
dependency ratio   128
deterministic approximation   63, 64
deterministic general epidemic   100
   maximum number infectious   101, 104
   number of survivors   102, 104
   threshold phenomenon   104, 111
deterministic model   60, 64
deterministic simple epidemic   92
differential–difference equations   20, 24

embedded process   53
embedded random walk   53
emigration   46
epidemic rate   91
equilibrium   69
equilibrium distribution   58
equilibrium queue size
   $M/G/1$ queue   84
   $M/M/n$ queue   79
   $M/M/1$ queue   69
expectation of life at birth   116
extinction   52

first partial derivative   22
force of mortality   117, 118
function of two variables   22

gambler's ruin   55
gambling against a casino   54
general epidemic   99
   assumptions   99
   deterministic model   100
   major outbreak   113
   minor outbreak   113
   stochastic model   99, 106
   threshold phenomenon   104, 111, 112

homogeneous mixing   89

idle period   74, 75
immigration   9
immigration process   10
immigration–birth process   18, 40

immigration–birth–death process   47
immigration–death process   56
immigration–emigration process   68
incubation period   88
individual birth rate   11, 38
individual death rate   14
infectious period   88
infective   88, 89
intrinsic growth rate   133

Kolmogorov forward equations   47

Lagrange's equation   26, 35
   general solution   27
   particular solution   33
Lagrange's method   27, 35
latent period   88
Lexis diagram   126
life line   126
life table   115, 116
life table function   116
limiting distribution   58

Markov process   16, 18, 44
   homogeneous   17, 18
Markov property   16
Markov queues   82
$M/G/1$ queue   84
mixed derivative   23
$M/M/\infty$ queue   81
$M/M/n$ queue   77, 79
$M/M/1$ queue   68

overall birth rate   13, 45
overall death rate   45

partial differential equation   25
partial differentiation   23
Poisson process   10
   postulates   10
   results   11
   waiting time   11
Pollaczek's formula   84
population pyramid   136
procedure for solving Lagrange's equation   35
   general solution   27
   particular solution   33
pure death process   14, 15
   extinction   14
   postulates   14
   waiting time   14

queue notation   66
queue size   69
queueing time   72, 73

removal   88
removal rate   99
removed   89, 99

second partial derivative   23
service rate   68, 70
simple birth process   11, 38
    postulates   13
    waiting time   12, 40
simple birth–death process   48, 49
    embedded random walk   53
    extinction   51
simple epidemic   90, 92
    assumptions   91
    deterministic model   92
    duration   94, 95
    stochastic model   93
    waiting time   93
simple queue   68, 70
stable age distribution   132
stable population   131
stationary   125
stationary age distribution   125, 127
stationary population   125
steady state   69, 70
stochastic general epidemic   99, 106
    major outbreak   113
    minor outbreak   113
    survivor distribution   107
    threshold phenomenon   112
stochastic simple epidemic
    waiting time   93
survivor distribution   107
susceptible   88, 89

threshold phenomenon   104, 111, 112
    deterministic general epidemic   104, 111
    stochastic general epidemic   112
traffic intensity   70, 78, 79, 84
transition probability   17